A FIRST COURSE IN ABSTRACT ALGEBRA

If the line L is defined to be the set of all real numbers, then the plane can be defined as the set of all ordered pairs (a,b) for all a and $b \in L$.

Definition 1.6.2 Let A and B be two sets. The *Cartesian product* of A and B is the set $A \times B = \{(a,b) \mid a \in A \text{ and } b \in B\}$.

Thus the plane is equal to $L \times L$.

Example 1.6.3 If $A = \{1,2,3\}$ and $B = \{3,4,5\}$, then $A \times B = \{(1,3), (2,3), (3,3), (1,4), (2,4), (3,4), (1,5), (2,5), (3,5)\}$ and $B \times A = \{(3,1), (4,1), (5,1), (3,2), (4,2), (5,2), (3,3), (4,3), (5,3)\}$.

Example 1.6.3 shows, of course, that except in special cases, $A \times B \neq B \times A$.

Exercises

1. Let $A = \{x \mid x \text{ is an integer}\}$ and $B = \{y \mid y \text{ is an integer and } -5 \leq y \leq 5\}$. What are each of the following sets: $A \times B$, $B \times A$, $A \times A$, $B \times B$? Can you describe them geometrically?
2. When does $A \times B = B \times A$?
3. Suppose $A = \phi$ and $B \neq \phi$. What are $A \times B$ and $B \times A$?
4. Let $A_1, A_2, \cdots, A_n$ be a finite collection of sets. How could you define $A_1 \times A_2 \times \cdots \times A_n$?

1.7 RELATIONS AND FUNCTIONS

One of the most important uses of the Cartesian product of two sets is in the formal definition of a relation. In ordinary usage the word "relation" concerns a pair of objects in some specified order. "A is the father of B" is an example of a relation, as is $a < b$ for real numbers. It is natural to define a relation in terms of ordered pairs. Thus, the $<$ relation between numbers could be defined as $R = \{(a,b) \mid a,b \text{ are real numbers and } b - a \text{ is positive}\}$.

Definition 1.7.1 Let A and B be sets. A *relation* R from A to B is a subset of $A \times B$. A *relation R on A* is a subset of $A \times A$.

Given this definition, we see that the relation $F = \{(x,x^2) \mid x \text{ is a real number}\}$ is quite familiar. In fact, we usually write $F(x) = x^2$, for all real numbers x. This relation F is recognized, from our experience in calculus, as an example of a function, that is, a rule or correspondence that associates to each element a in a set A a unique element in a set B. To cast the definition of a function in set-theoretic terms, we simply consider all ordered pairs (a, b) in which a is in A and b is the element in B that is associated with a.

Definition 1.7.2 A *function f from the set A to the set B*, written $f: A \to B$ or $A \xrightarrow{f} B$, is a relation f from A to B such that every $a \in A$ is the first member of precisely one ordered pair $(a,b) \in f$, that is,

i) if $a \in A$, there is $b \in B$ such that $(a,b) \in f$ and
ii) if $(a,b_1) \in f$ and $(a,b_2) \in f$, then $b_1 = b_2$.

We call A the *domain* of f and $\{b \mid (a,b) \in f\}$, denoted by $\text{Im } f$ or Af, the *range* or *image* of f. The set B is sometimes called the *codomain of f*.

The reader should note that in our definition, the domain of f is all of A, but the range of f may be a proper subset of B.

Although in calculus we usually denote the value of a function f at x by $f(x)$, we adopt the convention of writing the function on the right.[5] Hence, if $(a, b) \in f$, a function from A to B, we write $b = (a)f = af$. We call b the *image* of a under f (or the *value of f at a*) and say that a is a *preimage* of b. The set of preimages of a subset M of B is called the *preimage* of M or the inverse image of M. (The advantage of writing af instead of $f(a)$ will be discussed when function composition is introduced, and in particular when we multiply permutations in Chapter 3). The range of f may be written $\text{Im } f = \{af \mid a \in A\}$.

A function f from A to B is also called a *map* or a *mapping* from A to B. (a function is called a map simply because a cartographer's map can be thought of as the image of $f: A \to B$, where A is the region being mapped and B is the actual map.)

Definition 1.7.3 A function $f: A \to A$ is called a *function on A*.

Example 1.7.4 Let A be a set, $A \neq \phi$. Then $f = \{(a,a) \mid a \in A\}$ is called the *identity* function on A, that is, f is the function on A such that $af = a$, for all a in A.

Example 1.7.5 Let $A = \{1,-1,i,-i\}$ with $i^2 = -1$. Then $f = \{(a,a^4) \mid a \in A\}$ is the function defined by $af = 1$, for all $a \in A$.

Example 1.7.6 Let A be the set of all first-class letters mailed inside the United States. Let B be the set of positive integers. Let f be the function equal to $\{(a,b) \mid b$ is the cost in cents of postage on a, for all $a \in A\}$. Another way of defining f is as follows: if a denotes a letter whose weight is greater than $n - 1$ ounces but less than or equal to n ounces, then $af = 5n$.

Example 1.7.7 Let K denote the set of all real numbers and let F be a subset of K. We define the function $f: K \to \{0,1\}$ as $f = \{(k,a) \mid a = 0$ if $k \notin F$; $a = 1$ if $k \in F\}$. This function is called the *characteristic function* of the set F (relative to K).

[5] We will make an occasional exception to this convention.

Example 1.7.8 Let Z be the set of integers. Let $f:Z \times Z \to Z$ be defined by $(a,b)f = a + b$ and let $g:Z \times Z \to Z$ be defined by $(a,b)g = a \cdot b$. Thus the "operations" of addition and multiplication on the integers can be thought of as functions with domain $Z \times Z$ and range Z.

Definition 1.7.9 Let $A \neq \phi$ and let $f:A \times A \to A$. Then f is called a *binary operation* on A.

We see then that addition and multiplication are binary operations on the set of integers.

Exercises

1. Let $f:Z \to Z$ be defined by $xf = 2x + 1$. Express f as a set of ordered pairs of integers. What is the range of f?
2. Let $f = \{(x,x^3) \mid x \text{ is a real number}\}$. What are the domain and range of f?
3. Let $f = \{(x,x^4) \mid x \text{ is a real number}\}$. What are the domain and range of f?
4. Let $A = \{1,2,3\}$ and $B = \{4,5,6,7\}$. Which of the following subsets of $A \times B$ are functions from A to B?
 i) $\{(1,4), (2,5)\}$
 ii) $\{(1,5), (1,4), (2,6), (3,7)\}$
 iii) $\{(1,4), (2,5), (2,7), (1,6)\}$.
5. Find all functions on the set $A = \{1,2,3\}$. ●

Definition 1.7.10 Let $f:A \to B$.
i) If $a_1 f = a_2 f$ implies $a_1 = a_2$ for all $a_1, a_2 \in A$, then f is called a *one-to-one (1–1)* function (equivalently, $a_1 \neq a_2$ implies $a_1 f \neq a_2 f$).
ii) If $B = \text{Im} f (= Af)$, then f is called a function from A onto B or an *onto* function (equivalently, every $b \in B$ is the image of at least one $a \in A$).

A 1–1 function from A to B will often be denoted by $f:A \xrightarrow{1\text{–}1} B$, a function from A onto B by $f:A \xrightarrow{\text{onto}} B$. A 1–1 function from A onto B may be denoted by $f:A \xrightarrow[\text{onto}]{1\text{–}1} B$. In addition, if $f:A \xrightarrow[\text{onto}]{1\text{–}1} B$, we say that f is a *1–1 correspondence* between A and B, and that A and B are in 1–1 correspondence.

We remark that two sets have the same "number" of elements if they are in 1–1 correspondence. The property that distinguishes finite and infinite sets is that any infinite set S contains a proper subset T that is in 1–1 correspondence with S, while if F is a finite set, then there does not exist a 1–1 correspondence between F and any proper subset of F. We shall use these properties without special reference when they are needed in the sequel (see Exercises 9 and 10).

Example 1.7.11 Let $f:A \to B$ where $A = B = K$, the set of real numbers, and $f = \{(x,x^3) \mid x \in A\}$. Then f is 1–1 and onto.

Example 1.7.12 Let $A = B = K$, the set of real numbers, and let $f = \{(x,x^2) \mid x \text{ is a real number}\}$. In this example f is not 1–1, since $1f = (-1)f = 1$. Also, f is not onto since, for example, there is no real number x such that $xf = x^2 = -1$. However, if we consider $f:A \to K^+$, where K^+ is the set of all nonnegative real numbers, then f is onto K^+. Similarly, if $g = \{(x,x^2) \mid x \in K^+\}$, then $g:K^+ \xrightarrow[\text{onto}]{1\text{–}1} K^+$.

Example 1.7.13 Let $f:A \to B$ and let $A' \subset A$. The function $g:A' \to B$ defined by $(x)g = (x)f$ for all $x \in A'$ is called the *restriction* of f to A'. We denote g by $f \mid A'$.

In Example 1.7.12 the function g is the restriction of f to K^+.

Example 1.7.14 Let $A = \{1,-1,i,-i\}$ with $i^2 = (-i)^2 = -1$, and let $B = \{0,1\}$. Then again $f:A \to B$, $f = \{(a,a^4) \mid a \in A\}$, is a function that is neither 1–1 nor onto.

Example 1.7.15 Addition and multiplication on Z, the set of integers, are not 1–1 from $Z \times Z$ into Z, but they are onto.

Example 1.7.16 Let A be the set of all nondegenerate triangles in the plane, and let B be the set of all positive real numbers. Let $f:A \to B$ be defined as follows:

$$\text{If } \triangle \in A, \quad \text{then} \quad \triangle f = \text{Area } \triangle.$$

Clearly, f is not 1–1 but f is onto.

Although $f:A \to B$ may not be onto, there is always a subset B_1 of B such that $f:A \xrightarrow{\text{onto}} B_1$. Indeed, if $B_1 = \text{Im} f$, then B_1 satisfies this condition.

We shall return to the study of 1–1, onto functions in Chapter 3, where they will play an important role in our study of permutations.

Exercises

6. Let $A = \{1,2,3,4,5\}$, let $B = \{1,2,3\}$. Let $f:A \to B$ be defined as follows:

$$\text{If } a \text{ is odd,} \quad af = 1.$$

$$\text{If } a \text{ is even,} \quad af = 2.$$

Show that f is neither 1–1 nor onto.

7. Let $A = \{1,2,3,4,5\}$, $B = \{6,7,8,9,10\}$, and $C = \{11,12,13,14,15\}$. Let $f: A \to B$ be defined by $af = a + 5$, for all $a \in A$, and let $g: B \to C$ be defined by $bg = b + 5$, for all $b \in B$. Show that both f and g are 1–1 and onto.

8. Let f be the identity function on a set A. Prove that f is both 1–1 and onto.

9. Show that there exists a one-to-one correspondence between the set of even integers and the set of all integers.

10. Let F be a finite set, and let $f: F \xrightarrow{1-1} F$. Show that f is onto.

†11. Let A be a set and let P denote the collection of all subsets of A. Show that there does not exist a 1–1 function f from A onto P.

Hint: Suppose f is a 1–1 map from A onto P. Define a subset A' of A as follows:
$a \in A'$ if and only if $a \notin af$, the subset of A corresponding to a. Show that there does not exist an element $b \in A$ such that $bf = A'$.
This example shows that it would be impossible to index the collection of all subsets of the real number system by the real numbers.

1.8 EQUIVALENCE RELATIONS AND PARTITIONS

Certain relations on a set A have the property that they separate A into a collection of disjoint subsets. For example, the relation of equality on a set partitions the set into a collection of subsets, each of which contains precisely one element. As another illustration, congruence of triangles in the plane is a relation on the set T of all triangles, and this relation splits T into a collection of disjoint subsets, each subset being the collection of all triangles congruent to a given triangle. Relations that behave in this way are called *equivalence relations*. Their role in mathematics, as we shall see, is extremely important.

Let R be a relation on a set A. We shall denote the fact that $(a,b) \in R$ by aRb. This is in agreement with our use of the "$<$" and "$=$" symbols. For example, if S is the relation of "less than" on the real numbers, we write $a < b$ in place of $(a,b) \in S$.

Definition 1.8.1 An *equivalence relation* R on a set A is a relation R on A satisfying

i) aRa, for all $a \in A$. (reflexive law).
ii) If aRb, then bRa. (symmetric law).
iii) If aRb and bRc, then aRc. (transitive law).

† Exercises bearing a dagger are of more than routine difficulty.

Moreover, if aRb holds, we say that a is *equivalent* to b. Since aRb implies bRa, we see that b is equivalent to a as well. Thus, if aRb, we also say a and b are *equivalent*.

It is easily seen that "=" is an equivalence relation on K, the real number system. However, "<" is not an equivalence relation on K since $2<3$ does not imply $3<2$.

To illustrate further, let us consider the following relation defined for people: Person a is equivalent to person b if a and b were born on the same day of the year (possibly different years). We write aRb if this is the case. Clearly, a was born on his own birthday, so aRa. Also, if aRb, say a was born on July 22, 1944 and b on July 22, 1931, then bRa. And further, if aRb and bRc, then aRc. This relation is, hence, an equivalence relation on the set of all people.

Example 1.8.2 As another illustration, let R be the relation defined on the set of integers as follows: aRb if and only if $a - b$ is an integral multiple of 3, that is, $(a,b) \in R$ if and only if there is an integer d such that $a - b = 3d$. Now it is clear that $a - a = 0 = 3\cdot 0$, and so aRa holds for any integer a. Secondly, if aRb, then there is an integer d such that $a - b = 3\cdot d$. But then $b - a = 3(-d)$. Since $(-d)$ is an integer, we have bRa. Thus, if aRb, then also bRa. Thirdly, suppose aRb and bRc. Then there are integers d_1 and d_2 such that $a - b = 3d_1$ and $b - c = 3d_2$. But then $(a - b) + (b - c) = 3d_1 + 3d_2$, that is, $a - c = 3(d_1 + d_2)$. Since $d_1 + d_2$ is an integer, we have aRc. Thus, R is an equivalence relation on the set of all integers. We note, for example, that $3R0$, since $3 - 0 = 3\cdot 1$; $5R2$, since $5 - 2 = 3\cdot 1$, and $8R(-4)$, since $8 - (-4) = 3\cdot 4$.

Not all relations, of course, are equivalence relations. In fact, there exist relations that satisfy any two of the properties but not all of the properties of Definition 1.8.1. Examples of such relations are given in exercises 8, 9, and 10.

Exercises

1. Let R be the relation of Example 1.8.2. Show that if a is any integer, then exactly one of the following holds: i) $aR0$, ii) $aR1$, iii) $aR2$.

2. Let $\cong$ denote the relation of congruence among triangles in the plane. Show that $\cong$ is an equivalence relation.

3. Let $\sim$ denote the relation of similarity among triangles in the plane. Show that $\sim$ is an equivalence relation.

4. Let R be the relation defined on the set of integers Z as follows: aRb if and only if $a + b$ is an integral multiple of 2. Show that R is an equivalence relation on Z.

5. Let $A = \{1,2,3,4,5,6,7,8,9,0\}$. Let $A_1 = \{1,2,3,4\}$, $A_2 = \{5,6,7\}$, $A_3 = \{8,9\}$, $A_4 = \{0\}$. Define the relation R on A by aRb if and only

if $a \in A_i$ and $b \in A_j$ implies $i = j$. Show that R is an equivalence relation on A.

6. Let R be a relation defined on the set of all people as follows: aRb means that a is an ancestor of b. Is R an equivalence relation? Show that only iii) of Definition 1.8.1 is satisfied.

7. Let R be the relation defined on the set of integers Z as follows: aRb if and only if $a + b$ is an integral multiple of 3. Show that R is not an equivalence relation on Z. In particular, show that only ii) of Definition 1.8.1 is satisfied.

8. Let R be the relation defined on the set of integers Z as follows: aRb if and only if either a is an integral factor of b or b is an integral factor of a. Show that i) and ii) of Definition 1.8.1 are satisfied, but that iii) is not.

9. Show that weak inequality ($\leq$) on the real number system satisfies i) and iii) of Definition 1.8.1, but that it does not satisfy ii).

10. Let $S = Z \cup \{\sqrt{2}\}$ with Z the set of integers. Define aRb if $a + b \in Z$. Show that ii) and iii) of Definition 1.8.1 are satisfied, but not i). ●

In each of our examples, the equivalence relation R splits the set into a number of subsets as follows: two elements a and b are in the same subset if and only if aRb.

Definition 1.8.3 Let R be an equivalence relation on a set A. We call the set of elements equivalent to a given element a the *equivalence class determined by a*. This will be denoted by $\bar{a}$. Thus, $\bar{a} = \{x \mid x \in A \text{ and } xRa\}$.

It is easy to see that in Example 1.8.2, $\bar{0} = \{\cdots,-6,-3,0,3,6,9,\cdots\}$, $\bar{1} = \{\cdots,-5,-2,1,4,7,10,\cdots\}$, and $\bar{2} = \{\cdots,-7,-4,-1,2,5,8,\cdots\}$. Moreover, if $a \in Z$, then $\bar{a}$ is one of these three sets.

Lemma 1.8.4 Let $\sim$ be an equivalence relation on a set A. Then

$$\text{i)}\quad a \sim b \text{ if and only if } \bar{a} = \bar{b},$$

and

$$\text{ii)}\quad b \in \bar{a} \text{ if and only if } \bar{a} = \bar{b}.$$

Proof:

i) Let $a \sim b$. Let $x \in \bar{a}$. By definition of $\bar{a}$, $x \sim a$. Since $\sim$ is an equivalence relation, $x \sim a$ and $a \sim b$ implies $x \sim b$, and so $x \in \bar{b}$. Thus, $\bar{a} \subseteq \bar{b}$. Now, since $a \sim b$, by ii) of Definition 1.8.1, $b \sim a$. Interchanging the role of a and b in the above argument, we get $\bar{b} \subseteq \bar{a}$. Thus, $\bar{a} = \bar{b}$.

Conversely, suppose $\bar{a} = \bar{b}$. In particular, since $a \sim a$, $a \in \bar{a}$, and so $a \in \bar{b}$, that is, $a \sim b$.

ii) Let $b \in \bar{a}$. Then $b \sim a$, and by i), $\bar{b} = \bar{a}$. Conversely, if $\bar{b} = \bar{a}$, then by i), $b \sim a$ and so $b \in \bar{a}$.

Theorem 1.8.5 Let $\sim$ be an equivalence relation on a set A. Then,

i) For fixed a and b in A, either $\bar{a} \cap \bar{b} = \phi$ or $\bar{a} = \bar{b}$.

ii) If P is the collection of equivalence classes defined by $\sim$, then $A = \bigcup_{\bar{a} \in P} \bar{a}$.

Proof:

i) Either $\bar{a} \cap \bar{b} = \phi$ or $\bar{a} \cap \bar{b} \neq \phi$. If the latter is true, then there exists an element $c \in A$ such that $c \in \bar{a}$ and $c \in \bar{b}$. By ii) of Lemma 1.8.4, $\bar{c} = \bar{a}$ and $\bar{c} = \bar{b}$. Thus, $\bar{a} = \bar{b}$.

ii) For each $a \in A$, $a \in \bar{a}$. It is clear then that

$$A = \bigcup_{\bar{a} \in P} \bar{a}.$$

Theorem 1.8.5 proves that an equivalence relation splits a set into a collection of disjoint subsets. Such a collection is called a *partition.*

Definition 1.8.6 Let A be a set, $A \neq \phi$, and let P be a collection of subsets $\{A_\alpha\}$ of A such that

i) $A_\alpha \neq \phi$, all α,

ii) $A = \bigcup_\alpha A_\alpha$,

iii) If $A_\alpha \neq A_\beta$, then $A_\alpha \cap A_\beta = \phi$.

Then we say that P is a *partition* of the set A.

Theorem 1.8.5 shows that every equivalence relation on a set A gives rise to a partition of A. We now show that the converse is also true.

Theorem 1.8.7 Let P be a partition of a set A. Define the relation R on A as follows: aRb if a and b both belong to the same subset A_α of the partition P. Then R is an equivalence relation on A.

Proof: Let P be a partition of A. Let R be defined as in the statement of the theorem.

i) aRa, since a is in one and only one A_α.

ii) aRb implies bRa. (Why?)

iii) aRb and bRc imply aRc. (Why?)

Definition 1.8.8 In Theorem 1.8.7, the equivalence relation R is called the equivalence relation *induced* by the partition P. Similarly, in Theorem 1.8.5, we call P the partition *induced* by the equivalence relation $\sim$.

Exercises

11. (a) Define a relation R for points on the surface of Earth as follows: pRq if p and q have the same latitude. Is R an equivalence relation? If so, determine the partition induced by R on the surface of the earth, as in Theorem 1.8.5.

(b) In (a), replace R by the relation R': $pR'q$ if p and q have the same longitude.

12. Let $f: A \to B$ and define the relation R on A as follows: $a_1 R a_2$ if $a_1 f = a_2 f$, for $a_1, a_2 \in A$. Show that R is an equivalence relation on A.

13. Let $f: A \to A$. Show that f is an equivalence relation on A if and only if f is the identity function on A.

14. (a) Let $\sim$ be an equivalence relation on a set $A \neq \phi$. Let P be the partition of A induced by $\sim$. If R is the equivalence relation induced by this partition P according to Theorem 1.8.7, show that $a \sim b$ if and only if aRb.

(b) Let P be a partition of a set $A \neq \phi$. Let R' be the equivalence relation induced by P according to Theorem 1.8.7. Let P' be the partition induced by R' according to Theorem 1.8.5. Show that $P = P'$, that is, show that $A_\alpha \in P$ if and only if $A_\alpha \in P'$.

CHAPTER 2

Number Theory

Before one can begin to study almost any mathematical subject in an organized way, it is necessary to have some familiarity with properties of the integers. In fact, in Chapter 1 we have already made use of certain counting and ordering properties of the set of integers. A systematic study of the integers is itself an important and venerable branch of mathematics, known as the theory of numbers. Our purpose here, however, is neither to give a complete "definition" or "construction" of the integers nor to present a comprehensive view of the results of the theory of numbers. Rather, our goal is to establish certain results about the integers that we shall derive from a relatively small but familiar set of basic properties. In addition, the development of the material in this chapter will serve as a springboard and model in our study of abstract algebraic systems.

2.1 THE ARITHMETIC AND ORDER PROPERTIES OF THE INTEGERS

We begin our study of number theory by first listing the basic arithmetic properties of the set of integers $Z = \{\cdots,-2,-1,0,1,2,3,\cdots\}$, and deriving some of their elementary consequences. Following this, we discuss two of the basic order properties.

Arithmetic Properties.

A_0: There exists a function $f:Z \times Z \rightarrow Z$ called *addition*. For $a,b \in Z$, we call $(a,b)f$, denoted by $a + b$, the *sum* of a and b.

M_0: There exists a function $g:Z \times Z \rightarrow Z$ called *multiplication*. For $a,b \in Z$, we call $(a,b)g$, denoted by $a \cdot b$ (or ab), the *product* of a and b.

A_1: If $a,b,c \in Z$, then $(a + b) + c = a + (b + c)$ (associative law of addition).

A_2: If $a,b \in Z$, then $a + b = b + a$ (commutative law of addition).

A_3: There exists a unique integer 0 (zero) such that $a + 0 = a$, for all $a \in Z$. (0 is called an *identity for addition.*)

A_4: If $a \in Z$, then there exists a unique integer denoted by $-a$ such that $a + (-a) = 0$. $(-a)$ is called the *negative* of a, or the *additive inverse* of a.

M_1: If $a,b,c \in Z$, then $(a \cdot b) \cdot c = a \cdot (b \cdot c)$ (associative law of multiplication).

M_2: If $a,b \in Z$, then $a \cdot b = b \cdot a$ (commutative law of multiplication).

M_3: There exists a unique integer $1 \neq 0$ such that $a \cdot 1 = a$, for all $a \in Z$. (1 is called an *identity for multiplication*, or simply an *identity*.)

M_4: Let $a,b,c \in Z$, $a \neq 0$. If $a \cdot b = a \cdot c$, then $b = c$. (cancellation law of multiplication.)

D: If $a,b,c \in Z$, then $a \cdot (b + c) = (a \cdot b) + (a \cdot c) = a \cdot b + a \cdot c$.

(Distributive Law)

We recall from section 1.7 that $a + b$ and $a \cdot b$, being the images of (a,b) under the functions f and g respectively, are unique elements of Z. The fact that $a + b$ and $a \cdot b$ are in Z is also expressed by saying that Z is *closed* with respect to addition and multiplication. That $a + b$ and $a \cdot b$ are unique is also expressed by saying that addition and multiplication are *well-defined.* Further, if $a = b$ and $c = d$, then the ordered pairs (a,c) and (b,d) are equal. Therefore $(a,c)f = (b,d)f$, that is $a + c = b + d$. This expresses the familiar property that equal integers may be added to both sides of an equation.

Before examining some of the elementary consequences of these properties, we take a closer look at the associative laws and A_4 and M_4.

The associative laws permit us to extend meaningfully the concepts of addition and multiplication of two integers to "addition" and "multiplication" of three integers. Given the integers a, b, and c, the sum $a + b$ is a well-defined integer, and thus, so is $(a + b) + c$. Similarly, $a + (b + c)$ is a well-defined integer, since we have formed it by adding the two integers a and $(b + c)$. By the associative law, $(a + b) + c = a + (b + c)$. We may therefore now define the "sum" $a + b + c$ as either the integer $(a + b) + c$ or the integer $a + (b + c)$, since these two integers are precisely the same. Of course, $a \cdot b \cdot c$ can be defined analogously. Moreover, in Chapter 4 we prove that $a_1 + a_2 + \cdots + a_n$ has only one interpretation as an integer. This is known as the *generalized associative law.*

We should point out that there exist well-known binary operations that are not associative. For example, the operation of subtraction: $(2 - 3) - 5 \neq 2 - (3 - 5)$. Subtraction is also an example of a binary operation that is not commutative.

A_4 and M_4 are the first pair of properties that do not appear to be analogous. To have a complete parallelism between A_4 and M_4, since 1 is the multiplicative identity and 0 is the additive identity, we would hope to have in place of M_4 the following property: If $a \in Z$, then there exists an integer a^{-1} such that $a \cdot a^{-1} = 1$. This can happen in Z only when $a = 1$ or $a = -1$. M_4 is therefore a weakened version of a division property. For it says in effect that one can "divide out" a common nonzero factor that occurs on both sides of an equation. It is, in fact, the strongest possible "division" property that holds for the integers. The analogous "cancellation" law for addition is a consequence of the stronger property A_4.

Theorem 2.1.1 Let $a,b,c \in Z$. If $a + b = a + c$, then $b = c$.

Proof: By A_4, there exists an integer $(-a)$ such that $a + (-a) = 0$, and by A_2, $a + (-a) = (-a) + a$, whence $(-a) + a = 0$. By A_0, $(-a) + (a + b) = (-a) + (a + c)$, and by A_1, $((-a) + a) + b = (-a) + (a + b) = (-a) + (a + c) = ((-a) + a) + c$. Thus, $0 + b = 0 + c$, and by A_2, $b + 0 = 0 + b = 0 + c = c + 0$. Finally, by A_3, $b = b + 0 = c + 0 = c$, that is, $b = c$.

Exercises

1. Show that $-0 = 0$.

*2. Prove: If $a,b,c \in Z$ and $a + b = c + b$, then $a = c$. •

We shall now deduce several elementary and familiar theorems that follow from the arithmetic properties.

Theorem 2.1.2 If $a \in Z$, then $a \cdot 0 = 0 \cdot a = 0$.

Proof: By A_3, $0 = 0 + 0$. Using D, $a \cdot 0 = a \cdot (0 + 0) = a \cdot 0 + a \cdot 0$. By A_3, $a \cdot 0 + 0 = a \cdot 0$. Thus, $a \cdot 0 + 0 = a \cdot 0 + a \cdot 0$. By Theorem 2.1.1, $0 = a \cdot 0$. By M_2, $0 \cdot a = 0$.

The reader should note where A_0 is used in this proof.

Theorem 2.1.3 Let $a \in Z$. Then $-(-a) = a$.

Proof: By A_4, $a + (-a) = 0$ and $(-a) + [-(-a)] = 0$. By A_2, $(-a) + a = 0$. Thus, $(-a) + [-(-a)] = (-a) + a$. By Theorem 2.1.1, $-(-a) = a$.

Theorem 2.1.4 Let $a,b \in Z$. Then

$$(-a)b = a(-b) = -(ab).$$

Proof: $a \cdot 0 = a[b + (-b)] = ab + a(-b)$. (Why?) By Theorem 2.1.2, $a \cdot 0 = 0$, whence $ab + a(-b) = 0$. (What properties were used to get this equation?). Also, by A_4, $ab + [-(ab)] = 0$. Thus, $ab + a(-b) = ab + [-(ab)]$.

By the cancellation law for addition (Theorem 2.1.1), we now have

$$a(-b) = -(ab).$$

Similarly,
$$(-a)b = -(ab).$$

Corollary 2.1.5 Let $a,b \in Z$. Then $(-a)(-b) = ab$.

Proof: Exercise.

Exercises

3. Prove Corollary 2.1.5.

*4. Let $a,b \in Z$. Prove that $-(a+b) = (-a)+(-b)$. •

To simplify our notation, we agree to write $a - b$ in place of $a+(-b)$. That is, we *define* the symbol $a - b$ to be $a+(-b)$.

Order Properties

There exists a subset P of Z, called the set of positive integers, such that

O_1: if $a \in Z$, then one and only one of the following is true:
i) $a \in P$; ii) $a = 0$; iii) $-a \in P$ (law of trichotomy).

O_2: If $a,b \in P$, then $a+b \in P$ and $a \cdot b \in P$.

A third order property will be given in the next section. It is interesting to note that the arithmetic properties and O_1 and O_2 imply $1 \in P$.

Theorem 2.1.6 $1 \in P$.

Proof: By M_3, $1 \neq 0$, and therefore either $1 \in P$ or $-1 \in P$. But if $-1 \in P$, $(-1)(-1) = 1 \in P$ by O_2 and Corollary 2.1.5, a contradiction. Hence $1 \in P$.

Although O_1 and O_2 are very familiar, the use of the word "order" in connection with these properties may not be apparent. Since $1 \in P$, clearly $1+1 = 2 \in P$, $2+1 = 3 \in P$, $3+1 = 4 \in P$, and so forth. When we write 1, 2, 3, 4, we say that these four integers are in their "natural order." If the integer a is to the left of the integer b in this list, then we observe that $b - a$ is positive and in fact we can define "natural order" in precisely this way.

Definition 2.1.7 Let $a,b \in Z$. We say that *a is less than b* if $b - a$ is positive, and we write $a < b$. Alternatively, we say that *b is greater than a* and write $b > a$.

In the event that $a < b$ or $a = b$, we write $a \leq b$. Similarly, we write $a \geq b$ if either $a > b$ or $a = b$.

In view of the definition of $<$, it is now clear that $1 < 2, 2 < 3, \cdots$. Thus the "natural order" of the integers coincides with our concept of $<$, which we have defined in terms of positiveness.

Definition 2.1.8 Let $a \in Z$. If $(-a)$ is positive, we say that a is a *negative* integer, or that a is *negative.*

We observe that if a is negative, then a can be neither positive nor zero. For if a is both negative and positive, then both $-a$ and a are positive, contradicting O_1. For the case that a is both negative and zero, we see $-a \in P$ and $a = 0$, again contradicting O_1.

If a is positive, then $a - 0 = a + 0 = a$ is positive. Thus, $0 < a$. Also, if $0 < a$, then a is positive. In light of this, O_1 and O_2 become

O_1': If $a \in Z$, exactly one of the following is true: $a > 0$, $a = 0$, $(-a) > 0$.

O_2': If $a,b \in Z$, and if $0 < a$ and $0 < b$, then $0 < a + b$ and $0 < ab$.

Exercises

*5. Let $a \in Z$. Prove that a is negative if and only if $a < 0$.

*6. Show that O_1' is equivalent to O_1'': If $a \in Z$, then one and only one of the following is true:

$$\text{i) } a < 0, \quad \text{ii) } a = 0, \quad \text{iii) } (-a) < 0. \bullet$$

As we have previously remarked, our point of departure in studying the integers is to assume that the integers satisfy certain basic properties, namely, A_0, A_1, A_2, A_3, A_4, M_0, M_1, M_2, M_3, M_4, D, O_1 and O_2, and an additional property O_3 to be given in the next section. Any other properties of the integers that we shall use can be deduced from this basic set.

Although we have already given two statements of the law of trichotomy, we now give a third version, whose proof will again illustrate the use of our basic properties.

Theorem 2.1.9 Let $a,b \in Z$. Then one and only one of the following is true:

$$a < b; \quad a = b; \quad a > b.$$

Proof: Consider $b - a$. By O_1, exactly one of the following is true:
(i) $b - a$ is positive, (ii) $b - a = 0$, (iii) $-(b - a)$ is positive. If (i), then $b - a$ is positive and so $a < b$, by definition. If (ii), then $b - a = 0$, whence

$$b + (-a) = 0,$$

$$[b + (-a)] + a = 0 + a,$$

$$b + [(-a) + a] = a, \text{ (Why?)}$$
$$\text{and } b = a. \text{ (Why?)}$$

If (iii), then $-(b - a)$ is positive, whence, by Exercise 4 above,

$$a - b \text{ is positive. (Why?)}$$

Now, by definition, $a > b$.

Theorem 2.1.10 Let a, b, c be integers such that $a < b$ and $b < c$. Then $a < c$ (transitive law).

Proof: By definition of $<$, $b - a$ and $c - b$ are both positive. But

$$\begin{aligned}(c - b) + (b - a) &= [c + (-b)] + [b + (-a)] \\ &= c + \{(-b) + [b + (-a)]\} \quad \text{(Why?)} \\ &= c + \{[(-b) + b] + (-a)\} \\ &= c + \{0 + (-a)\} \\ &= c - a.\end{aligned}$$

Hence, $c - a$ is positive and $a < c$.

Exercise

7. Show that $\leq$ is a relation on Z. Which properties of an equivalence relation does it satisfy? •

We leave as exercises the following important properties of Z.

Theorem 2.1.11 Let $a,b,c \in Z$ and suppose $a < b$. Then

$$a + c < b + c.$$

Theorem 2.1.12 Let $a,b,c \in Z$, $a < b$ and $c > 0$. Then

$$ac < bc.$$

Theorem 2.1.13 Let $a,b,c \in Z$, $a < b$, $c < 0$. Then

$$bc < ac.$$

Exercises

8. Prove Theorems 2.1.11 through 2.1.13.
9. Let $a, b, c \in Z$ and suppose

$$a + c < b + c.$$

Prove that $a < b$.

10. Let $a, b, c \in Z$, $c > 0$ and suppose

$$ac < bc.$$

Prove that $a < b$.

11. Let $a, b, c \in Z$, $c < 0$ and suppose

$$bc < ac.$$

Prove that $a < b$.

12. Let $a_1, a_2, a_3, a_4 \in Z$. Prove that $((a_1 + a_2) + a_3) + a_4 = (a_1 + a_2) + (a_3 + a_4) = (a_1 + (a_2 + a_3)) + a_4 = a_1 + ((a_2 + a_3) + a_4) = a_1 + (a_2 + (a_3 + a_4))$.
Discuss the definition of $a_1 + a_2 + a_3 + a_4$.

*13. Prove that if $a \in Z$, $a \neq 0$, then $a^2 = a \cdot a > 0$.

14. a) Is property D' true in Z?
D': $a + (b \cdot c) = (a + b) \cdot (a + c)$.
b) Let A, B, and C be sets. Using $\cup$ instead of $+$ and $\cap$ instead of $\cdot$, then the following are analogous to D and D' in the calculus of sets: $A \cap (B \cup C) = (A \cap B) \cup (A \cap C)$ and $A \cup (B \cap C) = (A \cup B) \cap (A \cup C)$. Prove that these equations hold.

15. Define binary operations $\oplus$ and $\otimes$ on Z by $a \oplus b = a + b$, $a \otimes b = a$. Which of the properties $A_0 - A_4$, $M_0 - M_4$, and D are true when $+$ is replaced by $\oplus$ and $\cdot$ is replaced by $\otimes$?

*16. i) Let $a, b \in Z$, $a \neq 0$, $b \neq 0$. Show that $ab \neq 0$.
ii) Show that if $a \neq 0$, $b \neq 0$ implies $ab \neq 0$, then $A_0 - A_4$, $M_0 - M_3$, and D imply M_4.

17. Show that O_1, O_2, $A_0 - A_4$, $M_0 - M_3$, and D imply M_4.

2.2 WELL ORDERING AND MATHEMATICAL INDUCTION

Let P denote the set of positive integers. Let S be a nonempty subset of P. We wish to establish that S has a smallest integer, that is, that there is an integer $m \in S$ such that $m \leq n$, for all integers $n \in S$. To do this, we first choose any integer n_1 in S. If upon surveying the elements of S, $n_1 \leq n$ for all $n \in S$, then n_1 is the desired integer. If not, there is an integer $n_2 < n_1$. If $n_2 \leq n$, for all $n \in S$, n_2 is the integer we desire. If n_2 does not work, we pick n_3 from S, and so forth. In this way, we get a string of integers in S:

$$n_1 > n_2 > n_3 > \cdots > n_k > \cdots.$$

Since these integers are all positive, it is not difficult to be convinced that the string must stop at, say, $n_N = m$ and this will be our desired smallest integer.

There are, of course, certain problems with this line of reasoning. First, in order to determine if n_1 is the smallest integer of an infinite set S of positive integers, it is necessary to test in turn all integers of the form $n - n_1, n \in S$, for positiveness. Since S is infinite, there is no effective way of doing this. Second, even assuming we can tell when n_1 is not the smallest and we find an $n_2 < n_1$, and then an $n_3 < n_2$, and so forth, how do we really know that the chain $n_1 > n_2 > \cdots > n_k > \cdots$ must eventually end? The crux of the matter is this: In assuming that this chain ends, we are assuming that a certain nonempty set of positive integers, namely $\{n_1, n_2 \cdots, n_k, \cdots\}$, has a smallest element. This is tantamount to assuming from the very outset that S has a smallest integer. This fact, however, cannot be derived from the arithmetic and order properties already stated.[6] Thus, we assume it to be a basic property of the integers, and we add this third order property to our list.

O_3: *Law of Well Ordering for Positive Integers (LWO)* Let P denote the set of all positive integers. Let $S \subseteq P$, $S \neq \phi$. Then there exists an integer $m \in S$ such that $m \leq n$, for all $n \in S$. We call m the *smallest* or *least* integer (element) of S and we say that S has a least member.

Before we give a simple application of O_3, we prove two of its elementary consequences.

Lemma 2.2.1 The law of well ordering for positive integers implies that 1 is the smallest positive integer.

Proof: By Theorem 2.1.6, 1 is a positive integer. Now we let $M = \{m \mid m \in P \text{ and } 0 < m < 1\}$. If $M = \phi$, 1 is the smallest positive integer in P. Otherwise, $M \neq \phi$ and by O_3, there is a smallest integer n in M. Then $0 < n < 1$ and also $0 < n \cdot n < 1 \cdot n < 1$. But then $n^2 \in M$ and $n^2 < n$, a contradiction. Thus, $M = \phi$ and 1 is the smallest positive integer.

[6] This can be shown by displaying a mathematical system that satisfies all the other properties, but not this one. The rational number system is such an example, since the set of positive rational numbers does not have a smallest element.

Corollary 2.2.2 If $n \in P$, then there does not exist an integer k such that $n < k < n + 1$.

Proof: Suppose there exists an integer k such that $n < k < n + 1$. Then $0 < k - n < 1$, contradicting the theorem.

We now give a simple application of O_3, proving that the formula

$$(*)\ 1 + 2 + \cdots + n = n(n + 1)/2$$

is true for all positive integers n. We prove this by showing that the set E of positive integers for which (*) is true is equal to P. Thus, we observe that when $n = 1$, the formula becomes $1 = 1\cdot(1 + 1)/2 = 1$; this means that 1 is in E. For $n = 2$, we have

$$1 + 2 = \frac{2(2 + 1)}{2}, \text{ so again } 2 \in E$$

Continuing along these lines it is clear that we could only verify (*) for a finite collection of positive integers n.

We observe, however, that if $E \neq P$, then there is a positive integer n for which $1 + 2 + \cdots + n \neq \dfrac{n(n + 1)}{2}$. Let $S = \left\{n \mid n \in P \text{ and } 1 + 2 + \cdots + n \neq \dfrac{n(n + 1)}{2}\right\}$, that is, $S = P - E$. By our assumption that $E \neq P$, $S \neq \phi$. By O_3, S has a least element, say m. Hence, $1 + 2 + \cdots + m \neq \dfrac{m(m + 1)}{2}$. On the other hand, $m \neq 1$, since $1 \in E$, and so, by Lemma 2.2.1, $m > 1$. Thus, $m - 1 > 0$, that is, $m - 1 \in P$. But by the choice of m, $m - 1 \notin S$, since $m - 1 < m$. (Why is $m - 1 < m$?)

Thus,

$$1 + 2 + \cdots + (m - 1) = \frac{(m - 1)(m - 1 + 1)}{2} = \frac{(m - 1)m}{2}$$

Adding m to both sides of this equation,

$$\begin{aligned} 1 + 2 + \cdots + (m - 1) + m &= \frac{(m - 1)m}{2} + m \\ &= \frac{(m - 1)m}{2} + \frac{2m}{2} \\ &= \frac{m^2 + m}{2} \\ &= \frac{m(m + 1)}{2}, \end{aligned}$$

and so the formula is true for m. Hence, $m \in E$, that is, $m \notin S$, a contradiction. To avoid this contradiction we must conclude that $S = \phi$, and hence $E = P$, that is, the formula is true for all positive integers.

We see that the proof consists of two essential parts. First, we showed $1 \in E$. Secondly, we observed that if $m - 1 \in E$, with $m > 1$, then $m \in E$. Actually, as we shall see shortly, this result could have been proved by merely establishing the following about E:

i) $1 \in E$,
ii) whenever $n \in E$, then $n + 1 \in E$.

For, from an intuitive point of view, assuming that $1 \in E$, then by ii), $1 + 1 = 2 \in E$. By ii) again, since $2 \in E$, $2 + 1 = 3 \in E$. And again, $3 + 1 = 4 \in E$. To proceed once more along these lines would be futile. We shall show that i) and ii) together imply that $E = P$.

Theorem 2.2.3 Principle of Mathematical Induction (PMI) Let E be a subset of P such that

i) $1 \in E$ and
ii) whenever $n \in E$, also $n + 1 \in E$.

Then $E = P$.

Proof: To show that $E = P$, let $S = P - E$. If $S = \phi$, then $E = P$ and we are finished. Hence, assume $S \neq \phi$. Then by LWO, there exists a positive integer $m \in S$ such that $m \leq k$, for all $k \in S$. Since $1 \in E$, clearly $m \neq 1$, and so $m > 1$ by Lemma 2.2.1. Thus, $m - 1 > 0$. Since m is the least positive integer in S, $m - 1 \notin S$, that is, $m - 1 \in E$. Hence, by ii), $m \in E$, contradicting that $m \in S$. Therefore, $S = \phi$ and $E = P$.

There is another formulation of mathematical induction which is quite useful in application. This is often called "course-of-values" induction and is derived easily from the law of well ordering.

Theorem 2.2.4 Course-of-Values Formulation of PMI Let E be a set of positive integers such that

i) $1 \in E$ and
ii) Each integer $n > 1$ is in E, whenever $k \in E$ for all k satisfying $1 \leq k < n$.

Then $E = P$.

Proof: Exercise.

One very wide application of induction is to problems in which a statement involving positive integers is to be proved. Such a statement need not take the form of an equation as in the example following Corollary 2.2.2. As an illustration, consider the following statement which we denote by $Q(n)$: Any nonempty set of positive integers containing an integer less than or equal to n has a least element.

To prove that this statement is true for all positive integers n, we need only establish

i) that $Q(1)$ is true, that is, any nonempty set of positive integers containing an integer less than or equal to 1 has a least element, and
ii) that whenever $Q(k)$ is true, then $Q(k + 1)$ is true.

For if S is the set of positive integers for which $Q(n)$ is true, then i) and ii) above are equivalent to i') $1 \in S$ and ii') if $k \in S$, then $k + 1 \in S$, respectively. If i) and ii) have been proved, then by PMI, $S = P$, that is, $Q(n)$ is true for all positive integers n.

We shall actually carry out the proof of this statement, as outlined above, in Theorem 2.3.2. Clearly, any equation or inequality involving n can be viewed as some statement $Q(n)$.

Exercises

1. Prove Theorem 2.2.4, modeling your proof after that of Theorem 2.2.3.
2. Prove each of the following by mathematical induction.
   a) $2 + 4 + 6 + \cdots + (2n) = n(n + 1)$, for all positive integers n.
   b) $n < 2^n$, for each $n > 0$.
   c) $1 + 3 + 5 + \cdots + (2n + 1) = (n + 1)^2$, for each integer $n > 0$.
   d) $1 + 3 + 9 + \cdots + 3^n = (3^{n+1} - 1)/2$, for each integer $n > 0$.

*3. Prove: If a and b are in Z and $a < b$, then $a + 1 \leq b$.

4. Let a,b be positive integers. Show that there exists an integer m such that $ma > b$. (Archimedean property).
5. Let A be a nonempty subset of Z. A is said to be *well ordered* if whenever $B \subseteq A$, $B \neq \phi$, there exists an element $b \in B$ such that $b \leq c$, where c is any integer in B, that is, B has a least element b. Prove:
   i) Z is not well ordered.
   ii) If A is a well-ordered subset of Z and if $B \subseteq A$, $B \neq \phi$, then B is well ordered.
6. Let A be a nonempty subset of Z and let c be an integer satisfying $c \leq m$ for all $m \in A$. Show that A is well ordered.

   Hint: If $c < 0$ consider the set $A' = \{m - c + 1 \mid m \in A\}$. (This statement is equivalent to LWO).
7. If A is well ordered and if C is a subset of Z such that for each element $c \in C$, there is an $a \in A$ such that $a \leq c$, show that C is well ordered and that $A \cup C$ is well ordered.
8. Prove: Let S be a set of integers satisfying
   i) $-3 \in S$
   ii) whenever n is in S for $n \geq -3$, so is $n + 1 \in S$.
   Then all integers $k \geq -3$ are in S.

*9. Prove: Let S be a set of integers satisfying
i) $c \in S$ and
ii) whenever n is in S for $n \geq c$, then also $n + 1 \in S$.
Then all integers $k \geq c$ are in S.
Note: c need not be positive.

*10. Prove: Let S be a set of integers satisfying
i) $c \in S$ and
ii) whenever n is an integer $> c$ such that all k satisfying $c \leq k < n$ are in S, then also $n \in S$.
Then all $k \geq c$ are in S.

11. Prove by mathematical induction that for each positive integer n, there exists a positive integer c_n such that $5^{2n} - 1 = 24 \cdot c_n$.

12. What is wrong with the following proof?
Theorem: All horses have the same color.
"Proof": Let $P(n)$ be the proposition that all horses in a set of n horses are the same color.

For $n = 1$, $P(n)$ is clearly true. Let n be an integer for which $P(n)$ is true. We want to prove that $P(n + 1)$ is true.

Let $H_1, \cdots, H_{n+1}$ be the $n + 1$ horses in a set of $n + 1$ horses. Then consider the subset of n horses $S' = \{H_1, \cdots, H_n\}$. By assumption, these are all the same color. Now, replace H_n in S' by H_{n+1}. In the resulting set $S'' = \{H_1, \cdots, H_{n-1}, H_{n+1}\}$ of n horses, all are the same color since this is again a set of n horses. Since H_n and H_1 are the same color, and H_{n+1} and H_1 are the same color, all $n + 1$ horses are the same color. This concludes the "proof."

13. Let S be a nonempty set of negative integers. Suppose i) $-1 \in S$ and ii) whenever $-n \in S$, $n \geq 1$, then also $-n - 1 \in S$. Prove that S is the set of all negative integers.

*14. For $n \geq 0$ define $n!$ as follows:

$$0! = 1$$

and $n! = n(n-1)!$ for $n \geq 1$, that is $n! = n \cdot (n-1) \cdot (n-2) \cdots 2 \cdot 1$.

For $n \geq 0$ define the symbol $\binom{n}{k} = \dfrac{n!}{k!(n-k)!}$ if $0 \leq k \leq n$ and $\binom{n}{k} = 0$ if $k < 0$ or $k > n$.

i) Show that $\binom{n}{0} = 1$, $\binom{n}{n} = 1$, $\binom{n}{1} = n$, $\binom{n}{n-1} = n$ for $n \geq 0$, and $\binom{n}{n-k} = \binom{n}{k}$.
ii) Prove that $\binom{n+1}{k} = \binom{n}{k} + \binom{n}{k-1}$ for all $n \geq 0$ and all integers k. (This can be proved without PMI).
iii) Prove by induction on n that $\binom{n}{k}$ is an integer for all $n \geq 0$ and all integers k.
iv) Prove that $\binom{n}{0} + \binom{n}{1} + \binom{n}{2} + \cdots + \binom{n}{n} = 2^n$.

2.3 THE EQUIVALENCE OF THE LAW OF WELL ORDERING, THE PRINCIPLE OF MATHEMATICAL INDUCTION, AND COURSE-OF-VALUES INDUCTION

In section 2.2, we chose LWO as our last basic property of the integers. Theorem 2.2.3 (PMI) was proved using LWO with the other basic properties. In this section we shall show that LWO can be proved as a theorem under the assumption of PMI and the other properties, that is, we could just as well have chosen the principle of mathematical induction for this last property in place of LWO. In other words, the two mathematical statements—LWO and PMI—are logically equivalent.

In the proof of Theorem 2.2.3, the fact that 1 is the least positive integer (Lemma 2.2.1) is strongly used. This fact is also needed in the proof that PMI implies LWO. The reader will recall that LWO was used to prove Lemma 2.2.1. Hence, in order to avoid circularity, we now give a proof of this fact using only PMI.

Lemma 2.3.1 The principle of mathematical induction implies that 1 is the least positive integer.

Proof: Let $E = \{m \mid m \in P \text{ and } m \geq 1\}$. Clearly, $1 \in E$, since $1 \geq 1$. Next, assume that $n \in E$, that is, that $n \geq 1$. Then $n + 1 > 1$, whence $n + 1 \in E$. By PMI, $E = P$, that is, for any positive integer m, $m \geq 1$.

Theorem 2.3.2 The principle of mathematical induction implies the law of well ordering.

Proof: We must prove that if $S \neq \phi$, $S \subseteq P$, then S has a least element. To achieve this, let $Q(n)$ be the statement: Any set of positive integers containing an integer $\leq n$ has a least element. Let $E = \{m \mid m \in P$ and $Q(m)$ is true$\}$. Now, $Q(1)$ is true, since if a set of positive integers has an integer ≤ 1, it must, by Lemma 2.3.1, contain 1, which is its least element. Thus, $1 \in E$. Assume now that $n \in E$. That is, if B is a set of positive integers and if B contains an integer $\leq n$, B has a least integer. Now let C be a set of positive integers containing an integer $\leq n + 1$. If C has no integer less than $n + 1$, then clearly $n + 1$ is the least integer of C. If C has an integer less than $n + 1$, it follows from Lemma 2.3.1 that C has an integer $\leq n$. (Why?) Thus, since $n \in E$, C has a least integer. Thus under any circumstances, C has a least integer and $n + 1 \in E$. By PMI, $E = P$.

Now, for $S \subseteq P$, $S \neq \phi$, S has some integer $m > 0$. Since $Q(m)$ is true for all $m > 0$, S has a least integer. This completes the proof.

Theorems 2.2.3 and 2.3.2 show the logical equivalence of the law of well ordering and the principle of mathematical induction. It is also true that the course-of-values formulation of induction is logically equivalent to each of these statements. The proof of these facts is left as an exercise.

Exercise

1. Show that each of the following implies both of the other statements. a) LWO, b) PMI, c) course-of-values induction.

Hint: We have already shown that a) implies b), b) implies a), and, as an exercise, that a) implies c). It is not necessary to show all three of the other implications individually. It is enough to prove either that c) implies a) or that c) implies b). For, then using the transitivity of implication, we can get from any statement to any of the others.

2.4 ELEMENTARY CONCEPTS: DIVISORS AND PRIME NUMBERS

Although, as we have seen, the binary operation of division cannot be defined on the integers, some of the multiplicative properties of pairs of integers are most conveniently described by the use of words such as "divisor," "divisible," and "quotient." These terms are traditionally used in number theory, since division is possible for certain pairs of integers. We say, for example, that 18 is "exactly" divisible by 3, but not by 4. That is, the equation $18 = 3x$ has a solution in integers, while $18 = 4x$ does not.

Definition 2.4.1 Let b be an integer. We say the integer a is a *factor* of b or a *divisor* of b if there exists an integer c such that $b = ac$. We denote this by $a \mid b$. If a is not a divisor of b, we write $a \nmid b$. If $a \mid b$, we also say that b is a *multiple* of a, that b is *divisible* by a, or that *a divides b*.

As a consequence of this definition, we see that any integer a divides 0. Indeed, even $0 \mid 0$. We also observe that if $a \neq 0$, $a \in Z$, then $0 \nmid a$.

It also follows directly from our definition of divisibility that every integer a is divisible by 1, -1, a, and $-a$. For certain integers, such as 3 and 7, this list exhausts all possibilities. For other integers, such as 6 and 8, this list does not exhaust all divisors. Those integers that have only the obvious divisors play a special role in number theory. In fact, an important result obtained in this chapter will be that an integer $n > 1$ can be written as a product of integers with only the obvious divisors.

Definition 2.4.2 Let $p \in Z$, $p > 1$. If $n \mid p$ implies that $n = 1, -1, p$, or $-p$, then p is called a *prime number*, or simply a *prime*.

Definition 2.4.3 If $n \in Z$, $n > 1$, and n is not a prime number, then we say that n is a *composite number*, or n is *composite*.

It is clear that if n is composite, there exist integers $n_1 > 1$, $n_2 > 1$ such that $n = n_1 \cdot n_2$.

Definition 2.4.4 Let a be any integer. The *absolute value* of a, denoted by $|a|$, is defined as follows:

$$|a| = \begin{cases} a & \text{if} \quad a \geq 0 \\ -a & \text{if} \quad a < 0. \end{cases}$$

Clearly, $|-3| = 3$, $|1| = 1$, $|-17| = 17$, and $|0| = 0$.

Exercises

*1. Prove: Let $a, b \in Z$. Then

$$|ab| = |a|\,|b|.$$

*2. Prove: Let $a \in Z$. Then $|a| = 0$ if and only if $a = 0$. If $a \neq 0$, then $|a| > 0$.
*3. Prove: If $a \in Z$, then $1 \mid a$, $-1 \mid a$, $a \mid a$, and $-a \mid a$.
*4. Prove: If $a \in Z$, then $a \mid 0$.
*5. Prove: If $a, b \in Z$ and if $a \mid b$, then

$$a \mid (-b), \ (-a) \mid b, \ (-a) \mid (-b), \ |a| \mid |b|,$$

and $a \mid bc$, where c is any integer.
*6. Prove: Let $a, b \in Z$. Then $|a| = |b|$ if and only if $a = \pm b$, that is, $a = b$ or $a = -b$. ●

Theorem 2.4.5 Let $a, b \in Z$, $b \neq 0$. If $a \mid b$, then $|b| \geq |a|$.

Proof: Since $a \mid b$, there exists an integer c such that $b = ac$. Since $b \neq 0$, then necessarily $a \neq 0$ and $c \neq 0$. Thus, $|c| > 0$, by Exercise 2 above. Now, by Exercise 1 above, $|b| = |a|\,|c|$. Since $|c| > 0$, we have two cases:

a) If $|c| > 1$, then
$|a|\,|c| > |a| \cdot 1 = |a|$, so $|b| > |a|$
b) If $|c| = 1$, then $|b| = |a|$.

Exercises

*7. Prove: If $a, b, c \in Z$, $a \mid b$ and $b \mid c$, then $a \mid c$, that is, divisibility is transitive.
*8. Prove: If $c \in Z$, $c \neq 0$, and if $a, b \in Z$, then

$$(ca) \mid (cb) \text{ if and only if } a \mid b.$$

*9. Prove: If $a,b,c \in Z$, $a \mid b$ and $a \mid c$, then $a \mid (bu + cv)$, where u and v are any integers.

*10. Prove: If $m \mid n$ and $n \mid m$, then $m = \pm n$.

*11. Prove: If $0 \leq a < c$ and $0 \leq b < c$, then $|a - b| < c$.

12. Find all positive factors of 24.

*13. Prove: If p and q are prime numbers such that

$$p \mid q, \text{ then } p = q.$$

14. Prove that p is a prime if and only if whenever $p = n_1 n_2$, then $|n_1| = 1$ or $|n_2| = 1$.

15. Let $p > 1$ and suppose whenever $p \mid ab$, then $p \mid a$ or $p \mid b$. Prove that p is a prime.

16. Prove: If $a \in Z$, then

$$-|a| \leq a \leq |a|.$$

17. Prove: Let $c > 0$. Then $-c \leq b \leq c$ if and only if $|b| \leq c$.

18. Prove: If $b,c \in Z$, then

$$\big|\, |b| + |c| \,\big| = |b| + |c|.$$

19. Prove: If $b,c \in Z$, then

$$|b + c| \leq |b| + |c| \quad \text{(triangle inequality).}$$

2.5 THE DIVISION ALGORITHM

In the development of elementary number theory, a single theorem occurs that plays a key role in all that follows. This theorem is known as the division algorithm and establishes the elementary fact, known to all school children, that an integer b may be "divided" by an integer a in such a way that the remainder is less than $|a|$. A most important exercise for the reader, as he progresses through this book, is to examine the proofs carefully and see how the line of reasoning of many of them can be traced back to the division algorithm. Our proof of the division algorithm will rest on the law of well ordering for positive integers.

Theorem 2.5.1 Division Algorithm If a and b are in Z, $a \neq 0$, then there exist unique integers q and r such that

$$b = aq + r, \qquad 0 \leq r < |a|.$$

Proof:

I. Existence of q and r.

Case A: $a > 0$.

Let $S = \{b - ax \mid x \in Z, b - ax \geq 0\}$. We first show that $S \neq \phi$. If $b \geq 0$, then for $x = 0$, $b - a \cdot 0 = b$, whence $b - a0 \in S$ and $S \neq \phi$. If $b < 0$, then since $a > 0$, $a \geq 1$ and $ab \leq b$. Thus $b - ab \in S$ and $S \neq \phi$.

By the law of well ordering S has a least element r. (Why?) Thus there exists an integer q such that

$$b - aq = r, \qquad 0 \leq r.$$

To complete the proof of existence for the case $a > 0$ we need to show that $r < |a|$. Hence, assume that $r \geq |a| = a$. Then $r = a + c$ with $0 \leq c < r$ and $b - aq = a + c$. Hence $c = b - a(q + 1) \in S$, and since $c < r$, this contradicts the choice of r.

Case B: $a < 0$. Since $-a > 0$, by Case A there exist q', r such that

$$b = (-a)q' + r, \quad 0 \leq r < |a|.$$

Setting $q = -q'$,

$$b = aq + r, \quad 0 \leq r < |a|.$$

II. Uniqueness

Suppose $b = aq + r = aq' + r'$ with

$$0 \leq r < |a| \qquad \text{and} \qquad 0 \leq r' < |a|.$$

Then $a(q - q') = r' - r$. Hence, $a \mid (r - r')$ and, if $r - r' \neq 0$, $|a| \leq |r - r'|$ by Theorem 2.4.5. But, since $0 \leq r < |a|$ and $0 \leq r' < |a|$, by Exercise 11, Section 2.4, we have $|r - r'| < |a|$. This is a contradiction, hence $r - r' = 0$. Therefore $r = r'$ and since $a \neq 0$, $q = q'$.

The integer r of Theorem 2.5.1 is called the *remainder* in the division of b by a, and q is called the *quotient*.

Exercises

1. Prove Theorem 2.5.1 by induction on b.

   Hint: First consider the case $b \geq 0$. For $b < 0$, consider $-b$.

2. Let $b_1, b_2, a \in Z$, $a \neq 0$.

   Let $b_1 = aq_1 + r_1$, $0 \leq r_1 < |a|$,

   $b_2 = aq_2 + r_2$, $0 \leq r_2 < |a|$.

   Prove that if $b_1 + b_2 = aq_3 + r_3$, $0 \leq r_3 < |a|$, and if $r_1 + r_2 = aq_4 + r_4$, $0 \leq r_4 < |a|$, then $r_3 = r_4$.

3. Let $b_1, b_2, a \in Z$, $a \neq 0$.
   Let $b_1 = aq_1 + r_1$, $0 \leq r_1 < |a|$,
   $b_2 = aq_2 + r_2$, $0 \leq r_2 < |a|$.
   Prove that $a \mid (b_1 - b_2)$ if and only if $r_1 = r_2$.

2.6 GREATEST COMMON DIVISOR AND EUCLIDEAN ALGORITHM

Definition 2.6.1 Let a,b be integers. If $n \in Z$ and $n \mid a$ and $n \mid b$, then n is called a *common divisor* of a and b.

If a and b are integers and $a \neq 0$, then the set of common divisors of a and b is finite. The fundamental theorem of this section is the existence of a unique nonnegative common divisor that is divisible by all common divisors.

Definition 2.6.2 Let a and b be integers. The greatest common divisor (gcd) of a and b, denoted by (a,b), is defined as the nonnegative integer d such that

i) $d \mid a$ and $d \mid b$ and
ii) if $e \mid a$ and $e \mid b$, then $e \mid d$.

It is easy to show that $(132, 630) = 6$, $(14, 21) = 7$, and $(380, 95) = 95$. Moreover, we see that $(0,0) = 0$. The use of the word "greatest" is not a misnomer, for if either $a \neq 0$ or $b \neq 0$, then since any common divisor e of a and b divides d, $d \geq |e|$.

There is, of course, the problem of showing that any two integers a and b have a gcd, and that the gcd is indeed unique.

Theorem 2.6.3 Let $a,b \in Z$. Then (a,b) exists and is unique. Moreover, there exist integers s and t such that

$$(a,b) = as + bt$$

Proof: Since $(0,0) = 0 = 0 \cdot s + 0 \cdot t$ (any s and t), the theorem is true if $a = b = 0$. Thus, we will assume that at least $a \neq 0$.

Let $S = \{ax + by \mid x,y \in Z \text{ and } ax + by > 0\}$. Since $0 < a \cdot a + b \cdot 0 \in S$, $S \neq \phi$. By the law of well ordering S has a smallest positive integer d, whence there exist integers s and t such that $d = as + bt$. We shall show that d is (a,b).

By the division algorithm, there exist integers q and r such that $a = dq + r$, $0 \leq r < d$. Then $r = a - dq = a - (as + bt)q = a(1 - sq) + b(-tq)$. If $0 < r$, then $r \in S$. But this would contradict the fact that d is the smallest integer in S. Hence, $r = 0$, and $a = dq$, that is, $d \mid a$. Similarly, $d \mid b$.

Now, from the equation $d = as + bt$ and Exercise 9, section 2.4, we see that if $e \mid a$ and $e \mid b$, then $e \mid d$, completing the proof of the existence of (a,b).

We leave the proof of uniqueness of (a,b) as an exercise.

Exercises

1. Let $a,b \in Z$. Prove the uniqueness of (a,b).
2. Let $S \subseteq Z, S \neq \phi$ and assume that $a + b$ and $a - b$ are in S whenever $a,b \in S$. Prove there exists an integer $c \in S$ such that

$$S = \{nc \mid n \in Z\}. \bullet$$

Definition 2.6.4 If a,b,x and y are integers, then $ax + by$ is called a *linear combination* of a and b.

Although Theorem 2.6.3 shows the existence of (a,b), the proof of the theorem does not give us a systematic way of finding (a,b). An efficient method is available, however, and we present it here. This method, the *Euclidean algorithm*, also gives another proof of the existence of (a,b). In the exercises of Section 2.8, we give a fairly simple way of finding (a,b), which unlike the Euclidean algorithm, however, does not show how to find (a,b) as a linear combination of a and b.

Euclidean Algorithm Let a and b be integers, $a \neq 0$.

Then by the division algorithm there exist integers q_1 and r_1 such that

$$(1) \quad b = aq_1 + r_1, \qquad 0 \leq r_1 < |a|$$

If $r_1 = 0$, then $(a,b) = |a|$, and we are finished. If, however, $r_1 > 0$, then there are integers q_2 and r_2 such that

$$(2) \quad a = r_1q_2 + r_2, \qquad 0 \leq r_2 < r_1.$$

If $r_2 = 0$, then $r_1 \mid a$ and hence, by (1), $r_1 \mid b$. Also, if $c \mid a$ and $c \mid b$, then by (1), $c \mid r_1$. By Definition 2.6.2, $r_1 = (a,b)$ and $r_1 = b \cdot 1 + a(-q_1)$. If $r_2 > 0$, we continue, getting the complete chain:

$$\begin{array}{rll}
(1) & b = aq_1 + r_1, & 0 \leq r_1 < |a| \\
(2) & a = r_1q_2 + r_2, & 0 \leq r_2 < r_1 \\
(3) & r_1 = r_2q_3 + r_3, & 0 \leq r_3 < r_2 \\
 & \vdots & \\
(n-1) & r_{n-3} = r_{n-2}q_{n-1} + r_{n-1} & 0 \leq r_{n-1} < r_{n-2} \\
(n) & r_{n-2} = r_{n-1}q_n + r_n & 0 \leq r_n < r_{n-1} \\
(n+1) & r_{n-1} = r_nq_{n+1} &
\end{array}$$

Since $0 \le r_i < r_{i-1}$ at the ith step, we see that some remainder eventually must be zero. (Why?) This is our $(n + 1)$st step.

Now, starting with $(n + 1)$ and working back to (1), we see that $r_n \mid r_{n-1}$ by $(n + 1)$; by (n), $r_n \mid r_{n-2}$; by $(n - 1)$, $r_n \mid r_{n-3}$; and so by a simple induction argument, $r_n \mid a$ and $r_n \mid b$. Now, if $c \mid a$ and $c \mid b$, then by (1), $c \mid r_1$; by (2), $c \mid r_2$; by (3), $c \mid r_3$; and continuing, at (n), $c \mid r_n$. Since $r_n > 0$, $r_n = (a,b)$

We next show how to find s and t such that $(a,b) = r_n = as + bt$.

Starting at (n),

$$\begin{aligned} r_n &= r_{n-2} - r_{n-1}q_n \\ &= r_{n-2} - q_n(r_{n-3} - q_{n-1}r_{n-2}) \quad (\text{by } (n-1)) \\ &= -q_n r_{n-3} + (1 + q_n q_{n-1})r_{n-2} = \cdots \\ &= as + bt \end{aligned}$$

Example 2.6.5 Find (132, 630).

$$\begin{aligned} 630 &= 132 \cdot 4 + 102 \\ 132 &= 102 \cdot 1 + 30 \\ 102 &= 30 \cdot 3 + 12 \\ 30 &= 12 \cdot 2 + 6 \\ 12 &= 6 \cdot 2 + 0. \end{aligned}$$

Then, once again, $6 = (132, 630)$. Moreover,

$$\begin{aligned} 6 &= 30 + 12(-2) \\ &= 30 + (102 + 30(-3))(-2) \\ &= 102(-2) + 30(7) \\ &= 102(-2) + (132 + 102(-1))(7) \\ &= 132 \cdot 7 + 102(-9) \\ &= 132 \cdot 7 + (630 + 132(-4))(-9) \\ &= 630(-9) + 132 \cdot 43. \end{aligned}$$

Although (a,b) is unique, the integers s and t of Theorem 2.6.3 are not unique. The reader should find another set of values for s and t in the example above.

One last remark is necessary. Since the Euclidean algorithm implies the existence of (a,b) and shows how to express (a,b) as a linear combination of a and b, why did we first give an existence proof? The answer is that the first proof is easily applied to more general algebraic systems. This will be seen when we treat principal ideal domains in Chapter 5.

Exercises

3. Express (24, 63) as a linear combination of 24 and 63, (15, 23) as a linear combination of 15 and 23.

*4. Let $a, b \in Z$. Suppose there are integers s and t such that

$$as + bt = 1. \text{ Show that}$$

$$(a,b) = (a,t) = (s,b) = (s,t) = 1.$$

*5. Let $a,b,m \in Z$, $a \neq 0$, $m > 0$.
Prove: $(ma,mb) = m(a,b)$.

*6. Let $a,b,m \in Z$.
Prove: $(a,m) = (b,m) = 1$ if and only if

$$(ab,m) = 1.$$

*7. Let $(c,m) = d \neq 0$. Putting $c = dc_1$ and $m = dm_1$, prove that $(c_1,m_1) = 1$.

*8. Let $a,b \in Z$. Define the *least common multiple* (lcm) of a and b, denoted by $[a,b]$, to be the nonnegative integer ℓ such that
i) $a \mid \ell$ and $b \mid \ell$ and
ii) if $a \mid n$ and $b \mid n$, then $\ell \mid n$.
Prove that any two integers a and b have an lcm.

*9. Let $a_1,a_2,\cdots,a_n \in Z$. Define the *greatest common divisor* of a_1, $a_2,\cdots,a_n$, denoted by $(a_1,a_2,\cdots,a_n)$, as the nonnegative integer d satisfying
i) $d \mid a_i$, $i = 1,\cdots,n$
ii) if $e \mid a_i$, $i = 1,\cdots,n$, then $e \mid d$.
Prove that $(a_1,\cdots,a_n)$ exists and can be expressed in the form

$$(a_1,a_2,\cdots,a_n) = a_1b_1 + a_2b_2 + \cdots + a_nb_n$$

where the b_i are integers.

10. Let $a,b,c \in Z$ satisfy $(a,b,c) = 1$. Show that $(a + b,b,c) = 1$.

11. Let $a_1,a_2,\cdots,a_n \in Z$. Define the least common multiple of a_1, $a_2,\cdots,a_n$ and prove its existence.

2.7 *EUCLID'S LEMMA*

Definition 2.7.1 We say that the integers a and b are *relatively prime* (or that a is *prime to* b) if $(a,b) = 1$.

Clearly, if p is a prime and if $p \nmid a$, then $(a,p) = 1$ and a and p are relatively prime.

Theorem 2.7.2 Euclid's Lemma Let p be a prime number and let $p \mid ab$, $a,b \in Z$. Then $p \mid a$ or $p \mid b$.

Proof: Suppose $p \nmid a$. Then $(a,p) = 1$, whence, by Theorem 2.6.3, there exist integers s and t such that

$$1 = as + pt.$$

Then $b = b(as + pt) = (ab)s + p(bt)$.
Since $p \mid ab$ and $p \mid p$, clearly $p \mid (ab)s + p(bt)$, whence $p \mid b$.

Corollary 2.7.3 Let n be a positive integer and let $a_1,a_2,\cdots,a_n$ be integers such that $p \mid (a_1 \cdots a_n)$, p a prime. Then $p \mid a_i$, for some i such that $1 \le i \le n$.

Proof: We prove this corollary by using mathematical induction.

If $n = 1$, the theorem is trivially true.

Assume the theorem for $n - 1 \ge 1$. Let $p \mid (a_1 \cdots a_{n-1} \cdot a_n)$. By Euclid's lemma, either $p \mid a_n$ or $p \mid (a_1 \cdots a_{n-1})$. If $p \mid a_n$, we are finished. If $p \nmid a_n$, then $p \mid (a_1 \cdots a_{n-1})$. By our induction hypothesis, $p \mid a_i$ for some i satisfying $1 \le i \le n - 1$. In either case $p \mid a_i$ for some i such that $1 \le i \le n$. Thus, the theorem is true for n if it is true for $n - 1$. The theorem then follows from PMI.

Corollary 2.7.4 Let p be a prime number and let $a_1,a_2 \in Z$ satisfy $0 < a_i < p$, for $i = 1,2$. Then

$$p \nmid a_1 a_2.$$

Proof: Exercise.

Exercises

1. a) Find three integers a, b, and c such that $a \mid bc$, but $a \nmid b$ and $a \nmid c$.
   b) Find three integers a, b, and c, a not prime, such that $a \mid bc$ and $a \mid b$.
2. Prove Corollary 2.7.4.

*3. Let $a,b,c,d \in Z$ and suppose $ab = cd$. Show that any prime divisor of a is a prime divisor of c or d.

4. Let $p_1,p_2,\cdots,p_n$ be n distinct prime numbers. Let $a_1,a_2,\cdots,a_n$ be n integers such that for each i, $p_i \mid a_i$.
   Prove that $p_i \nmid (a_1 a_2 \cdots a_n) + 1$, $i = 1,2,\cdots,n$.
5. Let $p_1,p_2,\cdots,p_n$ be n distinct prime numbers. Let $a_1,a_2,\cdots,a_n$ be n integers such that for each $i = 1,2,\cdots,n$, $p_i \nmid a_j$, for $j \ne i$.

Prove that if $p_i \mid (a_1 a_2 \cdots a_n)$, then $p_i \mid a_i$. Also prove that if $p_i \nmid (a_1 a_2 \cdots a_n)$, then $p_i \nmid a_j, j = 1,2,\cdots,n$.

6. Let a, b, and m be integers such that $(a,m) = 1$ and $m \mid ab$. Show that $m \mid b$. (This is a generalization of Theorem 2.7.2.)

2.8 THE FUNDAMENTAL THEOREM OF ARITHMETIC

The fundamental theorem of arithmetic, to be proved in this section, states the familiar fact that any integer $n > 1$ can be expressed as the product of prime numbers in essentially one way. This theorem, an example of an algebraic structure theorem, shows the importance of prime numbers, since they "generate" the set of all positive integers greater than one. As we progress we shall see other examples of mathematical systems where certain elements act as the "building blocks" for the whole system.

Definition 2.8.1 Let n be a positive integer that is either itself a prime number or that can be expressed as a product of prime numbers. Then we say that n has a *factorization into prime numbers*, or that *n has a prime factorization*. If $n = p_1 p_2 \cdots p_s$, $s \geq 1$, and each p_i is a prime, we call this expression a *prime factorization* for n.

Theorem 2.8.2 The Fundamental Theorem of Arithmetic Let n be a positive integer, $n > 1$. Then n has a prime factorization and if

$$n = p_1 p_2 \cdots p_r \qquad \text{and} \qquad n = q_1 q_2 \cdots q_s$$

are two prime factorizations for n, then $r = s$ and the two factorizations differ only in the order of the factors.

Proof:

I. *Existence.* Let $S = \{k \mid k \text{ is an integer}, k > 1, k \text{ does not have a prime factorization}\}$. If $S = \phi$, then the theorem is proved. Thus, assume $S \neq \phi$. By the law of well ordering, S has a least member, say m. If the only positive factors of m are m and 1, then m is a prime and $m \notin S$. Thus, m can be written $m = m_1 \cdot m_2$, where $1 < m_1 < m$, $1 < m_2 < m$. By our choice of m, $m_1 \notin S$ and $m_2 \notin S$. Hence, $m_1 = u_1 u_2 \cdots u_g$, $g \geq 1$, where each u_i is prime, and $m_2 = v_1 v_2 \cdots v_h$, $h \geq 1$, where each v_i is prime. But

$$m = m_1 m_2 = u_1 \cdots u_g v_1 \cdots v_h$$

is a prime factorization for m. Thus, $m \notin S$, a contradiction. Therefore, $S = \phi$ and we have shown that every integer $n > 1$ has a prime factorization.

II. *Uniqueness.* The uniqueness is certainly true for $n = 2$. Thus, we shall assume that the theorem holds for all integers k such that $2 \leq k < n$

and prove that the theorem must then hold for n. Then by course-of-values induction, the theorem will follow for all integers $n > 1$.

Suppose, therefore, that

$$n = p_1 p_2 \cdots p_r = q_1 q_2 \cdots q_s$$

are two prime factorizations for n. If $r = 1$, then n is a prime, whence we must have $s = 1$ and also $p_1 = q_1$. Thus, we may assume $r > 1$ and $s > 1$. Now it is clear that $p_1 \mid q_1 q_2 \cdots q_s$, and so, by Corollary 2.7.3, $p_1 \mid q_t$ for some t. But since q_t is a prime, $p_1 = q_t$. We may assume that the q_i's are so arranged that $t = 1$. Thus,

$$p_1 p_2 \cdots p_r = p_1 q_2 \cdots q_s.$$

Since $p_1 \neq 0$, we may cancel and get $p_2 \cdots p_r = q_2 \cdots q_s = n'$. But $1 < n' < n$, and by our induction hypothesis we may conclude i) that $r - 1 = s - 1$ and ii) that the factorization $p_2 \cdots p_r$ is just a rearrangement of the q_i's, $i = 2, \cdots, r$. Thus, $r = s$, and since $p_1 = q_1$, we have proved the theorem for n. Hence, by induction, the theorem is true for all integers $n > 1$.

The fundamental theorem of arithmetic is often called the unique factorization theorem for positive integers. It is now clear that we excluded 1 from the set of prime numbers so that the fundamental theorem of arithmetic could be stated in the form of Theorem 2.8.2.

We remark that there exist mathematical systems very similar to the integers in which the analogue of the fundamental theorem of arithmetic is false. For example, let E be the set of even integers. E satisfies all the arithmetic and order properties of Z, except that E does not have a multiplicative identity. If in E we define a prime number n to be one that cannot be written as the product of two other numbers in E, then we see that 2, 6, and 18 are primes in E. There are, then, two distinct prime factorizations of 36 in E, since $36 = 2 \cdot 18 = 6 \cdot 6$.

Definition 2.8.3 Let x be a nonzero integer. Define x^n, $n \geq 0$, as follows:

1) $x^0 = 1$
2) For $n \geq 1$, $x^n = x^{n-1} \cdot x$.

This definition is an example of a *recursive* or *inductive definition.* It is not difficult to convince oneself that this provides a method for computing x^n for integers $x \neq 0$, $n \geq 0$. The complete proof that x^n is uniquely defined for all $x \neq 0$ and $n \geq 0$ utilizes the principle of mathematical induction and is rather subtle. We refer the interested reader to Halmos [16] or Stoll [48].

To look at a specific example, let $x = 3$.

Then $3^0 = 1$, $3^1 = 3^{1-1}\cdot 3 = 3^0\cdot 3 = 3$,

$3^2 = 3^{2-1}\cdot 3 = 3^1\cdot 3 = 3\cdot 3 = 9$

$3^3 = 3^{3-1}\cdot 3 = 3^2\cdot 3 = 9\cdot 3 = 27$

$3^4 = 3^{4-1}\cdot 3 = 3^3\cdot 3 = 27\cdot 3 = 81$, ad infinitum.

With our definition, we are now in a position to derive the usual laws of exponents. The derivations are left as exercises.

Exercises

*1. If $n \geq 0$ and $m \geq 0$ and if $x \neq 0$, prove that $x^n \cdot x^m = x^{n+m}$.

*2. Prove: $(xy)^n = x^n y^n$, if $n \geq 0$, all $x, y \in Z$, $x \neq 0$, $y \neq 0$.

*3. Let $a, b, n \in Z$, $n \geq 1$. Prove by induction on n that $(a+b)^n = \binom{n}{0}a^n + \binom{n}{1}a^{n-1}b + \binom{n}{2}a^{n-2}b^2 + \cdots + \binom{n}{i}a^{n-i}b^i + \cdots + \binom{n}{n}b^n$. ●

Our exponential notation allows the following useful restatement of Theorem 2.8.2.

Corollary 2.8.4 If $n > 1$ is a positive integer, then n has a unique representation in the form

$$n = p_1^{e_1} p_2^{e_2} \cdots p_r^{e_r},$$

where p_i is prime, $i = 1, 2, \cdots, r$, $p_i < p_j$, for $i < j$ and $e_i > 0$, all i.

Proof: Exercise.

Definition 2.8.5 The representation of n in Corollary 2.8.4 is called the *prime power factorization of n.*

Exercises

4. Let m and n be integers such that $m \mid n$. Show that if $n = p_1^{e_1} p_2^{e_2} \cdots p_r^{e_r}$, $e_i > 0$, p_i prime, for each i, then $m = p_1^{f_1} p_2^{f_2} \cdots p_r^{f_r}$, with $0 \leq f_i \leq e_i$, for each i.
5. Let $p_1, p_2, \cdots, p_s$ be distinct prime numbers. Let $j_1, j_2, \cdots, j_s, k_1, k_2, \cdots, k_s$ be integers ≥ 0. Let $m = p_1^{j_1} \cdots p_s^{j_s}$ and $n = p_1^{k_1} \cdots p_s^{k_s}$. Then $m \mid n$ if and only if $j_i \leq k_i$, $i = 1, 2, \cdots s$.
6. Let $m = p_1^{j_1} \cdots p_s^{j_s}$ and $n = p_1^{k_1} \cdots p_s^{k_s}$, where the p_i are distinct primes, and $j_i \geq 0$, $k_i \geq 0$, all i. Show that

$$(m,n) = p_1^{e_1} \cdots p_s^{e_s}$$

and

$$[m,n] = p_1^{f_1} \cdots p_s^{f_s},$$

where $e_i = \min(j_i, k_i)$ (the smaller of j_i and k_i), for each i, and $f_i = \max(j_i, k_i)$ (the larger of j_i and k_i), for each i.

7. Let $a,b \in Z$. Show that

$$|ab| = (a,b)\cdot[a,b].$$

*8. Let $a \mid m$, $b \mid m$ and $(a,b) = 1$. Show that $ab \mid m$.
*9. Let a,b,c, and $d \in Z$. If $ab \mid cd$ and $(a,d) = 1$, show that $a \mid c$.
10. Let $n \geq 1$ and suppose $2^n + 1$ is a prime. Show that $n = 2^j$, for some $j \geq 0$.
11. Let $p \geq 2$. Show that if $2^p - 1$ is a prime, then p is also a prime.
12. Let p and q be distinct primes. Show that $(1 + p + p^2)(1 + q + q^2 + q^3)$ is the sum of all the divisors of p^2q^3.
13. Let $m = p_1^{e_1}\cdots p_s^{e_s}$ be the prime power factorization for m. How many positive divisors of m are there, and what are they? Show that the sum of these divisors is $(1 + p_1 + \cdots + p_1^{e_1})\cdots(1 + p_s + \cdots + p_s^{e_s})$.
14. Prove that there are infinitely many prime numbers.

    Hint: See Exercise 4, Section 2.7. This is Euclid's proof.
15. Prove that there exist infinitely many primes of the form $6n - 1$.

    Hint: Consider $p_1p_2\cdots p_k - 1$, where $p_1 = 2$, $p_2 = 3, \cdots, p_k$ are the first k primes.
16. Prove that there are infinitely many primes of the form $4n - 1$.
17. Define $F_n = 2^{2^n} + 1$ (the nth Fermat number), $n = 0,1,2,\cdots$. Prove that $(F_n,F_m) = 1$, $n \neq m$.

    Hint: First prove by mathematical induction that

$$F_0F_1\cdots F_{n-1} + 2 = F_n, \qquad n = 1,2,\cdots.$$

Then observe that if $p \mid F_n$ and $p \mid F_m$, $n \neq m$, then p must be odd and even. Show that this exercise gives another proof of Exercise 14.

18. Show that an integer $n > 1$ is a square if and only if all exponents in its prime power factorization are even integers.
19. Prove that $\sqrt{2}$ is irrational, that is, $\sqrt{2}$ cannot be written as a ratio of integers.

    Hint: $\sqrt{2} = p/q$ implies $2q^2 = p^2$. Count the number of times 2 appears in the factorization of $2q^2$ and of p^2.
20. If n is a positive integer which is not a perfect square, then show $\sqrt{n}$ is irrational.

2.9 CONGRUENCES

If a and b are integers, then in view of the division algorithm, it makes sense to talk about the quotient and remainder obtained upon dividing a

by b. If b is kept fixed and we look at the remainders obtained by allowing a to take on successive integral values, then a periodic sequence of remainders always occurs. For example, if $b = 3$ and a assumes the values 0, 1, 2, 3, 4, 5, 6, 7, then the remainders obtained are, respectively, 0, 1, 2, 0, 1, 2, 0, 1. (What does the sequence of quotients look like?)

This property provides a way of classifying integers according to the remainder obtained upon division by a fixed integer. In fact, it is often the case that this remainder is the only thing of interest. For example, in counting the hours of the day, we begin again after reaching the number 12. With the sole exception of using 12 instead of 0, this is equivalent to counting the hours sequentially and naming each hour with the remainder obtained upon division by 12. In this section we shall study a relation on the integers that is defined in terms of remainders.

Definition 2.9.1 Let a, b, and m be integers, $m \geq 0$. Then we say that *a is congruent to b modulo m* if $m \mid (a - b)$. We denote this by $a \equiv b \pmod{m}$. If $m \nmid (a - b)$, we write $a \not\equiv b \pmod{m}$.

Exercise

*1. Prove that $a \equiv b \pmod{m}$ if and only if a and b have the same remainder upon division by m. (See Exercise 3, section 2.5.) •

Example 2.9.2 Let $m = 5$. It is easy to see that $5 \equiv 0 \pmod{5}$, $0 \equiv 5 \pmod{5}$, $6 \equiv 1 \pmod{5}$, $12 \equiv 2 \pmod{5}$, $-3 \equiv 7 \pmod{5}$ and $10^6 + 1 \equiv 1 \pmod{5}$.

We notice that if $m = 0$ then $a \equiv b \pmod{0}$ means $0 \mid (a - b)$. Since $0 \mid x$ only if $x = 0$, then $0 \mid (a - b)$ means $a - b = 0$, that is $a = b$. Therefore, $a \equiv b \pmod{0}$ is exactly the same as $a = b$.

For a fixed integer m, congruence modulo m is a relation on the set Z. Before proceeding, the reader should study Example 1.8.2.

Theorem 2.9.3 For a fixed integer $m \geq 0$, the relation $a \equiv b \pmod{m}$ defines an equivalence relation on the set of integers Z.

Proof: By the definition of equivalence relation, we must show that the set $\{(a,b) \mid a \equiv b \pmod{m}\}$ defines a relation that is reflexive, symmetric, and transitive.

i) Let $a \in Z$. Since $m \mid 0$, $m \mid (a - a)$. And so by definition, $a \equiv a \pmod{m}$. (reflexive)
ii) Let $a \equiv b \pmod{m}$. Then $m \mid (a - b)$ and $m \mid (-1)(a - b)$. Hence $m \mid (b - a)$ and $b \equiv a \pmod{m}$. (symmetric)
iii) Let $a \equiv b \pmod{m}$ and $b \equiv c \pmod{m}$. Then $m \mid (a - b)$ and $m \mid (b - c)$. Hence $m \mid [(a - b) + (b - c)]$ and $m \mid (a - c)$. Therefore $a \equiv c \pmod{m}$. (transitive)

Theorem 2.9.4 Let $a \equiv b \pmod{m}$ and $c \equiv d \pmod{m}$. Then
i) $a + c \equiv b + d \pmod{m}$
ii) $a - c \equiv b - d \pmod{m}$
iii) $ac \equiv bd \pmod{m}$.

Proof: We leave i) and ii) as exercises. To prove iii) we first note that since $a \equiv b \pmod{m}$, $m \mid (a - b)$. This means that there is an integer k_1 such that $mk_1 = a - b$ or $a = b + mk_1$. Similarly from $c \equiv d \pmod{m}$, $c = d + mk_2$ for some integer k_2. Then

$$ac = (b + mk_1)(d + mk_2) = bd + m(k_1 d + k_2 b + mk_1 k_2).$$

Hence $m \mid (ac - bd)$ and $ac \equiv bd \pmod{m}$.

Theorems 2.9.3 and 2.9.4 indicate that in many respects the relation $a \equiv b \pmod{m}$ behaves very much like the relation of equality. On the other hand, the cancellation law of multiplication holds only in a restricted sense. For example, if $ab \equiv ac \pmod{m}$ and $a \not\equiv 0 \pmod{m}$, the perfect analogue to the cancellation law for integers would imply that $b \equiv c \pmod{m}$. But this is not in general true. For if $a = 2$, $b = 3$, $c = 1$, $m = 4$, then $2 \cdot 3 \equiv 2 \cdot 1 \pmod{4}$, but $3 \not\equiv 1 \pmod{4}$. We now give the best possible analogue of the cancellation law.

Theorem 2.9.5 Let $ac \equiv bc \pmod{m}$, $c \not\equiv 0 \pmod{m}$. Let $d = (c,m)$ and $m_1 d = m$. Then $a \equiv b \pmod{m_1}$.

Proof: Let $m_1 d = m$ and $c_1 d = c$. By hypothesis $ac \equiv bc \pmod{m}$ and hence there exists an integer k such that $ac - bc = mk$. Substitution for c and m yields

$$ac_1 d - bc_1 d = m_1 dk.$$

Since $c \not\equiv 0 \pmod{m}$, $c \neq 0$ and $d \neq 0$. Hence

$$ac_1 - bc_1 = m_1 k,$$

and

$$(a - b)c_1 = m_1 k.$$

Now $(c_1, m_1) = 1$ (Exercise 7, section 2.6). Thus $m_1 \mid (a - b)$ (Exercise 9, section 2.8), and

$$a \equiv b \pmod{m_1}.$$

If we add the condition that $(c,m) = 1$, then the cancellation may be carried out without a change of modulus.

Corollary 2.9.6 If $ac \equiv bc \pmod{m}$ and if $(c,m) = 1$, then $a \equiv b \pmod{m}$.

Proof: Exercise.

Exercises

2. Since $10 \equiv 3 \pmod 7$, $100 \equiv 2 \pmod 7$, and $1000 \equiv 6 \pmod 7$, prove that $7 \mid (1000a_3 + 100a_2 + 10a_1 + a_0)$ if and only if $7 \mid (a_0 + 3a_1 + 2a_2 + 6a_3)$.
3. Let $f: Z \to Z$ be defined by $(x)f = a_n x^n + a_{n-1} x^{n-1} + \cdots + a_1 x + a_0$, $a_i \in Z$. Show that if $a \equiv b \pmod m$ then $(a)f \equiv (b)f \pmod m$.
4. Let n be an integer with decimal representation $n = a_k 10^k + a_{k-1} 10^{k-1} + \cdots + a_1 \cdot 10 + a_0$, $0 \le a_i \le 9$.
   a) Prove that the remainder, when n is divided by 3, equals the remainder when $a_0 + a_1 + \cdots + a_k$ is divided by 3. Hence prove that $3 \mid n$ if and only if $3 \mid a_0 + a_1 + \cdots + a_k$.
   b) Replace 3 in part a) by 9.
   c) Prove that $11 \mid n$ if and only if

$$11 \mid (a_0 - a_1 + a_2 - \cdots + (-1)^k a_k).$$

5. For $x \in Z$, let
   $(x)f = a_n x^n + \cdots + a_1 x + a_0$ and
   $(x)g = b_n x^n + \cdots + b_1 x + b_0$, $a_i, b_i \in Z$.

Show that if $c \equiv d \pmod m$ and $a_i \equiv b_i \pmod m$ for $i = 0, 1, \cdots, n$, then $(c)f \equiv (d)g \pmod m$.

6. Find the remainder of each of the following powers of 3 under division by 5: $3, 3^2, 3^3, \cdots, 3^{11}$.
7. Complete the proof of Theorem 2.9.4.
8. Prove Corollary 2.9.6.

2.10 RESIDUE CLASSES

Since for $m = 0$, $a \equiv b \pmod m$ is just usual equality, we shall henceforth assume that $m > 0$. Theorem 2.9.3 states that the relation $a \equiv b \pmod m$ defines an equivalence relation on the set Z of integers. Then, by Theorem 1.8.5, this relation partitions Z into a collection of disjoint subsets. In the special case of Example 1.8.2, congruence modulo 3 determined three equivalence classes. In this section we shall prove in general that congruence modulo m, $m > 0$, determines m equivalence classes.

Theorem 2.10.1 Let $Z_m = \{0, 1, 2, \cdots, m - 1\}$. If a and $b \in Z_m$, $a \neq b$, then $a \not\equiv b \pmod m$.

Proof: Since $a \neq b$, we may assume without loss of generality that $a < b$. Since $0 \le a < b \le m - 1$, we get $0 < b - a \le m - 1 - a < m$. Hence $b - a$ is not a multiple of m. Thus, $b \not\equiv a \pmod m$.

Theorem 2.10.2 Let z be any integer. Then there exists one and only one integer $r \in Z_m$ such that $z \equiv r \pmod{m}$.

Proof: By the division algorithm, there exist unique integers q and r such that $z = qm + r$, $0 \leq r < m$. By the definition of congruence, $z \equiv r \pmod{m}$. Clearly, $r \in Z_m$. To show that r is the only integer in Z_m such that $z \equiv r \pmod{m}$, assume $z \equiv r_1 \pmod{m}$, where $r_1 \in Z_m$. Then $z \equiv r \pmod{m}$ and $z \equiv r_1 \pmod{m}$ imply that $r \equiv r_1 \pmod{m}$. By Theorem 2.10.1, $r = r_1$.

Definition 2.10.3 The set of integers $Z_m = \{0,1,\cdots,m-1\}$ is called the set of *least positive residues modulo m*.

Theorem 2.10.4 If m is a positive integer, then there exist exactly m equivalence classes for the equivalence relation "congruence modulo m." These equivalence classes are $\bar{0},\bar{1},\cdots,\overline{m-1}$. (The equivalence class $\bar{z}$ is simply the set $\{x \mid x \in Z \text{ and } x \equiv z \pmod{m}\}$).

Proof: By Theorem 2.10.2, any $z \in Z$ is congruent to precisely one least positive residue and so $z \in \bar{r}$ for some $r \in Z_m$. Since no two distinct least positive residues are congruent modulo m, $\bar{r}_i \neq \bar{r}_j$ for $r_i \neq r_j$ and the theorem follows.

Definition 2.10.5 The equivalence classes of Theorem 2.10.4 are called *residue classes modulo m.*

If x belongs to the residue class $\bar{z}$, then by Lemma 1.8.4, $\bar{x} = \bar{z}$. Thus, if $x_0 \in \bar{0}$, $x_1 \in \bar{1},\cdots,x_{m-1} \in \overline{m-1}$, we see that $\{\bar{x}_0,\bar{x}_1,\cdots,\bar{x}_{m-1}\}$ consists of all the residue classes modulo m.

Definition 2.10.6 The *complete set of residue classes modulo m* is the collection $\{\bar{0},\bar{1},\cdots,\overline{m-1}\}$. A set of integers $\{x_0,x_1,\cdots,x_{m-1}\}$ is called a *complete set of residues* if $\{\bar{x}_0,\bar{x}_1,\cdots,\bar{x}_{m-1}\}$ is the complete set of residue classes.

To illustrate, let $m = 6$. Then $\{0,1,2,3,4,5\}$ is the set of least positive residues modulo 6. This set is also a complete set of residues modulo 6, as is the set $\{12,-5,20,-9,10,35\}$, since $\overline{12} = \bar{0}$, $\overline{-5} = \bar{1}$, $\overline{20} = \bar{2}$, $\overline{-9} = \bar{3}$, $\overline{10} = \bar{4}$, and $\overline{35} = \bar{5}$.

The residue classes modulo 6 are easily seen to be:

$$\bar{0} = \{\cdots,-12,-6,0,6,12,\cdots\}$$

$$\bar{1} = \{\cdots,-11,-5,1,7,13,\cdots\}$$

$$\bar{2} = \{\cdots,-10,-4,2,8,14,\cdots\}$$

$$\bar{3} = \{\cdots,-9,-3,3,9,15,\cdots\}$$

$$\bar{4} = \{\cdots,-8,-2,4,10,16,\cdots\}$$

$$\bar{5} = \{\cdots,-7,-1,5,11,17,\cdots\}.$$

Exercise

*1. Prove: The set $\{x_0, \cdots, x_{m-1}\}$ is a complete set of residues modulo m if no two x_i's belong to the same residue class. •

An interesting application of some of the ideas of this section is a proof of the fact that for all integers n, $30 \mid (n^5 - n)$. By Exercise 8, section 2.8, it will suffice to show that $n^5 - n$ is divisible by 2, 3, and 5. We begin by factoring as follows:

$$n^5 - n = n(n + 1)(n - 1)(n^2 + 1).$$

For any n, the integers $n - 1$, n, and $n + 1$ are consecutive, and since no two of these are congruent modulo 3, they constitute a complete set of residues, whence (exactly) one of them must be divisible by 3. For similar reasons one of these is divisible by 2. If it should happen that one of n, $(n - 1)$, and $n + 1$ is divisible by 5, then we are finished. If none of these is divisible by 5, then either $n + 2 \equiv 0 \pmod 5$ or $n + 3 \equiv 0 \pmod 5$, since these two integers together with the previous three are a set of five consecutive integers. But if $n + 2 \equiv 0 \pmod 5$, then $n \equiv -2 \pmod 5$ and $n^2 + 1 \equiv 0 \pmod 5$. If $n + 3 \equiv 0 \pmod 5$, then again $n^2 + 1 \equiv 0 \pmod 5$. Hence, in any event $5 \mid n^5 - n$, and we have proved that $30 \mid n^5 - n$.

Exercises

*2. Let $a, b \in Z$. Prove that $a \equiv b \pmod m$ if and only if each is congruent to the same least positive residue modulo m.

3. Let $m = 7$. Let x be any integer. i) Show that x, $x + 3$, $x + 3^2$, $x + 3^3$, $x + 3^4$, $x + 3^5$, and $x + 3^6$ is a complete set of residues modulo 7.
ii) Show that x, $x + 2$, $x + 2^2$, $x + 2^3$, $x + 2^4$, $x + 2^5$, and $x + 2^6$ is not a complete set of residues modulo 7.

*4. Let $a_0, a_1, \cdots, a_{m-1}$ be m integers such that $a_i \not\equiv a_j \pmod m$, $i \neq j$. Prove that the equivalence classes $\overline{a_0}, \overline{a_1}, \cdots, \overline{a_{m-1}}$ yield a complete set of residue classes modulo m.

5. Show that for every integer n, $11 \nmid 4(n^2 + 1)$.

6. Are there any integers n such that $13 \mid 4(n^2 + 1)$?

7. Let r_n be the product of a set of n consecutive integers. Show that $n \mid r_n$.

2.11 *RESIDUE CLASS ARITHMETIC*

In section 2.9 we saw that if $a \equiv b \pmod m$ and $c \equiv d \pmod m$, then $a + c \equiv b + d \pmod m$ and $ac \equiv bd \pmod m$. Using the concept of residue classes, we can rewrite this last statement as follows: If $\bar{a} = \bar{b}$ and

$\bar{c} = \bar{d}$, then

$$\overline{a + c} = \overline{b + d} \qquad \text{and} \qquad \overline{ac} = \overline{bd}.$$

In view of the above statement we can make a very natural definition for the "addition" and "multiplication" of two residue classes, namely

Definition 2.11.1 Let $\bar{a}$ and $\bar{c}$ be residue classes modulo m. Define $\bar{a} + \bar{c} = \overline{a + c}$ and $\bar{a} \cdot \bar{c} = \overline{a \cdot c}$, that is, the sum of $\bar{a}$ and $\bar{c}$ is the residue class containing the integer $a + c$ and the product of $\bar{a}$ and $\bar{c}$ is the residue class containing the integer ac.

Note that we have used the symbols "+" and "·" in two different ways. In $\bar{a} + \bar{c}$, the + is used to represent a binary operation between residue classes, whereas in $a + c$, the + is the usual addition of integers. We use · similarly.

From the discussion preceding Definition 2.11.1, we see that these operations are *well defined*, that is, if $\bar{a} = \bar{b}$ and $\bar{c} = \bar{d}$, then

$$\bar{a} + \bar{c} = \bar{b} + \bar{d} \qquad \text{and} \qquad \bar{a}\bar{c} = \bar{b}\bar{d}.$$

We now let $\bar{Z}_m$ denote the set of all residue classes of integers modulo m, with $m > 0$. Then by Definition 2.11.1, there exist binary operations + and · on $\bar{Z}_m$ which, we shall show, satisfy perfect analogues of all the arithmetic properties with the exception of M_4. We will formulate a modified version of M_4 that does hold. Thus, a kind of "miniature arithmetic," very similar in nature to the arithmetic of the integers, exists for $\bar{Z}_m$.

Theorem 2.11.2 Let $\bar{Z}_m$ be the set of residue classes modulo m. Then

$\bar{A}_0$: There exists a function $f: \bar{Z}_m \times \bar{Z}_m \to \bar{Z}_m$ called *addition*, that is, if $\bar{a}, \bar{b} \in \bar{Z}_m$, then their sum $\bar{a} + \bar{b} = \overline{a + b}$ is in $\bar{Z}_m$.

$\bar{A}_1$: If $\bar{a}, \bar{b}, \bar{c} \in Z_m$, then $(\bar{a} + \bar{b}) + \bar{c} = \bar{a} + (\bar{b} + \bar{c})$.

$\bar{A}_2$: If $\bar{a}, \bar{b} \in \bar{Z}_m$, then $\bar{a} + \bar{b} = \bar{b} + \bar{a}$.

$\bar{A}_3$: There exists an element $\bar{0}$ in Z_m such that $\bar{a} + \bar{0} = \bar{a}$, for all $\bar{a} \in \bar{Z}_m$. ($\bar{0}$ is called the *zero residue class* modulo m, or simply the zero element of $\bar{Z}_m$.)

$\bar{A}_4$: Given $\bar{a} \in \bar{Z}_m$, there exists $\bar{b} \in \bar{Z}_m$ such that $\bar{a} + \bar{b} = \bar{0}$.

$\bar{M}_0$: There exists a function $g: \bar{Z}_m \times \bar{Z}_m \to \bar{Z}_m$ called *multiplication*, that is, if $\bar{a}, \bar{b} \in \bar{Z}_m$, then their product $\bar{a} \cdot \bar{b} = \overline{ab}$ is in $\bar{Z}_m$.

$\bar{M}_1$: If $\bar{a}, \bar{b}, \bar{c} \in \bar{Z}_m$, then $(\bar{a}\bar{b})\bar{c} = \bar{a}(\bar{b}\bar{c})$

$\bar{M}_2$: If $\bar{a}, \bar{b} \in \bar{Z}_m$, then $\bar{a} \cdot \bar{b} = \bar{b} \cdot \bar{a}$.

$\bar{M}_3$: If $m > 1$, there exists an element $\bar{1} \in \bar{Z}_m$, $\bar{1} \neq \bar{0}$, such that $\bar{a} \cdot \bar{1} = \bar{a}$, for all $\bar{a} \in \bar{Z}_m$. ($\bar{1}$ is called the *multiplicative* identity of $\bar{Z}_m$.)

$\bar{M}_4$: Given $\bar{a}, \bar{b}, \bar{c} \in \bar{Z}_m$, if $(a,m) = 1$, then $\bar{a} \cdot \bar{b} = \bar{a} \cdot \bar{c}$ implies $\bar{b} = \bar{c}$.

$\bar{D}$: Given $\bar{a}, \bar{b}, \bar{c}$ in $\bar{Z}_m$, then

$$\bar{a}(\bar{b} + \bar{c}) = \bar{a}\bar{b} + \bar{a}\bar{c}.$$

Proof: $\overline{A}_0$ and $\overline{M}_0$ are consequences of Definition 2.11.1 and the discussion of that definition.

To prove $\overline{A}_1$, the associative law of addition in $\overline{Z}_m$, we see that $(\bar{a} + \bar{b}) + \bar{c} = \overline{(a + b)} + \bar{c} = \overline{(a + b) + c} = \overline{a + (b + c)}$ (by the associative law for addition on Z) $= \bar{a} + \overline{(b + c)} = \bar{a} + (\bar{b} + \bar{c})$. The proof of $\overline{M}_1$ is similar.

We leave the proofs of $\overline{A}_2$, $\overline{M}_2$, $\overline{A}_3$, $\overline{M}_3$ to the reader.

To prove $\overline{A}_4$, we observe that $\bar{a} + \overline{(-a)} = \bar{0}$. To prove $\overline{M}_4$, we note that $\bar{a}\cdot\bar{b} = \bar{a}\cdot\bar{c}$ implies $\overline{ab} = \overline{ac}$, that is, $ab \equiv ac \pmod{m}$. By Corollary 2.9.6, $ab \equiv ac \pmod{m}$ and $(a,m) = 1$ implies $b \equiv c \pmod{m}$, that is, $\bar{b} = \bar{c}$.

The proof of $\overline{D}$ is left as an exercise.

Although $\overline{M}_4$ is not as strong as M_4 (see section 2.1), it is, however, the best possible analogue. For example, if $m = 6$, then $\bar{2}\cdot\bar{3} = \bar{6} = \bar{0}$. Thus, $\bar{2}\cdot\bar{3} = \bar{2}\cdot\bar{0}$, yet $\bar{3} \neq \bar{0}$. In addition, in this example we see that the product of two nonzero elements may be zero.

In case m is a prime, then $\overline{M}_4$ is the exact analogue of M_4. For if m is a prime, $\overline{M}_4$ becomes: Given $\bar{a},\bar{b},\bar{c} \in \overline{Z}_m$, $\bar{a} \neq \bar{0}$, then $\bar{a}\cdot\bar{b} = \bar{a}\cdot\bar{c}$ implies $\bar{b} = \bar{c}$.

Exercises

1. Complete the proof of Theorem 2.11.2.
2. Let $\bar{a},\bar{b} \in \overline{Z}_m$. Let $S = \{a_i + b_j \mid a_i \in \bar{a}, b_j \in \bar{b}\}$. Show that $S = \bar{a} + \bar{b}$.
3. Let $\bar{a} \in \overline{Z}_5, \bar{a} \neq \bar{0}$. Show that there exists $\bar{x} \in \overline{Z}_5$ such that $\bar{a}\bar{x} = \bar{1}$.

2.12 LINEAR CONGRUENCES

We have already noted that an equation of the form $ax = b$, $a \in Z$, $b \in Z$, has a solution in Z if and only if $a \mid b$. In this section we will study those conditions under which $ax \equiv b \pmod{m}$ has solutions.

Definition 2.12.1 Any integer x_0 satisfying the *linear congruence* $ax \equiv b \pmod{m}$ is called a *solution* of the linear congruence.

For example, 3 and 7 are solutions of $3x \equiv 1 \pmod{4}$.

Theorem 2.12.2 If $(a,m) = 1$, then the linear congruence $ax \equiv b \pmod{m}$ has a solution. Further, if x_0 is a solution, then the set of all solutions is precisely $\bar{x}_0$. Thus we say the solution is unique modulo m.

Proof: Since $(a,m) = 1$, there are integers s and t such that $as + mt = 1$. Thus $asb = b - bmt$. Hence, $a(sb) \equiv b \pmod{m}$, or $x_0 = sb$ satisfies the linear congruence. Now if $y \in \bar{x}_0$, then $ax_0 \equiv ay \pmod{m}$

whence $ay \equiv b \pmod{m}$ and y is a solution. Conversely if $ay \equiv b \pmod{m}$, then $ax_0 \equiv ay \pmod{m}$ and, by Corollary 2.9.6, $x_0 \equiv y \pmod{m}$, that is, $y \in \bar{x}_0$.

Corollary 2.12.3 Let a, b, and p be integers, p a prime, $p \nmid a$. Then $ax \equiv b \pmod{p}$ always has a solution, which is unique modulo p.

Proof: Since $(a,p) = 1$, apply Theorem 2.12.2.

We see from Corollary 2.12.3 that for a prime modulus p, a linear congruence $ax \equiv b \pmod{p}$ has a solution as long as $a \not\equiv 0 \pmod{p}$. This is the direct analogue to the condition that $rx = s$, r,s rational numbers, has a solution in rational numbers if $r \neq 0$. Thus, "division" by any "nonzero" element is possible modulo a prime. Hence, as in the rational number system, any "nonzero" element has an "inverse."

Definition 2.12.4 a and a' are *inverses modulo m* if $aa' \equiv 1 \pmod{m}$.

Corollary 2.12.5 A number a has an inverse modulo m if and only if $(a,m) = 1$. If a has an inverse, say a', a' is unique modulo m.

Proof: I. Existence.

i) If $(a,m) = 1$, then by Theorem 2.12.2, $ax \equiv 1 \pmod{m}$ has a solution that is an inverse of a.

ii) Now suppose a has an inverse a'. Then $aa' \equiv 1 \pmod{m}$ and $aa' - 1 = km$, for some integer k, or $aa' - km = 1$. By Exercise 4, Section 2.6, $(a,m) = 1$.

II. Uniqueness. If a' and a'' are both inverses of a, then a' and a'' both satisfy $ax \equiv 1 \pmod{m}$, hence $aa' \equiv aa'' \pmod{m}$. Since $(a,m) = 1$, $a' \equiv a'' \pmod{m}$ by Corollary 2.9.6.

Our next result deals with the solution of a special class of simultaneous congruences in one unknown. The solution to the more general problem (see Exercise 5) was known by the Chinese Mathematician Sun-Tsu in the first century A.D.

Theorem 2.12.6 Chinese Remainder Theorem If $(m_1,m_2) = 1$, then the congruences (1) $x \equiv a_1 \pmod{m_1}$ and (2) $x \equiv a_2 \pmod{m_2}$ have a common solution, which is unique modulo m_1m_2.

Proof: (1) has a solution, since $a_1 + km_1$ satisfies (1) for all integers k. All that remains is to prove there is an integer k_1 such that

$$a_1 + k_1m_1 \equiv a_2 \pmod{m_2}.$$

This is equivalent to showing that $m_1k \equiv a_2 - a_1 \pmod{m_2}$ has a solution for k. But, since $(m_1,m_2) = 1$, this last congruence has a solution by Theorem 2.12.2.

Now suppose x_0 and x_1 are both common solutions to (1) and (2). Then $x_0 \equiv a_1 \pmod{m_1}$ and $x_1 \equiv a_1 \pmod{m_1}$. This implies that $x_0 - x_1 \equiv 0 \pmod{m_1}$, or that $m_1 \mid (x_0 - x_1)$. Similarly, $m_2 \mid (x_0 - x_1)$. Thus $m_1 m_2 \mid (x_0 - x_1)$ by Exercise 8, Section 2.8. This means simply that $x_0 \equiv x_1 \pmod{m_1 \cdot m_2}$, and we have proven the uniqueness of the solution modulo $m_1 m_2$.

Exercises

*1. Let $\bar{a},\bar{b} \in \bar{Z}_p$, $\bar{b} \neq \bar{0}$, and p a prime. Show that $\bar{b}\bar{x} = \bar{a}$ has a solution in $\bar{Z}_p$.

2. Solve each of the following congruences:
   a) $3x \equiv 4 \pmod 5$
   b) $8x \equiv 3 \pmod{27}$

3. Solve the simultaneous congruences:
   $x \equiv 7 \pmod{21}$, $\quad x \equiv 3 \pmod 8$.

4. Prove the following generalization of Theorem 2.12.2:

The linear congruence $ax \equiv b \pmod m$ has a solution if and only if $d \mid b$, where $d = (a,m)$. Moreover, if a solution exists, there is a unique solution (mod m_1), where $m_1 = m/d$, and thus there are exactly d solutions modulo m, that is, there are exactly d solutions x_i, $0 \leq x_i < m$, no two of which are congruent modulo m.

5. Prove the following more general case of the Chinese remainder theorem.

If $(m_i,m_j) = 1$, $i \neq j$, $i,j = 1,2,\cdots,n$, then $x \equiv a_1 \pmod{m_1}$, $x \equiv a_2 \pmod{m_2}, \cdots, x \equiv a_n \pmod{m_n}$ have a common solution, and this solution is unique modulo $m_1 \cdot m_2 \cdots m_n$.

6. Prove: A necessary and sufficient condition that $x \equiv a_1 \pmod{m_1}$, $x \equiv a_2 \pmod{m_2}$, $\cdots x \equiv a_n \pmod{m_n}$ have a common solution is that

$$(m_i,m_j) \mid (a_i - a_j), \quad i \neq j.$$

There is just one solution x that satisfies

$$0 \leq x < \text{lcm} \quad [m_1,m_2,\cdots m_n].$$

Hint: First do the cases where $n = 2, 3$. Then proceed by induction.

Remark: Observe that the Chinese remainder theorem is a special case of this exercise.

2.13 EULER φ-FUNCTION

The least positive residues modulo m that have inverses modulo m are those relatively prime to m. An important function that counts the number of these integers is called the Euler φ-function, or the totient. It will occur in several applications.

Definition 2.13.1 Let $m \geq 1$. The *Euler φ-function* is the function φ with domain P, the set of positive integers, defined as follows: $(m)\varphi$ equals the number of integers in Z_m that are prime to m.

To illustrate, $(1)\varphi = 1$, $(2)\varphi = 1$, $(4)\varphi = 2$, and if p is any prime, $(p)\varphi = p - 1$.

Definition 2.13.2 The residue class $\bar{r}$ modulo m is *prime to m* if $(r,m) = 1$.

We note that if $x \in \bar{r}$, then $(x,m) = (r,m)$. Hence, Definition 2.13.2 is independent of the choice of the residue class representative.

As a consequence of Definitions 2.13.1 and 2.13.2 $(m)\varphi$ is equal to the number of residue classes prime to m.

Definition 2.13.3 A *reduced set of residues modulo m* is a set of integers $\{r_1, r_2, \cdots, r_{(m)\varphi}\}$ such that exactly one of them lies in each residue class prime to m. If each r_i satisfies $0 \leq r_i < m$, we call $\{r_1, r_2, \cdots, r_{(m)\varphi}\}$ the *reduced set* of *least positive residues modulo m*.

As an example, suppose $m = 6$. Then $\{0,1,2,3,4,5\}$ is a complete set of residues modulo 6, and $\{1,5\}$ is a reduced set of residues modulo 6. In addition, $\{6,13,26,39,10,17\}$ is also a complete set of residues, while $\{13,17\}$ is a reduced set of residues modulo 6.

Exercises

*1. a) Prove that if A and B are two complete sets of residues modulo m, then there is a $1 - 1$ correspondence between A and B such that corresponding pairs are congruent modulo m.

b) In a), let A and B be reduced sets of residues.

*2. Prove that a necessary and sufficient condition that a set of integers is a reduced set of residues modulo m is that each be prime to m, that no two be congruent to each other, and that they be $(m)\varphi$ in number. •

In deriving an explicit formula for $(m)\varphi$, we shall proceed in two steps. First, we shall determine $(p^k)\varphi$ explicitly where p is a prime and k a positive integer. Secondly, we shall show that if $(m_1,m_2) = 1$, then $(m_1 \cdot m_2)\varphi = (m_1)\varphi \cdot (m_2)\varphi$. Then combining these two steps with the fundamental theorem of arithmetic, we shall derive the complete formula for $(m)\varphi$.

Theorem 2.13.4 Let p be a prime number, $k \in Z$, $k > 0$. Then

$$(p^k)\varphi = p^k(1 - 1/p).$$

Proof: We need count only those integers in the set $S' = \{0,1,2, \cdots, p^k - 1\}$ that are prime to p^k, or equivalently, in the set $S = \{1,2,\cdots,$

$p^k - 1, p^k\}$ those that are prime to p^k. We shall count the number of integers in S that are not prime to p^k and subtract that number from p^k. Now, if $a \in S$ and $(a, p^k) \neq 1$, then $p \mid (a, p^k)$ and also $p \mid a$, since p is a prime. Thus, we may write $a = np$. But then $p \mid a$ for any value of n satisfying $1 \leq n \leq p^{k-1}$ and so there are p^{k-1} integers in S not prime to p^k. Thus, $(p^k)\varphi = p^k - p^{k-1} = p^k(1 - 1/p)$.

Theorem 2.13.5 If $(m_1, m_2) = 1$, m_1, m_2 positive integers, then $(m_1 \cdot m_2)\varphi = (m_1)\varphi \cdot (m_2)\varphi$.

Proof: If either m_1 or m_2 is 1, the proof is trivial. Thus, we may assume $m_1 > 1$, $m_2 > 1$.

Now let $X = \{x_1, x_2, \cdots, x_{(m_1)\varphi}\}$ be the reduced set of least positive residues modulo m_1 and let $Y = \{y_1, y_2, \cdots, y_{(m_2)\varphi}\}$ be the reduced set of least positive residues modulo m_2. Finally, let $W = \{w_1, w_2, \cdots, w_{(m_1 m_2)\varphi}\}$ be the reduced set of least positive residues modulo $m_1 m_2$. We shall show that the number of elements in $X \times Y$ is equal to the number of elements in W, which will establish the result. This will be done by showing that to each (x_i, y_j) in $X \times Y$, there exists a unique w_k in W, and that to each w_k in W there exists an element (x_i, y_j) in $X \times Y$. Moreover, we shall see that if we start with (x_i, y_j) and get w_k, then the pair (x_m, y_n) determined by w_k will be precisely the original (x_i, y_j). That is, we shall establish that there exists a 1–1 correspondence between $X \times Y$ and W.

i) Thus, let $x_i \in X$, $y_j \in Y$. Then the congruences

$$w \equiv x_i \pmod{m_1} \qquad \text{and} \qquad w \equiv y_j \pmod{m_2}$$

have a common solution w_k since $(m_1, m_2) = 1$, and this solution is unique modulo $m_1 m_2$ (Chinese remainder theorem). Moreover, $(w_k, m_1 m_2) = 1$, by Exercise 6, section 2.6. Thus, $w_k \in W$, that is, the pair (x_i, y_j), $x_i \in X$, $y_j \in Y$, determines a unique element w_k of W.

ii) Conversely, suppose, that $w_k \in W$. Then clearly, $(w_k, m_1 m_2) = 1$, and so again by Exercise 6, section 2.6, $(w_k, m_1) = (w_k, m_2) = 1$. By Theorem 2.12.2, there is a unique element $x_i \in X$ such that $x_i \equiv w_k \pmod{m_1}$, and there is a unique element $y_j \in Y$ such that $y_j \equiv w_k \pmod{m_2}$. Thus, any $w_k \in W$ gives rise to a unique pair (x_i, y_j), where $x_i \in X$, $y_j \in Y$.

Now let w_k be the element that coresponds to (x_i, y_j) in i), and let (x_m, y_n) be the ordered pair that corresponds to w_k in ii). We see that by i) $w_k \equiv x_i \pmod{m_1}$, and in part ii) we have that $x_m \equiv w_k \pmod{m_1}$. Thus, $x_i \equiv x_m \pmod{m_1}$, that is, $x_i = x_m$. Similarly, $y_j = y_n$, and the proof is complete.

Theorem 2.13.6 If $m = p_1^{e_1}p_2^{e_2}\cdots p_s^{e_s}$ is the prime power factorization of m, then

$$(m)\varphi = m(1 - 1/p_1)(1 - 1/p_2)\cdots(1 - 1/p_s).$$

Proof: Exercise.

Exercises

3. Find $(36)\varphi$, $(81)\varphi$, $(101)\varphi$.
4. Prove Theorem 2.13.6.
5. Show that $(n)\varphi$ is even for all $n > 2$.
6. Find all integers n such that $(n)\varphi = 2$.
7. Let p^α be a power of the prime p. Show that

$$(1)\varphi + (p)\varphi + \cdots + (p^\alpha)\varphi = p^\alpha.$$

8. Let m be a positive integer. Show that

$$\sum_{d \mid m} (d)\varphi = m, \quad \text{where } \sum_{d \mid m} (d)\varphi = (d_1)\varphi + (d_2)\varphi + \cdots + (d_r)\varphi,$$

with $\{d_1,d_2,\cdots,d_r\}$ the set of all positive divisors of m, and $d_i \neq d_j$, for $i \neq j$.
9. Find all pairs of positive integers m, p, such that $(m)\varphi = m/p$, where p is a prime.[7]
10. Let $n > 1$ and let k_i, $i = 1,\cdots,(n)\varphi$, be the integers satisfying $0 < k_i < n$ and $(k_i,n) = 1$. Show that $k_1 + k_2 + \cdots + k_{(n)\varphi} = (n/2)\cdot(n)\varphi$.

2.14 THE THEOREMS OF FERMAT AND EULER

The theorems of Fermat and Euler proved in this section will be used for illustrative purposes in Chapter 4, although different proofs will be given there.

Theorem 2.14.1 Euler Let a and m be integers, $m > 0$. If $(a,m) = 1$, then $a^{(m)\varphi} \equiv 1 \pmod{m}$.

Proof: Let $r_1,r_2,\cdots,r_{(m)\varphi}$ be a reduced set of residues modulo m. Now if $ar_i \equiv ar_j \pmod{m}$, for some i and j, $i \neq j$, then since $(a,m) = 1$, we have $r_i \equiv r_j \pmod{m}$ by Corollary 2.9.6, contradicting the statement

[7] *American Mathematical Monthly*, Vol. 70 (1963), p. 331.

that $r_1, \cdots, r_{(m)\varphi}$ is a reduced set of residues modulo m. Hence $ar_i \not\equiv ar_j \pmod{m}$, for all $i, j, i \neq j$. Moreover, for each i, by Exercise 6, Section 2.6, we have $(ar_i, m) = (a,m)(r_i,m) = 1 \cdot 1 = 1$. Thus, since the integers $ar_1, \cdots, ar_{(m)\varphi}$ are $(m)\varphi$ in number, each prime to m, and since no two are congruent modulo m, they form a reduced set of residues modulo m by Exercise 2, Section 2.13. By Exercise 1, Section 2.13, the ar_i's and the r_j's can be paired off into congruent pairs modulo m. Thus, by Theorem 2.9.4

$$ar_1 \cdot ar_2 \cdots ar_{(m)\varphi} \equiv r_1 r_2 \cdots r_{(m)\varphi} \pmod{m},$$

whence

$$a^{(m)\varphi} r_1 r_2 \cdots r_{(m)\varphi} \equiv r_1 r_2 \cdots r_{(m)\varphi} \pmod{m}.$$

Since $(r_i, m) = 1$, for all i, clearly $(r_1 r_2 \cdots r_{(m)\varphi}, m) = 1$, and thus $a^{(m)\varphi} \equiv 1 \pmod{m}$ by Corollary 2.9.6.

Corollary 2.14.2 If p is a prime and if a is an integer such that $p \nmid a$, then $a^{p-1} \equiv 1 \pmod{p}$.

Proof: Let $m = p$ in Theorem 2.14.1.

Theorem 2.14.3 Fermat If p is a prime, then $a^p \equiv a \pmod{p}$, for all integers a.

Proof: If $a \equiv 0 \pmod{p}$, then $a^p \equiv 0 \equiv a \pmod{p}$. If $a \not\equiv 0 \pmod{p}$, then $(a, p) = 1$. By Corollary 2.14.2, $a^{p-1} \equiv 1 \pmod{p}$. Then $a^p \equiv a \pmod{p}$.

Exercises

1. Let $a, u, m \in Z$ be such that $(a,m) = 1$ and u is the smallest positive integer such that $a^u \equiv 1 \pmod{m}$. Prove that $u \mid (m)\varphi$.

2. Let a and b be relatively prime integers. Show that there exist integers m and n such that $a^m + b^n \equiv 1 \pmod{ab}$.[8]

[8] *American Mathematical Monthly*, Vol. 69 (1962), p. 57.

CHAPTER 3

Composition of Functions and Permutations

In this chapter our main interest will be to study a special class of functions, called permutations, which are one-to-one functions from a set onto itself. We shall see how a binary operation can be defined on a very large set of functions, and we shall be particularly concerned to study this operation on sets of permutations.

Many of the concepts and results of this chapter will be utilized in our study of groups in Chapter 4.

3.1 COMPOSITION OF FUNCTIONS

Definition 3.1.1 Let $f:A \to B'$ and $g:B \to C$ with $B' \subseteq B$. Then the *composite* of f and g (or the *product*) is defined to be the function $h:A \to C$ where $ah = (af)g$ for all $a \in A$. We shall denote h by $f \circ g$.

The convention of writing xf instead of $f(x)$ allows us, in the definition of the composite of f and g, to apply $h = f \circ g$ to an element $a \in A$ in the order "first f, then g," that is, in the order in which f and g are written. On the other hand, using the notation $f(x)$, we have $(f \circ g)(x) = f(g(x))$, that is, $f \circ g$ must be interpreted as "first g, then f," opposite to the written order of f and g. The advantage in applying f and g in their written order justifies our convention of writing f to the right of x. We feel this advantage is especially seen when multiplying permutations, as we shall do shortly.

Frequently h is called a "function of a function," and we note that the range of f is contained in the domain of g. Were this restriction not made, there would be no natural way of defining $f \circ g$.

To illustrate let

$$xf = \sqrt{x} \qquad \text{and} \qquad xg = x^2,$$

where the domain of f is the set of all nonnegative real numbers and the domain of g is the set of all real numbers. The ranges of f and g are as suggested by the notation. We see that both $f \circ g$ and $g \circ f$ are defined, since the range of each function is a subset of the domain of the other. Thus, on the one hand,

$$x(f \circ g) = (xf)g = (\sqrt{x})g = (\sqrt{x})^2 = x,$$

where x is in the domain of f, that is, x is greater than or equal to zero. On the other hand,

$$x(g \circ f) = (xg)f = (x^2)f = \sqrt{x^2} = |x|,$$

and the domain of $g \circ f$ is the set of all real numbers. Since the domain of $f \circ g$ is a proper subset of the domain of $g \circ f$, these two functions are not the same. However, $g \circ f | K^+ = f \circ g$ where K^+ is the set of nonnegative real numbers.

It is easy to find functions f and g whose composites $f \circ g$ and $g \circ f$ are defined but not equal and such that neither $f \circ g$ nor $g \circ f$ is a restriction of the other. For example, if K is the set of real numbers, let f, g be functions on K defined by $xf = x^2$ and $xg = x + 1$. Then $(x)f \circ g = x^2 + 1$ and $(x)g \circ f = (x + 1)^2$.

Given three functions,

$$f{:}A \rightarrow B', \quad g{:}B \rightarrow C', \quad \text{and} \quad h{:}C \rightarrow D,$$

with $B' \subseteq B$, and $C' \subseteq C$, we may form the two composites $f \circ (g \circ h)$ and $(f \circ g) \circ h$. As with addition and multiplication of the integers, there is an associative law for composition of functions which states that $f \circ (g \circ h) = (f \circ g) \circ h$.

Theorem 3.1.2 Let $f{:}A \rightarrow B'$, $g{:}B \rightarrow C'$, and $h{:}C \rightarrow D$, with $B' \subseteq B$, $C' \subseteq C$. Then $(f \circ g) \circ h = f \circ (g \circ h)$.

Proof: To show that $(f \circ g) \circ h = f \circ (g \circ h)$, we must show that the image of any element $x \in A$ is the same under both of these functions. This is easily seen, since

$$\begin{aligned} x[(f \circ g) \circ h] &= [x(f \circ g)]h = [(xf)g]h = (xf)(g \circ h) \\ &= x[f \circ (g \circ h)]. \end{aligned}$$

In the special case of Theorem 3.1.2, in which $A = B = C$ and $f = g = h$, we have $f \circ (f \circ f) = (f \circ f) \circ f$. By defining $f^2 = f \circ f$, we may also define f^3 unambiguously by setting $f^3 = f^2 \circ f = f \circ f^2$. Given $f:A \to A$, no matter how we insert parentheses into the expression

$$\underbrace{f \circ f \circ \cdots \circ f}_{n \text{ times}}$$

in a meaningful way, we always get the same result. (See the discussion of associative laws in Chapter 2. The proof mentioned in Chapter 2, also applicable here, will be given in Section 4.5.)

***Definition* 3.1.3** Let $f:A \to A$. Define f^n for all $n \geq 0$ as follows:
$f^0 = I$, the identity function on A
$f^1 = f$
$f^{n+1} = f^n \circ f,\ n \geq 1.$

This definition is another example of an inductive definition (see Section 2.8).

Exercises

In the following exercises, K denotes the set of real numbers.

1. Let Q be the set of rational numbers. Let $f:Q \to K$, where $xf = \sqrt[3]{x}$, $g:K \to K$, where $xg = x^6$. What is the function $f \circ g$?

2. Let $A = \{(a,a') \mid a,a' \in K\}$. Let $f:A \to K$, where $(a,a')f = a^2 + (a')^2$ and $g:K \to K$, where $xg = \sqrt{x}$. What is $f \circ g$? What is $g \circ f$?

3. Let $f:K \to K$, where $xf = -x$, and let $g:K \to K$, where $xg = 1/x$, for $x \neq 0$ and $xg = 0$, for $x = 0$. Show that $f^2 = I$ (the identity function), $g^2 = I$, and $f \circ g = g \circ f$.

4. Let $f:K \to K$, where $xf = x + \pi$. For $n > 0$, show that f^n is defined by $xf^n = x + n\pi$.

5. Let $f:K \to K$, where $xf = x^3$ and $g:K \to K$ where $xg = 1 + x^2$. Determine $f \circ g$ and $g \circ f$. Are they equal?

6. Let $f:K \to K$, where $xf = 2x - 1$. Find a function $g:K \to K$ such that $x(f \circ g) = x$, all $x \in K$, and $x(g \circ f) = x$, all $x \in K$.

*7. Let $f:A \xrightarrow[\text{onto}]{1-1} B$, $g:B \xrightarrow[\text{onto}]{1-1} C$. Show that $f \circ g:A \xrightarrow[\text{onto}]{1-1} C$. •

The reader should note in Exercise 6 that the 1–1 and onto properties of f are crucial. The existence of the function g is assured by the following theorem.

***Theorem* 3.1.4** Let $f:A \xrightarrow[\text{onto}]{1-1} B$. Then there exists a unique function

$g: B \xrightarrow[\text{onto}]{1-1} A$ such that $f \circ g = I_A$, the identity on A, and $g \circ f = I_B$, the identity on B. Indeed, the function g is defined as follows: For all $b \in B$, $bg = a$, where $af = b$.

Proof: Since f is onto, for each $b \in B$, there is an $a \in A$ such that $af = b$. Furthermore this choice of a is unique since f is 1–1. We define $g: B \to A$ as follows:

$$bg = a, \quad \text{where} \quad af = b.$$

Since f is 1–1 and onto, g is a function from B to A. And g is in fact 1–1 and onto. (Why?)

For any $a \in A$, $a(f \circ g) = (af)g = bg = a$. Hence $f \circ g = I_A$. For any $b \in B$, $b(g \circ f) = (bg)f = af = b$, and $g \circ f = I_B$.

To prove the uniqueness of g let $g': B \to A$ satisfy $f \circ g' = I_A$ and $g' \circ f = I_B$. Then for each $b \in B$, $bg' = (bg')f \circ g = (b(g' \circ f))g = bg$.

Definition 3.1.5 Let $f: A \xrightarrow[\text{onto}]{1-1} B$. Then the function g of theorem 3.1.4 is called the *inverse function* of f. We denote g by f^{-1}.

For example, let K be the set of real numbers and let $f: K \to K$ be defined by:

$$xf = x^3.$$

It is easy to see that f is 1–1 and onto. By Theorem 3.1.4 the function f^{-1} is defined by: $af^{-1} = b$, where $bf = a$. But $bf = b^3$ and hence $b = \sqrt[3]{a}$. This gives $af^{-1} = \sqrt[3]{a}$, and f^{-1} is defined for all real numbers.

On the other hand, let $h: K \to K$ be defined by:

$$xh = x(x - 1)(x + 1).$$

Then h is onto but not 1–1, since $1h = (-1)h = 0$. Hence if there were a function g such that $h \circ g = I_K$, then $(0)g = 1$ and $(0)g = -1$, which contradicts the definition of a function. Hence we see that it would not be possible to define the inverse of a non-one-to-one function.

Let $f: A \xrightarrow[\text{onto}]{1-1} B$. Then f is a collection of ordered pairs such that every $a \in A$ occurs in precisely one ordered pair and every $b \in B$ occurs in precisely one ordered pair. Then the function $f^{-1} = \{(b,a) \mid (a,b) \in f\}$. For example, if $f = \{(x,x^3) \mid x \in K\}$, then $f^{-1} = \{(x^3,x) \mid x \in K\}$. The reader should verify that $\{(x^3,x) \mid x \in K\} = \{(x, \sqrt[3]{x}) \mid x \in K\}$.

Exercises

*8. Show that the function g defined in Theorem 3.1.4 is 1–1 and onto.

9. Let $f:K \to K$ and $g:K \to K$, where $xf = -x$ and $xg = 1/x$, $x \neq 0$ and $0g = 0$. Show that f^{-1}, g^{-1}, and $(f \circ g)^{-1}$ exist. Moreover, show that $(f \circ g)^{-1} = f^{-1} \circ g^{-1}$.

10. Let $f:A \xrightarrow[\text{onto}]{1-1} B$ and $g:B \xrightarrow[\text{onto}]{1-1} A$. Show that $g = f^{-1}$ if and only if $f = g^{-1}$.

11. Let $f:A \to B$ and $g:B \to A$. If $f \circ g = I_A$, show that f is 1–1 and g is onto.

12. Give an example illustrating each of the following:

a) $f:A \xrightarrow[\text{onto}]{1-1} B$, $g:B \xrightarrow[\text{onto}]{1-1} A$, but $f \circ g \neq I_A$ and $g \circ f \neq I_B$.

b) $f:A \to B$, $g:B \to A$, $f \circ g = I_A$, but f is not onto and g is not 1–1.

c) $f:A \to B$, $g:B \to A$, $f \circ g = I_A$, but $g \circ f \neq I_B$.

*13. Let $f:A \xrightarrow[\text{onto}]{1-1} A$. For each integer $n \geq 0$, show that f^n is 1–1 and onto.

*14. Let $f:A \xrightarrow[\text{onto}]{1-1} A$. Prove that $(f^n)^{-1} = (f^{-1})^n$, for all $n \geq 0$.

3.2 PERMUTATIONS: INTRODUCTION

Definition 3.2.1 Let A be a set, $A \neq \phi$. A *permutation* T on the set A is a function $T:A \xrightarrow[\text{onto}]{1-1} A$.

Theorem 3.2.2 Let T_1, T_2, T_3 be permutations on a set A. Then

i) $T_1 \circ T_2$ is a permutation on A,

ii) $T_1 \circ (T_2 \circ T_3) = (T_1 \circ T_2) \circ T_3$.

Proof: i) See Exercise 7, Section 3.1; ii) See Theorem 3.1.2.

Of special interest are the permutations on the set $X_n = \{1,2,3,\cdots,n\}$. We denote the set of all permutations on X_n by S_n.

Let $T \in S_n$. For each integer $j \in X_n$, jT is again an integer in X_n. Moreover, since T is 1–1, $jT = hT$ if and only if $j = h$. Since T is also onto, we now easily observe that the set

$$\{1T, 2T, \cdots, nT\} = X_n.$$

Therefore, T can be thought of as effecting a rearrangement of integers $1, 2, \cdots, n$.

One simple way to display the permutation T on X_n is to write

(1) $$T = \begin{pmatrix} 1 & 2 & \cdots & n \\ 1T & 2T & \cdots & nT \end{pmatrix},$$

where the image jT of j under T, is written directly below j. For example, $T = \begin{pmatrix} 1 & 2 & 3 \\ 3 & 1 & 2 \end{pmatrix}$ is the permutation on X_3 defined by $1T = 3, 2T = 1, 3T = 2$. Of course, any array of the form $\begin{pmatrix} 1 & 2 & \cdots & n \\ j_1 & j_2 & & j_n \end{pmatrix}$, where $j_1, \cdots, j_n$ is just a rearrangement of X_n, defines a permutation.

Theorem 3.2.3   There exist $n!$ permutations on X_n, that is, S_n has $n!$ elements.

   Proof: Exercise.

The notation (1) provides us with a ready means of finding the composite, or product, of two permutations. Suppose

$$T = \begin{pmatrix} 1 & 2 & \cdots & n \\ 1T & 2T & & nT \end{pmatrix} \quad \text{and} \quad U = \begin{pmatrix} 1 & 2 & \cdots & n \\ 1U & 2U & & nU \end{pmatrix}.$$

To find $T \circ U$, we must determine $j(T \circ U)$, for each j in X_n. Since $j(T \circ U) = (jT)U$, we find jT under j in the display for T, and then we find $(jT)U$ under jT in the display for U.

   For example, let $T = \begin{pmatrix} 1 & 2 & 3 & 4 \\ 1 & 4 & 2 & 3 \end{pmatrix}$ and $U = \begin{pmatrix} 1 & 2 & 3 & 4 \\ 3 & 4 & 1 & 2 \end{pmatrix}$. Then to find $T \circ U$, we trace out the successive images of each $j \in X_n$ as follows:

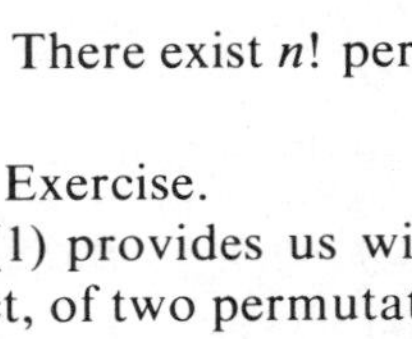

$$T = \begin{pmatrix} 1 & 2 & 3 & 4 \\ 1 & 4 & 2 & 3 \end{pmatrix}$$
$$U = \begin{pmatrix} 1 & 2 & 3 & 4 \\ 3 & 4 & 1 & 2 \end{pmatrix} \qquad \begin{pmatrix} 1 & 2 & 3 & 4 \\ 3 & 2 & 4 & 1 \end{pmatrix} = T \circ U$$

Moreover, $U \circ T = \begin{pmatrix} 1 & 2 & 3 & 4 \\ 3 & 4 & 1 & 2 \end{pmatrix} \circ \begin{pmatrix} 1 & 2 & 3 & 4 \\ 1 & 4 & 2 & 3 \end{pmatrix} = \begin{pmatrix} 1 & 2 & 3 & 4 \\ 2 & 3 & 1 & 4 \end{pmatrix}$. We note that $U \circ T \neq T \circ U$.

Exercises

1.   Let $T = \begin{pmatrix} 1 & 2 & 3 & 4 & 5 \\ 2 & 1 & 4 & 3 & 5 \end{pmatrix}$, $U = \begin{pmatrix} 1 & 2 & 3 & 4 & 5 \\ 3 & 2 & 1 & 5 & 4 \end{pmatrix}$, $V = \begin{pmatrix} 1 & 2 & 3 & 4 & 5 \\ 5 & 4 & 2 & 3 & 1 \end{pmatrix}$ be in S_5.
Find each of the following: $T \circ U$, $T \circ V$, $V \circ U$, $U \circ V$, $T \circ (U \circ V)$, $(T \circ V) \circ V$, T^2, V^6.

2.   List the elements of S_3 in the form: $\begin{pmatrix} 1 & 2 & 3 \\ 1T_i & 2T_i & 3T_i \end{pmatrix}$, $i = 1, \cdots, 6$, and find T_1 and T_2 such that $T_1 \circ T_2 \neq T_2 \circ T_1$.

3.   Prove Theorem 3.2.3.

*4.   Let A be a set, $A \neq \phi$. Let T be a permutation on A. Show that T^{-1} exists and that T^{-1} is also a permutation on A.

*5. Let $T \in S_n$. Show that T^m, $m \geq 0$, is in S_n and hence, $(T^m)^{-1}$ is also in S_n.

*6. Let $i \in X_n$ and let $T \in S_n$. Suppose that $iT = i$. Prove that for all integers m, $iT^m = i$.

*7. Let $T \in S_m$. For $n \geq 0$, define $T^{-n} = (T^n)^{-1}$. Show that

$$T^{-n} = (T^{-1})^n.$$

(Thus $T^{-n} = (T^{-1})^n = (T^n)^{-1}$, for all integers n.)

*8. Let k, ℓ be integers, and let $T \in S_n$. Show that $T^k \circ T^\ell = T^{k+\ell}$.

Hint: See Theorem 4.5.10.

*9. Let T be a permutation. Show that $(T^k)^\ell = T^{k\ell}$, for all integers k and ℓ.

3.3 CYCLES AND CYCLIC DECOMPOSITION

Definition 3.3.1 Let $T \in S_n$, and let x and y belong to X_n. Then x is *T-equivalent* to y, written $x \overset{T}{\sim} y$, if for some integer k, $xT^k = y$.

To illustrate, let $T = \begin{pmatrix} 1 & 2 & 3 & 4 & 5 \\ 3 & 1 & 2 & 5 & 4 \end{pmatrix}$. Then $1 \overset{T}{\sim} 3$, since $1T = 3$, and $1 \overset{T}{\sim} 2$, since $1T^{-1} = 2$.

Theorem 3.3.2 *T*-equivalence is an equivalence relation on the set X_n.

Proof:

i) Recalling that T^0 is the identity function on X_n, $xT^0 = x$, for all $x \in X_n$, whence $x \overset{T}{\sim} x$.

ii) If $x \overset{T}{\sim} y$, there exists an integer k such that $y = xT^k$. By exercise 7, Section 3.2, $(T^k)^{-1} = T^{-k}$, whence $yT^{-k} = (xT^k)T^{-k} = x(T^k \circ T^{-k}) = xT^0 = x$, and so $y \overset{T}{\sim} x$.

iii) If $xT^k = y$ and $yT^\ell = z$, then $xT^{k+\ell} = (xT^k)T^\ell = yT^\ell = z$, whence $x \overset{T}{\sim} y$ and $y \overset{T}{\sim} z$ imply $x \overset{T}{\sim} z$.

Definition 3.3.3 Let $T \in S_n$ and let $\{A_\alpha\}$ be the partition of the set X_n induced by the relation of *T*-equivalence. Then the subsets A_α of X_n are called the *orbits* of T.

Recall that if A_α and A_β are orbits of T, then $A_\alpha = A_\beta$ or $A_\alpha \cap A_\beta = \phi$.

Definition 3.3.4 Let $T \in S_n$. T is a *cycle of length r* if i) there exists an orbit A of T with r elements and ii) any orbit of T different from A has precisely one element.

For example, if $n = 6$, then $T = \begin{pmatrix} 1 & 2 & 3 & 4 & 5 & 6 \\ 1 & 5 & 3 & 4 & 6 & 2 \end{pmatrix}$ is a cycle of length 3 since the orbits of T are $\{1\}$, $\{2,5,6\}$, $\{3\}$, $\{4\}$.

The permutation $U = \begin{pmatrix} 1 & 2 & 3 & 4 & 5 & 6 \\ 1 & 6 & 3 & 4 & 2 & 5 \end{pmatrix}$ is also a cycle of length 3, which has the same orbits as T. But U and T are not equal, hence the orbits of a permutation do not determine it completely.

If every orbit of $T \in S_n$ has one element, then T is a cycle of length 1, and conversely. A cycle of length 1 must therefore necessarily be the identity permutation, for if $x \in X_n$ and $xT \neq x$, then T would have an orbit with more than one element.

Theorem 3.3.5 Let $T \in S_n$ and let A be an orbit of T with r elements. Then for any $x \in A$, $A = \{x, xT, \cdots, xT^{r-1}\}$.

Proof: Let $x \in A$. Then it follows from the definition of A that $\{x, xT, \cdots, xT^{r-1}\} \subseteq A = \{xT^i \mid i \in Z\}$. Since it is given that A contains r elements, it remains only to show that $xT^{\ell} \neq xT^j$, for all ℓ and j satisfying $\ell \neq j$, and $0 \leq \ell, j \leq r - 1$.

Hence suppose that $xT^j = xT^{\ell}$, for some j and ℓ satisfying $0 \leq j < \ell \leq r - 1$. Then by Exercise 8, Section 3.2, and the fact that T^0 is the identity permutation,

$$\begin{aligned}(xT^j)T^{-j} &= (xT^{\ell})T^{-j} \\ xT^0 &= xT^{\ell-j} \\ x &= xT^{\ell-j}, \quad \text{where} \quad 0 < \ell - j \leq r - 1.\end{aligned}$$

Since A has r elements, there must exist an integer k such that $xT^k \in A$, but $xT^k \notin \{x, xT, \cdots, xT^{r-1}\}$.

By the division algorithm there exist unique integers q and s such that

$$k = (\ell - j)q + s, \quad \text{with} \quad 0 \leq s < \ell - j.$$

Thus,

$xT^k = xT^{q(\ell-j)+s} = (xT^{(\ell-j)q})T^s$

$= xT^s$ by Exercise 6, Section 3.2. But since s satisfies $0 \leq s < \ell - j < r - 1$, $xT^k = xT^s \in \{x, xT, \cdots, xT^{r-1}\}$, a contradiction. Hence $xT^j \neq xT^{\ell}$ for all $j \neq \ell$, $0 \leq j, \ell \leq r - 1$.

Corollary 3.3.6 Let $T \in S_n$. Let A be an orbit of T with r elements. Then

$$A = \{x, xT, \cdots, xT^{r-1}\} = \{xT^i, xT^{i+1}, \cdots, xT^{r+i-1}\}$$

for all $i \in Z$. Further, $xT^r = x$.

Proof: Since $xT^i \in A$, replace x by xT^i in the theorem, so that

$A = \{xT^i, xT^{i+1}, \cdots, xT^{r+i-1}\}$. To show that $xT^r = x$, consider $\{x, xT, \cdots, xT^{r-1}\} = \{xT, \cdots, xT^{r-1}, xT^r\}$. Hence $\{x\} \cup \{xT, \cdots, xT^{r-1}\} = \{xT, \cdots, xT^{r-1}\} \cup \{xT^r\}$, and therefore $x = xT^r$. (See Exercise 6, Section 1.3.)

Let T be a cycle of length r. If $r = 1$, then T is the identity and we shall often denote T by $T = (1)$ or $T = (i)$ for any $i = 1, \cdots, n$. If $r \geq 2$, and if A is the orbit of length r, then by Theorem 3.3.5, for any $x \in A$, $A = \{x, xT, \cdots, xT^{r-1}\}$. In view of this, we shall frequently denote the cycle T of length r by $T = (x\ xT \cdots xT^{r-1})$. In this notation, we see that the image of an element y moved by T is the element immediately to the right of y, or if y is at the extreme right of the list, yT is the element at the extreme left of the list. Moreover, given any subset $\{y_1, \cdots, y_k\} \subseteq X_n - A$, we may also denote T by $(x.xT \cdots xT^{r-1})\ (y_1) \cdots (y_k)$, since each (y_i) denotes the identity. To illustrate, let $T = \begin{pmatrix} 1 & 2 & 3 & 4 & 5 & 6 & 7 \\ 3 & 4 & 2 & 5 & 1 & 6 & 7 \end{pmatrix} \in S_7$. Then T is a cycle of length 5, which may be denoted equally well by any of the following:

$$(1\ 3\ 2\ 4\ 5), \qquad (2\ 4\ 5\ 1\ 3), \qquad (5\ 1\ 3\ 2\ 4),$$

$$(1\ 3\ 2\ 4\ 5)(7), \qquad (6)(1\ 3\ 2\ 4\ 5), \qquad (6)(7)(3\ 2\ 4\ 5\ 1).$$

Note that cycles of length 1 can be added or deleted without affecting the permutation. Although it is unclear to which S_n the cycle T belongs without the addition of the missing letters, we shall usually rely on context to suggest the proper S_n.

Definition 3.3.7 Let $T, U \in S_n$ be cycles of lengths r and s, respectively. If $r > 1$ and $s > 1$, we say that T and U are *disjoint* cycles if $A \cap B = \phi$, where A is the orbit of T with r elements and B the orbit of U with s elements. If either $r = 1$ or $s = 1$, we also say that T and U are *disjoint*.

With T, U, A, and B as in the above definition, we observe that if $r > 1$ and if $x \in A$, then i) x is moved by T, that is, $xT \neq x$, and ii) $x \notin B$, whence U leaves x fixed, that is $xU = x$. Thus, it will be easy for the reader to verify (Exercise 2 below) that if T and U are disjoint cycles, then $T \circ U = U \circ T$. We see, for example, that if $T = \begin{pmatrix} 1 & 2 & 3 & 4 & 5 & 6 \\ 3 & 2 & 5 & 4 & 1 & 6 \end{pmatrix}$ and $U = \begin{pmatrix} 1 & 2 & 3 & 4 & 5 & 6 \\ 1 & 6 & 3 & 4 & 5 & 2 \end{pmatrix}$, then $A = \{1,3,5\}$ and $B = \{2,6\}$ and T and U are disjoint. Thus, we know that $T \circ U = U \circ T$, without even finding these products.

Exercises

*1. Prove that the cycles T and U are disjoint if and only if whenever $iT \neq i$, $iU = i$, and whenever $iU \neq i$, $iT = i$.

*2. Let T and $U \in S_n$, T and U disjoint cycles. Show that $T \circ U = U \circ T$.

3. Let V_1, V_2 be disjoint cycles in S_n such that $V_1 \circ V_2 = (1)$. Show that $V_1 = V_2 = (1)$.

Extend this to a product of ℓ cycles, $\ell \geq 2$, disjoint in pairs.

4. Let T be a cycle of length $r > 1$. Show that if $iT \neq i$, then $iT^n \neq iT^{n-1}$, for all integers $n > 0$. ●

If T is a cycle of length $r > 1$ and U a cycle of length $s > 1$, with $T = (y_1 \cdots y_r)$, $U = (z_1 \cdots z_s)$, we write

$$T \circ U = (y_1 \cdots y_r)(z_1 \cdots z_s)$$

Let $T = \begin{pmatrix} 1 & 2 & 3 & 4 & 5 \\ 2 & 3 & 1 & 4 & 5 \end{pmatrix}$ and $U = \begin{pmatrix} 1 & 2 & 3 & 4 & 5 \\ 1 & 4 & 3 & 5 & 2 \end{pmatrix}$ be in S_5. Then T and U are cycles, $T = (1\ 2\ 3)$ and $U = (2\ 4\ 5)$. Using our original notation, we see that $T \circ U = \begin{pmatrix} 1 & 2 & 3 & 4 & 5 \\ 2 & 3 & 1 & 4 & 5 \end{pmatrix}\begin{pmatrix} 1 & 2 & 3 & 4 & 5 \\ 1 & 4 & 3 & 5 & 2 \end{pmatrix} = \begin{pmatrix} 1 & 2 & 3 & 4 & 5 \\ 4 & 3 & 1 & 5 & 2 \end{pmatrix} = (1\ 4\ 5\ 2\ 3)$. Using cycle notation, we find the product as follows:

$$T \circ U = (1\ 2\ 3)(2\ 4\ 5).$$

The cycle T takes 1 to 2, and U takes 2 to 4, whence the product $T \circ U$ takes 1 to 4. T leaves 4 fixed, U moves it to 5, and so $T \circ U$ takes 4 to 5. Similarly, T leaves 5 fixed, and U takes 5 to 2. Then T takes 2 to 3 and U leaves 3 fixed. Finally, T takes 3 to 1, and U leaves 1 fixed. Hence we see that the product takes 1 to 4, 4 to 5, 5 to 2, 2 to 3, and 3 to 1; and so $T \circ U = (1\ 4\ 5\ 2\ 3)$. Despite this long description, the reader will find it more convenient to multiply permutations using cycle notation. As another example: $(1\ 2\ 3)(1\ 4)(1\ 3) = (1\ 2)(3\ 4)$.

A product of cycles is clearly a single permutation. Conversely, we shall prove that any permutation can be written as a product of cycles. This will provide a very convenient method for expressing and multiplying permutations.

Example 3.3.8 Let $T = \begin{pmatrix} 1 & 2 & 3 & 4 & 5 & 6 & 7 & 8 \\ 2 & 4 & 5 & 1 & 3 & 7 & 8 & 6 \end{pmatrix}$

Then we may write T as a product of disjoint cycles as follows:

$$1T = 2, \quad 2T = 4, \quad \text{and} \quad 4T = 1.$$

Hence one of the cycles will be $(1\ 2\ 4)$.

$$3T = 5 \quad \text{and} \quad 5T = 3.$$

Therefore a second cycle will be $(3\ 5)$.

$$6T = 7, \quad 7T = 8, \quad \text{and} \quad 8T = 6.$$

The final cycle will be $(6\ 7\ 8)$.
Thus $T = (1\ 2\ 4)(3\ 5)(6\ 7\ 8)$.

Theorem 3.3.9 Let $T \in S_n$, $T \neq (1)$, the identity permutation. Then T can be uniquely written as a product of disjoint cycles. That is, there exist cycles $T_1, T_2, \cdots, T_k \in S_n$, T_i and T_j disjoint for $i \neq j$, each of length at least 2, such that $T = T_1 \circ T_2 \circ \cdots \circ T_k$. Moreover, if $U_1, U_2, \cdots, U_m$ is another set of disjoint cycles each of length at least 2 such that $T = U_1 \circ U_2 \circ \cdots \circ U_m$, then $m = k$ and for some arrangement $U_{j_1}, \cdots, U_{j_k}$ of the U_j's, $U_{j_i} = T_i$, $i = 1, \cdots, k$, that is, the set of cycles $\{T_i\}$ = the set of cycles $\{U_j\}$.

Proof:

I. *Existence.* Let $T \in S_n$, $T \neq (1)$. Let $A_1, \cdots, A_k$ be the distinct orbits of T with more than one element. Say A_j has n_j elements. Then by Theorem 3.3.5, for any x_j in A_j, $x_j, x_jT, x_jT^2, \cdots, x_jT^{n_j-1}$ are all distinct and form the set of elements in A_j. Hence $T = (x_1 x_1T \cdots x_1T^{n_1-1})(x_2 x_2T \cdots x_2T^{n_2-1}) \cdots (x_k x_kT \cdots x_kT^{n_k-1})$ is a factorization of T into disjoint cycles.

II. *Uniqueness.* Let $T = T_1 \circ \cdots \circ T_k$ be the factorization obtained above, and note that k is the number of orbits of T containing more than one element. Let $T = U_1 \circ \cdots \circ U_m$ be a factorization of T into disjoint cycles, each of length greater than 1. Let $x_1 \in A_1$ as above. Hence for some i, $x_1U_i \neq x_1$. Then, since U_i is disjoint from U_j, $j \neq i$, it follows from Exercise 1 in this section that $x_1U_j = x_1$ for all $j \neq i$. Since by Exercise 2, $U_i \circ U_j = U_j \circ U_i$, we may renumber the U_i's such that U_i becomes U_1. Since x_1 is in the orbit of U_1 containing more than one element, it follows that $U_1 = (x_1 x_1T \cdots x_1T^{n_1-1}) = T_1$, and therefore

$$U_2 \circ \cdots \circ U_m = U_1^{-1} \circ T = T_1^{-1} \circ T = T_2 \circ \cdots \circ T_k.$$

We now complete the proof by induction on k. If $k = 1$, then $T_1^{-1} \circ T = (1) = U_2 \circ \cdots \circ U_m$. By Exercise 3, $U_i = (1)$ for $i = 2, \cdots, m$ and hence $m = 1$ and $U_1 = T_1 = T$.

If $k > 1$, assuming the theorem for $k - 1$, we see that $m - 1 = k - 1$ and for some rearrangement $U_2 = T_2$, $U_3 = T_3, \cdots, U_k = T_k$. This completes the proof.

Exercises

5. Write $\begin{pmatrix} 1 & 2 & 3 & 4 & 5 & 6 & 7 & 8 \\ 2 & 4 & 1 & 3 & 6 & 8 & 7 & 5 \end{pmatrix}$ as a product of disjoint cycles.
6. Express each of the following products in terms of disjoint cycles (assume all permutations are in S_7):

i) (123)(467)(345)(146)
ii) (43)(156)(712)
iii) (1234)(123)(12)

Verify each of your answers by writing all the permutations in the form

$$\begin{pmatrix} 1 & 2 & 3 & 4 & 5 & 6 & 7 \\ 1T & 2T & 3T & 4T & 5T & 6T & 7T \end{pmatrix}$$

7. Let T be a permutation in S_n. Define the *order* of T to be the smallest positive integer m such that T^m is the identity permutation.
   a) Prove that for any $T \in S_n$, the order of T exists.
   b) Show that if T is a cycle of length r, then T has order r.
   c) Show that if T and S are disjoint cycles of orders t, s, respectively, then the order of $T \circ S$ is lcm$[t,s]$.
8. If p is a prime, describe all elements of S_n of order p.
9. Find an element of largest order in S_n, for $n = 2,3,4,5,6,7,8,9,10,17$.

3.4 PARITY OF PERMUTATIONS

Although the factorization of a permutation into disjoint cycles is unique up to the arrangement of the factors, there is another important way of factoring a permutation in which the uniqueness of the factors is no longer present. This method is factorization into 2-cycles (*transpositions*). We shall see, however, that the parity (evenness or oddness) of the number of factors is an invariant of the permutation.

Definition 3.4.1 A cycle of length 2 is called a *transposition*.
(1 2) is a transposition and (1 2)(3) is a transposition.

Lemma 3.4.2 For $n \geq 2$, any cycle $C \in S_n$ can be factored into a product of transpositions

Proof: The proof is by induction on the length of the cycle. If C is of length 1, then $C = (1)$. Hence $C = (1\ 2)(1\ 2)$. If C is a cycle of length $r \geq 2$, it is easily verified that $(i_1 i_2 \cdots i_r) = (i_1 i_2)(i_1 i_3 \cdots i_r)$. By induction, $(i_1 i_3 \cdots i_r)$ can be factored into transpositions, and thus, so can $(i_1 i_2 i_3 \cdots i_r)$.

Theorem 3.4.3 Any permutation can be factored into a product of transpositions.

Proof: If T is the identity, the result follows from Lemma 3.4.2. Otherwise, T can be written as a product of disjoint cycles, and each cycle can be factored into a product of transpositions by Lemma 3.4.2.

It is clear that the decomposition of a permutation into a product of transpositions is not at all unique. For example,

$$\begin{aligned}(1\,2\,3\,4) &= (1\,2)(1\,3)(1\,4)\\ &= (2\,3)(2\,4)(2\,1)\\ &= (1\,2)(1\,3)(1\,4)(2\,3)(2\,3)(1\,2)(2\,4)(2\,4)(1\,2).\end{aligned}$$

Although the first two factorizations require 3 transpositions each, and the last requires 9, both 3 and 9 are odd.

Theorem 3.4.4 Let $T \in S_n$. If $T = C_1 \circ C_2 \circ \cdots \circ C_r$ and $T = D_1 \circ D_2 \circ \cdots \circ D_s$ are two factorizations of T into transpositions, then r and s are either both even, or both odd, that is, $r + s$ is always even.

Proof: By Theorem 3.3.9, if $T \neq (1)$, then T has a unique (up to order) factorization into disjoint cycles, say

$$(*) \qquad T = (i_1 \cdots i_{n_1})(j_1 \cdots j_{n_2}) \cdots (k_1 \cdots k_{n_t}).$$

If the element $s \in X_n$ does not appear in (*), then we may add the 1 cycle (s) without changing T. Similarly if $T = (1)$, then $T = (1)(2)\cdots(n)$. Therefore by adding sufficient 1-cycles to (*) we can assume that every element of X_n appears exactly once in (*). Let N be the function defined by: $(T)N = (n_1 - 1) + (n_2 - 1) + \cdots + (n_t - 1)$. (If $T = (1)$, then $(T)N = ((1))N = 0$).

Now let $a,b \in X_n$. Then a and b belong either to the same orbit in (*) or to different orbits.

I. a,b are in the same orbit. Then $T = T' \circ (a\ell_1 \cdots \ell_{m_1} bh_1 \cdots h_{m_2})$, where T' is the product of the remaining disjoint cycles. Then $T \circ (ab) = T' \circ (a\ell_1 \cdots \ell_{m_1} bh_1 \cdots h_{m_2}) \circ (ab) = T' \circ (a\ell_1 \cdots \ell_{m_1}) \circ (bh_1 \cdots h_{m_2})$ is a factorization of $T \circ (ab)$ into disjoint cycles. Hence

$$(T \circ (ab))N = (T)N - 1,$$

since $(T)N = (T')N + (m_2 + m_1 + 2 - 1)$ and $(T \circ (ab))N = (T')N + (m_2 + 1 - 1) + (m_1 + 1 - 1)$.

II. a,b are in different orbits. Then $T = T'' \circ (a\ell_1 \cdots \ell_{m_1}) \circ (bh_1 \cdots h_{m_2})$, where T'' is the product of the disjoint cycles not containing a or b. Then $T \circ (ab) = T'' \circ (a\ell_1 \cdots \ell_{m_1}) \circ (bh_1 \cdots h_{m_2}) \circ (ab) = T'' \circ (a\ell_1 \cdots \ell_{m_1} bh_1 \cdots h_{m_2})$, whence $(T \circ (ab))N = (T)N + 1$.

Thus

$$(T \circ (ab))N = (T)N \pm 1.$$

Now let $T = (i_1 j_1) \circ \cdots \circ (i_r j_r)$ be a factorization of T into a product of r transpositions. We will show by induction on r that $(T)N$ is even if r is even, or odd if r is odd. If $r = 1$, T is a 2-cycle and $(T)N = 1$; hence r and $(T)N$ have the same parity.

Assume the theorem for $r - 1 \geq 1$. Then, if $T' = T \circ (i_r j_r)$, $(T')N = (T)N \pm 1$. But $T' = (i_1 j_1) \circ \cdots \circ (i_{r-1} j_{r-1}) \circ (i_r j_r) \circ (i_r j_r) = (i_1 j_1) \circ \cdots$

$\circ(i_{r-1}j_{r-1})$ is a product of $r - 1$ transpositions. Hence by induction $(T')N$ has the same parity as $r - 1$. Therefore, r and $(T)N$ have the same parity. (Note that in general $(T)N \neq r$).

Now, let $T = (\ell_1 m_1)\circ\cdots\circ(\ell_s m_s)$ be another factorization of T into transpositions. As above, $(T)N$ has the same parity as s, and hence s and r have the same parity.

Definition 3.4.5 A permutation $T \in S_n$, $n \geq 2$, is *even* (*odd*) if it can be written as a product of an even (odd) number of transpositions. We say that the *parity* of T is even (odd), accordingly.

It is easy to determine the parity of a product of two permutations from their respective parities. For, if

$$T = (i_1 j_1)\cdots(i_r j_r) \text{ and}$$

$$S = (m_1 n_1)\cdots(m_s n_s), \text{ then}$$

$T \circ S$ is a product of $r + s$ 2-cycles. Hence, the parity of $T \circ S$ is given by the following table:

T	S	$T \circ S$
even	even	even
even	odd	odd
odd	odd	even
odd	even	odd

The set of permutations S_n on X_n, is partitioned into two classes, the even and the odd permutations. We conclude this section by showing that both these classes have the same number of elements.

Theorem 3.4.6 If $n \geq 2$, and A_n is the set of all even permutations on X_n, then A_n contains $n!/2$ elements.

Proof: Let B_n be the set of all odd permutations in S_n. Then $S_n = A_n \cup B_n$, $A_n \cap B_n = \phi$. Let $\alpha: A_n \to B_n$ be defined as follows: For $T \in A_n$, $(T)\alpha = T \circ (12)$. We claim that α is 1–1 and onto. For, if $(T)\alpha = (U)\alpha$, we have $T \circ (1\ 2) = U \circ (1\ 2)$. Then $T \circ (1\ 2) \circ (1\ 2) = U \circ (1\ 2) \circ (1\ 2)$. But $(1\ 2) \circ (1\ 2) = (1)$, whence $T = U$, and α is 1–1. Next, let $U \in B_n$. Then U is odd and $U \circ (1\ 2)$ is even. Hence $(U \circ (1\ 2))\alpha = U \circ (1\ 2) \circ (1\ 2) = U$, and α is onto. This shows that A_n and B_n have the same number of elements, say m. Clearly, $m + m = n!$ and $m = n!/2$.

Exercises

1. Find the parity of each of the following permutations:

   i) $\begin{pmatrix} 1 & 2 & 3 & 4 & 5 & 6 & 7 \\ 2 & 3 & 4 & 1 & 6 & 7 & 5 \end{pmatrix}$

ii) (1 2 3)(2 4 5)(1 6 7)
iii) (1 4 5 6 3)(1 4 6 5 3)(1 4 3 6 5).

2. Show that, for $r \geq 2$,

$$(i_1 i_2 \cdots i_r) = (i_1 i_2)(i_1 i_3)(i_1 i_4)\cdots(i_1 i_r).$$

3. Show that the cycle $(1\ 2 \cdots n)$ is even if and only if n is odd.
4. Let $T \in A_n$, $U \in S_n$. Show that $U^{-1}TU \in A_n$.
5. Let $T \in A_n$. Show that $T^{-1} \in A_n$.
6. Show that the set A_n is "closed" under permutation multiplication. That is, if $T, S \in A_n$, then $T \circ S \in A_n$. Is a similar statement true about B_n?
7. a) Let $T \in S_n$, $n \geq 4$, and $U = (1\ 2\ 3\ 4)$. Show that $T^{-1}UT = (1T\ 2T\ 3T\ 4T)$.
   b) Let $T \in S_n$, $n \geq 5$, and $U = (1\ 2\ 3)(4\ 5)$. Find $T^{-1}\ UT$ as a product of disjoint cycles.
8. Let $T, U \in S_n$. Let $U = C_1 \cdots C_k$ be a factorization of U into disjoint cycles, where $C_i = (j_1 j_2 \cdots j_{t_i})$. Show that $T^{-1}UT = D_1 \cdots D_k$, where $D_i = (j_1 T\, j_2 T \cdots j_{t_i} T)$.
9. Let $T, U \in S_n$.
   $T = C_1 \circ \cdots \circ C_k$ is a factorization of T into disjoint cycles and $U = D_1 \circ \cdots \circ D_k$ is a factorization of U into disjoint cycles. Suppose C_i and D_i have the same length, $i = 1, 2, \cdots, k$. Prove that there exists $V \in S_n$ such that $V^{-1}TV = U$.
10. Let p be a prime. Let $Z_p^* = \{1, 2, \cdots, p-1\}$.
    a) For each $x \in Z_p^*$ define a map $\tau_x : Z_p^* \to Z_p^*$ as follows: $y\tau_x = r$, where r is the least positive residue congruent to yx modulo p. Show that τ_x is a permutation of Z_p^*.
    b) Show that for $x \in Z_p^*$, $y \in Z_p^*$, $\tau_x \tau_y = \tau_{xy} = \tau_z$, $z \in Z_p^*$, $z \equiv xy$ (mod p).
    c) Let $f: Z_p^* \to \{\tau_x \mid x \in Z_p^*\}$ be defined by $xf = \tau_x$. Show that f is 1–1 and onto and that $(xy)f = (xf)(yf)$.

CHAPTER 4

The Theory of Groups

4.1 DEFINITION OF GROUP AND EXAMPLES

In Chapter 2 we saw that a great many theorems about the integers are deducible from the relatively short list of properties stated in Section 2.1. These properties could have been stated in the "abstract," using the terminology and notation of set theory.

For example, if we replace the set Z of integers by an arbitrary non-empty set S and the operation of addition by a function $f:S \times S \rightarrow S$, then properties A_0, A_1, and A_2 become:

B_0: There is a function $f:S \times S \rightarrow S$.
B_1: If $a,b,c \in S$, then
$((a,b)f,c)f = (a,(b,c)f)f$.
B_2: If $a,b \in S$, then
$(a,b)f = (b,a)f$.

Notice that in this form no direct mention is made of integers. We merely define a function and list some of its properties. In a similar way we can define an abstract "multiplication" and state the distributive law. Such a procedure has the obvious advantage of simultaneously including all mathematical systems that share these abstract properties.

Historically, the important abstractions developed (often in very slow stages) from specific problem areas. The theory of groups, which we will study in this chapter, arose from the theory of equations, more specifically from the attempt to find roots of a polynomial in terms of its coefficients. Considerations far too involved to explain here led to a systematic study of sets of permutations, which in turn led to the formulation of the concept of a group. The study of groups, although very much influenced by its historical origins, has developed in many different directions. The richness and breadth of this development has given the theory of groups a central position in mathematics.

Definition 4.1.1 Let G be a nonempty set and f a binary operation on G, that is, $f: G \times G \to G$. We denote the element $(a,b)f$ by $a \circ b$. The pair (G,f) will be called a *group* if

i) f is associative, that is, $a \circ (b \circ c) = (a \circ b) \circ c$ for all $a,b,c \in G$.
ii) There is an element $e \in G$ such that $a \circ e = a$ for all $a \in G$. e is called a *right identity element* for (G,f).
iii) There exists a right identity e of (G,f), with the property that for each $a \in G$ there is an element $b \in G$ such that $a \circ b = e$. b is called a *right inverse* of a.

For purposes of brevity, when no ambiguity of meaning exists, we shall simply denote the group (G,f) by G. The context should clearly indicate whether we are concerned with the abstract set or with a set together with an associated binary operation.

When the function denoting the binary operation is not indicated, we shall usually use juxtaposition, as in the multiplication of numbers, to denote the group operation. That is, the element $(a,b)f$ will be denoted by ab. Following this convention, if b is a right inverse of a, we write $b = a^{-1}$, and $ab = aa^{-1} = e$. On occasion we shall use $a + b$ or $a * b$ in place of $a \circ b$. With the notation $a + b$, a right inverse of a will be denoted by $(-a)$ and a group identity by 0.

Definition 4.1.2 Let G be a group. If $a \circ b = b \circ a$, for all $a,b \in G$, we say that G is *commutative* or *abelian*.[9] If there exists a pair of elements $a,b \in G$ such that $a \circ b \neq b \circ a$, we say that G is *noncommutative* or *non-abelian*. When $a \circ b = b \circ a$, we say that the elements a and b *commute.*

Definition 4.1.3 A group with a finite number of elements is called a *finite group*; otherwise, it is called an *infinite group*. If a group G is finite, and G consists of exactly n elements, we say that the *order of* G is n and we write $|G| = n$. If G is infinite, we write $|G| = \infty$.

The following list of examples will illustrate the diversity of mathematical systems that satisfy the axioms given above and that are, therefore, groups.

Example 4.1.4 Let G be the set of all integers and f the operation of addition, that is, $(a,b)f = a + b$. Property A_1 in Section 2.1 is the statement that f is associative. The integer 0 satisfies the requirement for a right identity and $-a$ is clearly a right inverse of a, since $a + (-a) = 0$. Thus $(G,+)$ is a group.

Example 4.1.5 Let G be the set of all rational numbers excluding 0. That is, G is the set of all real numbers that can be written in the form a/b,

[9] After the Norwegian mathematician N. H. Abel (1802–1829).

with a and b integers, $a \neq 0$, $b \neq 0$. For $u, v \in G$, let $u \circ v = uv$, the usual product of two real numbers. The associative property of multiplication of rational numbers follows from the associative law of multiplication for integers (see Section 5.7). The rational number $1/1 = 1$ is a right identity and a right inverse of a/b is simply b/a. Hence $(G,\circ)$ is a group.

Exercises

1. Is $(Z, -)$ a group?
2. Why is it necessary in Example 4.1.5 above to exclude 0 from the set G?
3. Let H be the set of even integers. Show that $(H, +)$ is a group. ●

Example 4.1.6 Let G be the set of residue classes of integers modulo m, that is $G = \overline{Z}_m$, and let f be the addition of residue classes defined in Section 2.11. We showed there that f satisfies the associative law. Also $\bar{0}$ is a right identity and the residue class $\overline{(m - a)}$ is a right inverse of $\bar{a}$. Thus $(\overline{Z}_m, +)$ is a group.

Example 4.1.7 Let R be a nonsquare rectangle in the plane whose vertices are labeled as in Figure 6 below.

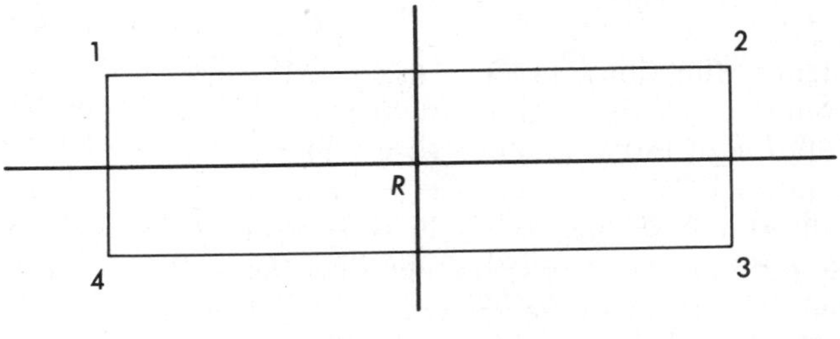

Figure 6

Consider the following rigid motions of R (called the *symmetries* of R):
r: Rotation of 180° about its center
h: Reflection in the horizontal axis
v: Reflection in the vertical axis
e: No movement at all (equivalent to a rotation of 360°).

Each of these movements can be thought of either as a transformation of R or as a permutation on its vertices. In either case these movements can be composed or "multiplied" as functions (Section 3.1) and it is easy to verify that the product of any pair of these is again one of the four. For example, $r \circ h = v$, as illustrated in Figure 7.

The element e is the identity function and each element is its own inverse. Since we have already shown that composition of functions is an associative operation, it follows that the set of symmetries of R is a group

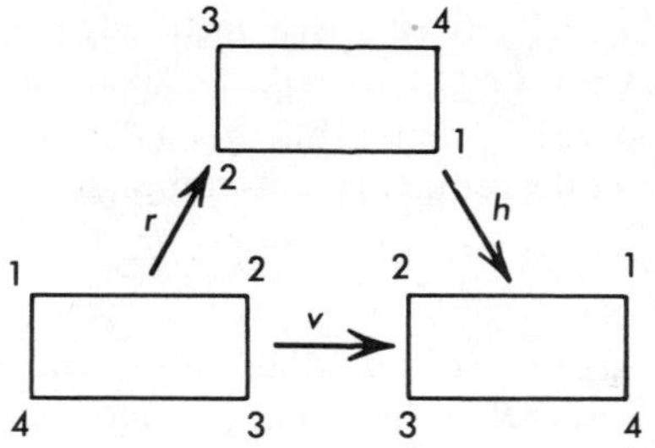

Figure 7

with respect to the operation of function composition. This group is sometimes called the Klein 4-group.

Exercise

4. Compute all products of pairs of elements of the Klein group above. Is the group commutative? What is its order? •

Example 4.1.8 Let E_2 denote the points of the plane with Cartesian coordinates, that is, $E_2 = \{(x,y) \mid x,y \text{ are real numbers}\}$. Let D_4 represent the following set of permutations of E_2.

e (identity function): $(x,y) \to (x,y)$
r_1 (counterclockwise rotation of 90°): $(x,y) \to (-y,x)$
r_2 (rotation of 180°): $(x,y) \to (-x,-y)$
r_3 (rotation of 270°): $(x,y) \to (y,-x)$
v (reflection in the y axis): $(x,y) \to (-x,y)$
h (reflection in the x axis): $(x,y) \to (x,-y)$
d_1 (reflection through the line $y = x$): $(x,y) \to (y,x)$
d_{-1} (reflection through the line $y = -x$): $(x,y) \to (-y,-x)$.

This set of transformations can also be thought of as the set of all symmetric movements of a square with center at the origin (0,0) and vertical and horizontal edges.

The set D_4 together with the composition of functions satisfies all of the requirements for a group. The associativity of this product follows from Theorem 3.1.2. The fact that the product of any two of these transformations is again in D_4 can be verified directly. For example,

$$(x,y)(r_1 \circ d_1) = ((x,y)r_1)d_1 = (-y,x)d_1 = (x,-y).$$

But

$$(x,y)h = (x,-y),$$

hence,

$$r_1 \circ d_1 = h.$$

The reader is asked to verify that e is a right identity and that for each element of D_4 there exists a right inverse. This group is called the *group of symmetries of a square*. Note that $d_1 \circ r_1 = v$ and $r_1 \circ d_1 = h$ and observe that D_4 is our first example of a nonabelian group.

Exercises

5. Show that D_4 is a group. (Fill in all details of the discussion above.)
6. Show that the subset $R = \{e, r_1, r_2, r_3\}$ together with the operation $\circ$ of D_4 restricted to R is a group. Can you find any other subsets of D_4 that form a group with respect to $\circ$? ●

Example 4.1.9 Let $G = \{1, -1, i, -i\}$ where $i^2 = -1$. If f is the usual multiplication of complex numbers, it is easy to see that (G, f) is a group of four elements.

Example 4.1.10 Let S be an arbitrary set and let G be the set of all 1–1 mappings from S onto itself, that is, the set of all permutations on the set S. Let f be the binary operation of permutation multiplication. Then, by Theorem 3.1.2, f is associative on G. The identity function satisfies the requirements for a group identity, and if $g \in G$, then the function g^{-1} defined in Definition 3.1.5 is a group inverse for g. The group G is usually called the *transformation group* for S. If the set S consists of n elements, say $\{1, 2, \cdots, n\}$, then G is called the *symmetric group on n letters*, denoted by S_n.

Exercises

7. Show that in D_4 there is a unique right identity and each element has a unique right inverse.
8. Show that $(a^{-1})^{-1} = a$ for all elements a of the group D_4.
9. Show that if a, b are elements of the group D_4, then $(ab)^{-1} = b^{-1}a^{-1}$
10. Find the orders of S_2, S_3, S_n.
11. Let $G = \{\bar{1}, \bar{3}, \bar{5}, \bar{7}\} \subset Z_8$. Show that G is a group with respect to residue class multiplication modulo 8.
12. Let $G = \{\bar{1}, \bar{5}, \bar{7}, \overline{11}\} \subset Z_{12}$. Show that G is a group with respect to residue class multiplication modulo 12.
13. Let G be the set of all symmetries of an equilateral triangle. Show that G is a group with respect to the operation of function composition.

4.2 ELEMENTARY CONSEQUENCES OF THE DEFINITION OF A GROUP

The list of examples given above offers a fairly wide sample of infinite and finite groups. They all share some rather obvious properties that do not appear explicitly in the definition of a group. In particular, in each group there appears to be only one choice for an identity element and for the inverse of an element. Another elementary property common to all is that if e is an identity of the group G, then $ea = ae = a$ for all $a \in G$. This holds even in those examples in which the binary operation is not commutative. We shall show in this section that many of the properties that appear common to all of these examples do indeed follow from the group axioms and thus hold for all groups.

We begin with a lemma that has some independent interest. Throughout we denote an arbitrary group by G.

Lemma 4.2.1 Let e be a right identity of G (Definition 4.1.1 iii), that is, $ae = a$ for all $a \in G$ and $aa^{-1} = e$. If $cc = c$ for some $c \in G$, then $c = e$.

Proof: If $cc = c$, then $(cc)c^{-1} = cc^{-1}$, which implies that $c = ce = c(cc^{-1}) = (cc)c^{-1} = cc^{-1} = e$.

Theorem 4.2.2 Every right inverse is also a left inverse. That is, if $aa^{-1} = e$ then $a^{-1}a = e$.

Proof: Consider the element $a^{-1}a$. We shall prove that $a^{-1}a = e$ by showing that $a^{-1}a$ satisfies the hypothesis of Lemma 4.2.1. For

$$(a^{-1}a)\,(a^{-1}a) = ((a^{-1}a)a^{-1})a = (a^{-1}(aa^{-1}))a = (a^{-1}e)a = a^{-1}a.$$

Hence, $a^{-1}a = e$.

Theorem 4.2.3 Every right identity is a left identity and there is precisely one right identity. That is, in every group G there is a unique element e such that $ea = ae = a$ for all $a \in G$.

Proof: Let e be a fixed right identity of the group G, and let e_1 be another identity, either right or left. Then $e_1e_1 = e_1$. Hence, by Lemma 4.2.1, $e_1 = e$. Therefore, any identity of G is equal to e. Further, for all $a \in G$, $ea = (aa^{-1})a = a(a^{-1}a) = ae = a$.

Theorem 4.2.4 If $a,b,c \in G$, then $ab = ac$ implies that $b = c$ and $ba = ca$ implies $b = c$. That is, cancellation on the left and the right is always permissible.

Proof: If $ab = ac$, then $a^{-1}(ab) = a^{-1}(ac)$. Hence, $(a^{-1}a)b = (a^{-1}a)c$, and $eb = ec$ by Theorem 4.2.2. Therefore, by Theorem 4.2.3, $b = c$. Similarly, if $ba = ca$, then $(ba)a^{-1} = (ca)a^{-1}$ and $b(aa^{-1}) = c(aa^{-1})$. Hence, $be = ce$ and $b = c$.

Theorem 4.2.5 If $a \in G$, then there is precisely one element $a^{-1} \in G$ such that $aa^{-1} = a^{-1}a = e$.

Proof: Suppose that $ba = e$ and $ca = e$ for some $a,b,c \in G$. Then, since $ba = ca$, $b = c$.

Corollary 4.2.6 If $a \in G$, then $(a^{-1})^{-1} = a$.

Proof: The element $(a^{-1})^{-1}$ is the unique element satisfying $a^{-1}x = e$. But $a^{-1}a = e$, and hence $(a^{-1})^{-1} = a$.

As a consequence of the previous theorems it is possible to think of a group G as a nonempty set together with a binary operation $\circ$ satisfying the following properties:

1) $a \circ (b \circ c) = (a \circ b) \circ c$. That is, $\circ$ is associative.
2) G contains a unique element e such that $a \circ e = e \circ a = a$ for all a in G.
3) For each a in G, G contains a unique element b, denoted by a^{-1}, such that $a \circ a^{-1} = a^{-1} \circ a = e$.

That such a set $(G,\circ)$ satisfies our definition of a group is obvious, and the theorems in this section prove that every group satisfies these properties. (This list of properties is often used as the definition of a group.)

It should also be clear that we could have begun by defining a group in terms of the existence of a *left identity* and a *left inverse* and proved the appropriate analogues of the theorems above. The definition of a group that we have given is only one of many other possible and, of course, logically equivalent definitions. The theorem below gives one such alternate.

Theorem 4.2.7 Let G be a nonempty set and $\circ$ a binary operation on G satisfying:

1) $a \circ (b \circ c) = (a \circ b) \circ c$ for all $a,b,c \in G$.
2) The equation $a \circ x = b$ has a solution in G for all $a,b \in G$.
3) The equation $y \circ a = b$ has a solution in G for all $a,b \in G$.

Then $(G,\circ)$ is a group.

Proof: Exercise.

Exercises

1. Verify that the associative law holds in Example 4.1.9.

* 2. Show that if G is a group and $a,b \in G$, then $(ab)^{-1} = b^{-1}a^{-1}$.

3. Show that if a group G contains an element c with the property that $ca = c$ for all $a \in G$, then G consists of a single element.

* 4. Show that the set $\bar{Z}_p{}^* = \{\bar{1},\bar{2},\cdots,\overline{(p-1)}\}$ and the operation of multiplication of residue classes forms a group if and only if p is a prime.

† 5. Prove Theorem 4.2.7.

6. Let G be a group. Show that G is abelian if and only if $(ab)^2 = a^2b^2$.

7. Show that if $a^2 = e$ for all elements a of a group G, then G is abelian.

* 8. Let $gG = \{gh \mid h \in G\}$ for some fixed g in the group G. Show that $G = gG$.

9. Let H be a nonempty finite set and let $\circ$ be an associative binary operation on H. Suppose that $a \circ b = a \circ c$ implies $b = c$ and $a \circ c = b \circ c$ implies $a = b$. Show that H is a group. Show that the hypothesis that H is finite cannot be omitted.

10. Let G be a nonempty set and $\circ$ an associative binary operation on G. Assume that there exists $e \in G$ such that $a \circ e = e \circ a = a$ for all $a \in G$, and further, that for each $a \in G$ there exists $b \in G$ such that either $a \circ b = e$ or $b \circ a = e$. Show that G is a group.

*11. Let H be a nonempty subset of the group G. For $g \in G$, define $gH = \{gh \mid h \in H\}$ and let $Hg = \{hg \mid h \in H\}$. If g_1 and g_2 are elements of G, prove that there exist mappings f_1, f_2, f_3 such that

$$f_1: g_1H \xrightarrow[\text{onto}]{1-1} H, \quad f_2: g_1H \xrightarrow[\text{onto}]{1-1} g_2H,$$

$$f_3: g_1H \xrightarrow[\text{onto}]{1-1} Hg_2.$$

12. Let A be the set of reduced residue classes modulo m, $m > 0$. Show that A is a group with respect to residue class multiplication.

13. Let $(G, \circ)$ be a group. Show that the equations $a \circ x = b$ and $y \circ a = b$ have unique solutions, and that these solutions are $x = a^{-1} \circ b$ and $y = b \circ a^{-1}$, respectively.

14. Let H be a collection of permutations on the set S such that
   i) the identity permutation on S is in H
   ii) if $T \in H$, then $T^{-1} \in H$
   iii) if $T_1, T_2 \in H$, then $T_1 \circ T_2 \in H$.
   Show that $(H, \circ)$ is a group. (H is called a *group of permutations*).

4.3 MULTIPLICATION TABLE FOR A FINITE GROUP

Let G be a finite group of order n. Then it is possible to define its binary operation $\circ$ by listing the values of the n^2 products $a \circ b$ for all $a,b \in G$. One particularly convenient way to do this is by means of a "multiplication table," a table analogous to the ones used in grade school to illustrate addition or multiplication of numbers. In the case of a finite group, many of the group axioms can be translated into "geometrical" statements about the multiplication table. We illustrate this with the group S_3 of all permutations on the three numbers 1, 2, 3. Here the binary operation is permutation multiplication defined in Section 3.1. The elements of S_3 are: $a_1 = (1)$, $a_2 = (1\ 2)$, $a_3 = (2\ 3)$, $a_4 = (1\ 3)$, $a_5 = (1\ 2\ 3)$ and $a_6 = (1\ 3\ 2)$. The multiplication table is constructed by listing the elements of G along the top and left side in the same order. We refer to the column headed by a_j as the jth column and to the row with a_i on the left as the ith row. We then fill in the boxes according to the rule: the contents of the box in the ith row and jth column is the element $a_i a_j$.

$\circ$	a_1	a_2	a_3	a_4	a_5	a_6
a_1	a_1	a_2	a_3	a_4	a_5	a_6
a_2	a_2	a_1	a_6	a_5	a_4	a_3
a_3	a_3	a_5	a_1	a_6	a_2	a_4
a_4	a_4	a_6	a_5	a_1	a_3	a_2
a_5	a_5	a_3	a_4	a_2	a_6	a_1
a_6	a_6	a_4	a_2	a_3	a_1	a_5

Exercises

1. Verify that all entries above are correct.
2. Construct the multiplication table for Example 4.1.9.
3. Construct the multiplication table for Example 4.1.7.
4. State and prove a criterion for commutativity based on the multiplication table of a group.

It is now possible, by examining the formal properties of the table, to decide whether certain of the axioms are fulfilled. One of the elements is a right identity if and only if its column contains elements in exactly the same order as in the labeling column. Notice that if there are two such columns, then either the two elements are equal or else the set is not a group. This follows from the fact that the identity element is unique. In the illustration above a_1 is the identity element.

The presence of a_1 in each row guarantees that each element has an inverse. More generally, every element must appear in every row and every column. For otherwise one element would have to appear twice in a row (or a column) and this would contradict the fact that the elements are distinct, since $uv = uw$ implies that $v = w$. The only group property that is difficult to check directly from properties of the multiplication table is associativity.[10]

Exercises

5. Let $G = \{a,b,c,d\}$ with binary operation defined by the following table. Is G a group? Why?

[10]See, e.g., H. Zassenhaus [53].

	a	b	c	d
a	a	b	d	c
b	b	a	c	d
c	d	c	a	b
d	c	d	b	a

6. In Exercise 5 replace G by $H = \{a, b, c, d, e\}$ and the table by:

	a	b	c	d	e
a	a	b	c	d	e
b	b	a	d	e	c
c	c	d	e	b	a
d	d	e	a	c	b
e	e	c	b	a	d

4.4 ISOMORPHISM

It should be evident from the examples already given that a great many different mathematical systems are groups. In order to obtain a clear picture of how many different types of groups there are, we must be able to distinguish between those properties of a group that are "relevant" and those that are not.

As a trivial example of such a distinction, consider the Klein group described in Example 4.1.7 and suppose that the rectangle in question has sides of length two inches and four inches. If now we form the group of symmetries of a rectangle with sides of length one inch and three inches, then we may say that the two groups are "essentially" the same.

A slightly less trivial example is given by the groups $G = \{e, r_1, r_2, r_3\}$ described in Exercise 6, Section 4.1, and H, the group $\overline{Z}_4$ of Example 4.1.6 ($m = 4$). To demonstrate the similarity between these two groups, we define a mapping $f: G \rightarrow \overline{Z}_4$ as follows:

$$ef = \overline{0}$$
$$r_1 f = \overline{1}$$
$$r_2 f = \overline{2}$$
$$r_3 f = \overline{3}.$$

Any product of elements of G corresponds to the sum of corresponding elements in $\overline{Z}_4$. For example, $(r_1 r_2)f = \overline{1} + \overline{2} = r_1 f + r_2 f$. We see then, that the operations of $\overline{Z}_4$ and of G behave in "essentially" the same way. This can be most easily demonstrated by examining the multiplication tables of G and $\overline{Z}_4$.

TABLE FOR G

	e	r_1	r_2	r_3
e	e	r_1	r_2	r_3
r_1	r_1	r_2	r_3	e
r_2	r_2	r_3	e	r_1
r_3	r_3	e	r_1	r_2

TABLE FOR $\overline{Z}_4$

	$\bar{0}$	$\bar{1}$	$\bar{2}$	$\bar{3}$
$\bar{0}$	$\bar{0}$	$\bar{1}$	$\bar{2}$	$\bar{3}$
$\bar{1}$	$\bar{1}$	$\bar{2}$	$\bar{3}$	$\bar{0}$
$\bar{2}$	$\bar{2}$	$\bar{3}$	$\bar{0}$	$\bar{1}$
$\bar{3}$	$\bar{3}$	$\bar{0}$	$\bar{1}$	$\bar{2}$

The statement above can now be completely checked by noting that if all of the entries in the table for G are replaced by elements of $\overline{Z}_4$ according to the function f, then the two tables are identical. Alternatively, if the table for G is superimposed on the table for Z_4, the set of pairs of elements occurring in the same box are the ordered pairs in the function f.

We now formalize this discussion in the following definition.

Definition 4.4.1 Two groups $(G,\circ)$ and $(H,*)$ will be called *isomorphic* if there exists a 1–1 onto function $f:G \to H$ such that for all $a,b \in G$,

$$(a \circ b) f = af * bf.$$

We shall also say that *G is isomorphic to H* and use the notation $G \simeq H$. The function f is called an *isomorphism*.

We see then that two groups are isomorphic if their elements can be put into 1–1 correspondence in such a way that their respective binary operations correspond.

Example 4.4.2 Let $(Z,+)$ and $(W,+)$ be the groups of integers and even integers respectively under addition. Let $f:Z \to W$ be defined by $nf = 2n$ for all $n \in Z$. Clearly f is 1–1 and onto. Since $(a+b)f = 2(a+b) = 2a + 2b = af + bf$, f is an isomorphism and $Z \simeq W$.

Exercises

1. Show that if H is the additive group $(\overline{Z}_4,+)$ and G is the group of Example 4.1.9, then $G \simeq H$.
2. Show that the groups of Exercises 11 and 12, Section 4.1, are both isomorphic to the Klein group (Example 4.1.7).
3. Show that the group of symmetries of an equilateral triangle (Exercise 13, Section 4.1) is isomorphic to S_3.

4. Let G be the group of all permutations on the set of three symbols $\{a,b,c\}$. Show that $G \simeq S_3$.
5. Show that the Klein group is not isomorphic to $(\overline{Z}_4, +)$.
6. Show that S_3 is not isomorphic to $(\overline{Z}_6, +)$.
7. Let f be an isomorphism from the group G to the group H.
 a) If e is the identity of G, show that ef is the identity of H.
 b) Show that $(a^{-1})f = (af)^{-1}$.
8. Let G be an abelian group and H a nonabelian group. Prove that G and H are not isomorphic.
* 9. Show that the relation $A \simeq B$ is an equivalence relation on any set of groups.
10. Let $f: G \to G$ be defined as follows: $gf = a^{-1}ga$ for a fixed in G, and all $g \in G$. Show that f is an isomorphism.

4.5 THE GENERALIZED ASSOCIATIVE LAW AND THE LAW OF EXPONENTS

Let $(G,\circ)$ be a group. Since $\circ$ is a *binary* operation, it makes sense to form products of *pairs* of elements, that is, to combine elements of G two at a time. Hence, given three elements a_1, a_2, a_3 we may form a single product in this order in two distinct ways, namely, $(a_1 \circ a_2) \circ a_3$ and $a_1 \circ (a_2 \circ a_3)$. The associative law states that both of these products represents the same element of G. Hence we may write $a_1 \circ a_2 \circ a_3$ with no ambiguity. In the case of four elements, the number of products that can be formed is five and it is not difficult to show that they are all equal in G.

Exercise

1. Form the five products of a_1, a_2, a_3, a_4 in that order and, using the associative law, show that they are all equal. •

In this section we extend the results mentioned above for three and four elements to an arbitrary string of n elements. The procedure will be as follows. First, we inductively define all "meaningful" products of n elements in some order. Then we inductively define the "standard" product of n elements of a group in some fixed order. Finally we show that every meaningful product of n elements in some order is equal to the standard product, and hence represents the same group element. This result is known as the *generalized associative law* and it allows us to use the notation $a_1 \circ a_2 \circ \cdots \circ a_n$ for any product of n elements in that order with no ambiguity.

Since, in what follows, we must distinguish between products that, as will be shown, are equal in a group G but formally appear different, we let G be a set with a binary operation that is not necessarily associative.

Definition 4.5.1 Let G be a set with a binary operation $\circ$ and an identity e. For each integer $n \geq 1$, we define an *n product* of a sequence of n elements from G as follows:

If $n = 1$, the 1 product of a_1 is simply a_1.

If $n > 1$, an n product of the sequence $a_1, \cdots, a_n$ is defined to be any product of the form: $(a_1 \circ \cdots \circ a_m) \circ (a_{m+1} \circ \cdots \circ a_n)$, where $(a_1 \circ \cdots \circ a_m)$ is an m product, and $(a_{m+1} \circ \cdots \circ a_n)$ is an n–m product, $1 \leq m < n$.

(This definition utilizes the second form of the principle of induction, since an n product is defined in terms of m products for $1 \leq m < n$.)

We now introduce the "standard" n product and show that any n product is equal to our standard one.

Definition 4.5.2 For each integer $n \geq 0$, we define $\prod_{i=1}^{n} a_i$ as follows: For $n = 0$, $\prod_{i=1}^{0} a_i = e$. For $n \geq 1$, $\prod_{i=1}^{n} a_i = \left(\prod_{i=1}^{n-1} a_i\right) \circ a_n$. (This is another inductive definition.)

It is easy to see by induction that for all integers $n \geq 1$, $\prod_{i=1}^{n} a_i$ is one of the n products of Definition 4.5.1.

For purposes of illustration we write out $\prod_{i=1}^{n} a_i$ in full, for $n = 1,2,3,4$. Thus,

$$\prod_{i=1}^{1} a_i = a_1$$

$$\prod_{i=1}^{2} a_i = a_1 \circ a_2$$

$$\prod_{i=1}^{3} a_i = \left(\prod_{i=1}^{2} a_i\right) \circ a_3 = (a_1 \circ a_2) \circ a_3$$

$$\prod_{i=1}^{4} a_i = \left(\prod_{i=1}^{3} a_i\right) \circ a_4 = ((a_1 \circ a_2) \circ a_3) \circ a_4.$$

The general pattern should now be clear.

Theorem 4.5.3 Generalized Associative Law Let G be a group. Let $a_1, a_2, \cdots, a_n$ be n elements from G. Then any n product of $a_1, a_2, \cdots, a_n$ in that order is equal to $\prod_{i=1}^{n} a_i$, and hence all n products of $a_1, \cdots, a_n$ in that order are equal.

Proof: The theorem is proved by induction on n.

For $n = 1$ the theorem is trivially true.

Now assume that the theorem is true for all k products $1 \leq k < n$. That is, assume that any k product of k elements $b_1,\cdots,b_k$ in that order is equal to $\prod_{i=1}^{k} b_i$.

Thus, let $\alpha = (a_1 \circ \cdots \circ a_m) \circ (a_{m+1} \circ \cdots \circ a_n)$, $1 \leq m < n$, be an n product. By our induction hypotheses,

$$(a_{m+1} \circ \cdots \circ a_n) = \prod_{i=1}^{n-m} a_{m+i}.$$

Then, using the definition of $\prod_{i=1}^{k} b_i$, and the usual associative law, we get

$$\begin{aligned}\alpha &= (a_1 \circ \cdots \circ a_m) \circ \prod_{i=1}^{n-m} a_{m+i} \\ &= (a_1 \circ \cdots \circ a_m) \circ \left(\left(\prod_{i=1}^{n-m-1} a_{m+i} \right) \circ a_n \right) \\ &= \left((a_1 \circ \cdots \circ a_m) \circ \prod_{i=1}^{n-m-1} a_{m+i} \right) \circ a_n .\end{aligned}$$

By our induction assumption, the $(n - 1)$ product

$$(a_1 \circ \cdots \circ a_m) \circ \prod_{i=1}^{n-m-1} a_{m+i}$$

is equal to $\prod_{i=1}^{n-1} a_i$ and so

$$\alpha = \left(\prod_{i=1}^{n-1} a_i \right) \circ a_n = \prod_{i=1}^{n} a_i$$

by definition. This completes the proof of the theorem.

We mention at this point that the above proof can be slightly modified to show the following: Let H be a nonempty set and let $\circ$ be an associative binary operation on H. Then the generalized associative law holds for $(H,\circ)$. Thus, although Theorem 4.5.3 shows that the generalized associative law holds for addition of integers ($(Z,+)$ is a group), the modification will show that the generalized associative law also holds for multiplication of integers (Z is not a group with respect to multiplication, but multiplication is an associative binary operation on Z). We leave the details of this modification to the reader (Exercise 6).

Corollary 4.5.4 Let $(G,\circ)$ be a commutative group. Let $a_1,a_2,\cdots,a_n$ be elements of G and let $a_{i_1},a_{i_2},\cdots,a_{i_n}$ be the same n elements listed in some order. Then $a_1\circ a_2\circ\cdots\circ a_n = a_{i_1}\circ a_{i_2}\circ\cdots\circ a_{i_n}$.

Proof: Exercise.

Now that we have the generalized associative law, it is quite simple to prove the basic facts concerning exponents.

Definition 4.5.5 Let a be an element of the group G. Then we denote the product $\prod_{i=1}^{n} a_i$ where $a_i = a$ for $i = 1,\cdots,n$, by $\prod_{i=1}^{n} a$, and we define a^n by

$$a^n = \prod_{i=1}^{n} a, \text{ for } n \geq 0.$$

We recall that $a^0 = \prod_{i=1}^{0} a = e$, and for $n \geq 1$

$$a^n = a^{n-1}\circ a$$

It will be helpful to the reader to think of a^n as $a\circ a\circ\cdots\circ a$, where a appears n times.

Lemma 4.5.6 Let G be a group and let $a \in G$. Then $a^n = a^{n-1}\circ a = a\circ a^{n-1}$, for all $n \in Z$, $n \geq 0$.

Proof: Exercise.

Theorem 4.5.7 Let G be a group and let $a \in G$. Then $(a^n)^{-1} = (a^{-1})^n$, for $n \in Z, n \geq 0$.

Proof: The proof is by induction on n. If $n = 0$, then $(a^0)^{-1} = e^{-1} = e = (a^{-1})^0$, by definition. Assume that for $n = k \geq 0$, $(a^k)^{-1} = (a^{-1})^k$. Then

$$a^{-1}\circ(a^k)^{-1} = a^{-1}\circ(a^{-1})^k, \text{ and}$$
$$(a^k\circ a)^{-1} = (a^{-1})^k\circ a^{-1} \text{ by Exercise 2, Section 4.2 and Lemma 4.5.6.}$$

Hence $(a^{k+1})^{-1} = (a^{-1})^{k+1}$ by Definition 4.5.5, and the theorem is proved.

Definition 4.5.8 Let G be a group and let $a \in G$. We define $a^{-n} = (a^{-1})^n$, where $n > 0$.

Lemma 4.5.9 Let G be a group and let $a \in G$. Then $a^{-n} = (a^{-1})^n$ for all integers n.

Proof: If $n \geq 0$, this follows from the definition. If $n < 0$, let $n = -m, m > 0$. Then $a^{-n} = a^{-(-m)} = (a^{-1})^{-m}$ by definition. Hence $a^{-n} = (a^{-1})^n$.

Theorem 4.5.10 If $a \in G$, then

i) $a^n \circ a^m = a^{n+m}$ and
ii) $(a^n)^m = a^{nm}$, for all $n,m \in Z$.

Proof: i) We first consider the case $n \geq 0$ and $m \geq 0$. Then $a^n \circ a^m = \prod_{i=1}^{n} a \circ \prod_{i=1}^{m} a = \prod_{i=1}^{n+m} a$, since the product of an n product and an m product is an $n + m$ product equal to the standard $n + m$ product by the generalized associative law.

If $n < 0$ and $m < 0$, we may repeat the above argument by first replacing $a^n \circ a^m$ by $(a^{-1})^{-n} \circ (a^{-1})^{-m}$.

Finally, let $n \geq 0$ and $m < 0$. If $n = 0$, the theorem follows trivially. Thus assume the result holds for all k such that $0 \leq k < n$ and all $m < 0$. Then $a^n \circ a^m = a^n \circ (a^{-1})^{-m} = a^n \circ (a^{-1} \circ (a^{-1})^{-m-1}) = (a^n \circ a^{-1}) \circ (a^{-1})^{-m-1} = ((a^{n-1} \circ a) \circ a^{-1}) \circ (a^{-1})^{-m-1} = (a^{n-1} \circ (a \circ a^{-1})) \circ (a^{-1})^{-m-1} = a^{n-1} \circ (a^{-1})^{-m-1} = a^{n-1} \circ a^{m+1} = a^{(n-1)+(m+1)} = a^{n+m}$, and the result follows by induction.

The case $n < 0$, $m \geq 0$ can be handled similarly. This completes the proof of i).

ii) If $m = 0$, then $(a^n)^0 = e = a^0 = a^{n \cdot 0}$. Assume that the theorem holds for all k such that $0 \leq k < m$ and all n. Then $(a^n)^m = (a^n)^{m-1} \circ a^n = a^{n(m-1)} \circ a^n = a^{n(m-1)+n} = a^{nm}$ and the result follows by induction for all nonnegative m.

If $m < 0$, then $(a^n)^m = ((a^n)^{-1})^{-m} = ((a^{-1})^n)^{-m}$. But as $-m > 0$, by the previous case $(a^n)^m = (a^{-1})^{n(-m)} = (a^{-1})^{-nm} = ((a^{-1})^{-1})^{nm} = a^{nm}$.

We recall that when a group G is written *additively*, that is, when $+$ is used to represent the group operation, then the inverse of an element a is written as $-a$ and 0 is used to represent the group identity. The element $\underbrace{a \circ a \circ \cdots \circ a}_{n \text{ times}}$, which we have written above as a^n, becomes na, and the theorem above can be restated as follows:

i) $na + ma = (n + m)a$.
ii) $n(ma) = (nm)a$.

Exercises

1. Prove Corollary 4.5.4.
2. Prove Lemma 4.5.6.

*3. Let a be an arbitrary element of the group G, and let m,n be integers. Show that $a^n \circ a^m = a^m \circ a^n$.

4. Let G be a group. Show that G is abelian if and only if $(ab)^n = a^n b^n$ for all $a,b \in G$ and all $n \in Z$.

*5. Let a,b be elements of a group G. And let $a^{-1}ba = b^j$ for some integer $j \geq 0$. Prove that $a^{-r}ba^r = b^{j^r}$ for all integers $r \geq 0$. (Note that if $j = 1$, then $a^{-1}ba = b$ implies that $a^{-r}ba^r = b$, for all integers $r \geq 0$).

6. Let H be a nonempty set and let $\circ$ be an associative binary operation on H. Show that the generalized associative law holds for $(H,\circ)$, that is, show that all n products of $a_1,\cdots,a_n$ in that order are equal, where $a_1,\cdots,a_n \in H$.

4.6 SUBGROUPS

The reader may have noticed from some of the examples in Section 4.1 that there are certain subsets of a group $(G,\circ)$ which are themselves groups with respect to the binary operation $\circ$ of G. That is, if the binary operation defined for G is restricted to a subset H of G, then it may happen that this subset with the restricted operation is a group. When this occurs, we say that the group $(H,\circ)$ is a *subgroup* of $(G,\circ)$. For example, the set of even integers under addition is easily seen to be a subgroup of the group of all the integers with respect to addition.

Definition 4.6.1 Let $(G,\circ)$ be a group. Let $H \subseteq G$, $H \neq \phi$. Let $*$ be the restriction of $\circ$ to H, that is, $a * b = a \circ b$, for all $a,b \in H$. If $(H,*)$ is a group, we call H a *subgroup* of G.

Since $*$ is simply the operation $\circ$ restricted to the elements of H, we shall ordinarily write $(H,\circ)$ or simply H in place of $(H,*)$.

It is easy to see that every group G has at least two subgroups: the group G itself and the subgroup that has only one element, namely the identity element. If $(H,\circ)$ is a subgroup of $(G,\circ)$, but $H \neq G$, that is, $H \subset G$, we say that H is a *proper subgroup* of G. The subgroup consisting of only the identity element is called the *trivial subgroup* of G, and will be denoted by E.

Since the binary operation of a subgroup H is essentially the same as in the full group G, we should expect that the elements that act as inverse and identity in H will be the same as in G.

Theorem 4.6.2 Let G be a group and let H be a subgroup of G. Then

i) the identity element of H is the identity of G.

ii) If $a \in H$ and a^{-1} is the inverse of a in G, then $a^{-1} \in H$ and a^{-1} is the inverse of a in H.

Proof: i) Let e' be the identity element of the group H. Then $e'e' = e'$ in H and hence in G. Therefore, by Lemma 4.2.1, $e' = e$, the identity of G.

ii) Let $a \in H$. Let b be the inverse in H of a. By i), $ab = e$, the identity of both H and G. Hence b is the inverse of a in G.

The problem often arises to determine when a subset of elements of a group constitutes a subgroup with respect to the group operation. The determination can be made, of course, by directly testing each of the group axioms for the set in question. The task is simplified, however, when we realize that since the elements of the subset are elements of the group, certain of the group axioms are automatically true. (Name one.) It is necessary only to verify closure, that is, $a \circ b \in H$, for all $a,b \in H$, and to verify that $a^{-1} \in H$ for all $a \in H$. This can be accomplished in a single step, as we prove next.

Theorem 4.6.3 Let H be a nonempty subset of a group G. Then H is a subgroup of G if and only if for all $a,b \in H$, the element $ab^{-1} \in H$.

Proof: Suppose H is a subgroup of G. Then, if $a,b \in H$, also $b^{-1} \in H$, whence $ab^{-1} \in H$.

Suppose, conversely, whenever $a,b \in H$, also $ab^{-1} \in H$. We verify that all of the group axioms hold for H.

i) H contains e, the identity of G. For, since $H \neq \phi$, there is an $a \in H$. By hypothesis, with $b = a$, $aa^{-1} = e \in H$. (Note that it is not necessary to assume that $a^{-1} \in H$).

ii) For each $a \in H$, $a^{-1} \in H$. For, by i), $e \in H$, whence for each $a \in H$, $ea^{-1} = a^{-1} \in H$, by hypothesis.

iii) H is closed with respect to the binary operation on G, that is, the binary operation of G restricted to H is a binary operation on H. To show this, let $a,b \in H$. By ii), $b^{-1} \in H$. Then, by hypothesis, $a(b^{-1})^{-1} \in H$, that is, $ab \in H$.

iv) The associative law holds in H. Let $a,b,c \in H$. Since $H \subseteq G$,

$$a,b,c \in G$$

whence $a(bc) = (ab)c$.

Properties i), ii), iii), and iv), taken together, show that H is a group and the theorem is proved.

We can use this criterion to show quickly that the set of even integers does form a subgroup of the group of all integers under addition. For, if a and b are even integers, then $a - b$ is an even integer.

Example 4.6.4 Let $G = (\overline{Z}_6, +)$. Then the subgroups of $\overline{Z}_6$ are $E = \{\overline{0}\}$, $A_1 = \{\overline{0},\overline{2},\overline{4}\}$, $A_2 = \{\overline{0},\overline{3}\}$, $A_3 = \overline{Z}_6$. Note that $\overline{0}$ is contained in each of these. Why is $\{\overline{0},\overline{2},\overline{3}\}$ not a subgroup of $\overline{Z}_6$?

Exercises

1. Find all subgroups of the groups S_3 and the Klein group. Find a subgroup of S_3 isomorphic to a subgroup of the Klein group.

*2. Let A be a subgroup of a group G and B a subgroup of A. Show that B is a subgroup of G.

3. Let G be a finite group and H a nonempty subset of G. Show that H is a subgroup of G if and only if $H \circ H = \{ab \mid a \in H, b \in H\} = H$.

4. Restate the result of Exercise 3 in terms of a multiplication table for G.

5. Let $L_m = \{x \mid x \in Z \text{ and } m \mid x\}$. Show that L_m is a subgroup of the additive group of integers.

6. Show that if A is a subgroup of the additive group of integers, then $A = L_m$ for some integer m (see Exercise 5 above).

7. Let A be the set of all 3-cycles of S_4, that is, $A = \{(1\ 2\ 3), (1\ 2\ 4), (1\ 3\ 4), (2\ 3\ 4), (1\ 3\ 2), (1\ 4\ 2), (1\ 4\ 3), (2\ 4\ 3)\}$. Find the smallest subgroup of S_4 containing A. This subgroup is called the subgroup *generated* by A. What is its order? Find all of its subgroups.

8. Let A be the set of all 3-cycles of S_n. Show that A generates A_n.

Hint: Show that the product of two disjoint transpositions is equal to the product of two 3-cycles.

9. Let S be a subset of a group G. Let the relation $\sim$ on G be defined as follows: $a \sim b$ if and only if $ab^{-1} \in S$. Show that $\sim$ is an equivalence relation if and only if S is a subgroup of G.

*10. Let H be a subgroup of the group G. Suppose that

$$gH = \{gh \mid h \in H\}.$$

Show that $g \in H$ if and only if $gH = H$.

4.7. CYCLIC GROUPS

As the reader may have already observed, it is comparatively easy to recognize certain subgroups of a group G. One need only choose an element a, and the set of all powers (including negative powers) of a. Since every element in such a set has the form a^m for some integer m, and since $a^n \circ (a^m)^{-1} = a^n \circ a^{-m} = a^{n-m}$, it follows that such a set forms a subgroup of G. We have therefore proved the following theorem.

Theorem 4.7.1 Let a be an element of a group G. Then the set $A = \{a^n \mid \text{all } n \in Z\}$ is a subgroup of G.

If it should occur that for some choice of $a \in G$, the subgroup A is actually all of G, then G is called *cyclic* and has some very special properties which we investigate in this section.

Definition 4.7.2 Let G be a group. If there is an element $a \in G$ such that $G = \{a^m \mid m \in Z\}$, then G is called a *cyclic group (generated by the element a)*, and a is called a *generator* of G. We denote this by $G = (a)$.

We observe that if $G = (a)$, every element $g \in G$ can be expressed in the form a^m, for some integer m. As we shall see by later examples, the choice of m need not be unique.

In additive notation, the definition becomes: There exists an element $a \in G$ such that for each $g \in G$ there exists an integer m such that $g = ma$. It is immediate that $(Z,+)$ is cyclic.

Example 4.7.3 Let G be the Klein group. If we let a be the rotation of 180°, then $a^2 = e$, $a^{-1} = a$, and hence the set of powers of a forms a cyclic subgroup of order 2. The reader can easily check that each nonidentity element of the group generates a cyclic subgroup of order 2. Therefore, G is not a cyclic group.

Example 4.7.4 Let $G = (\overline{Z}_6,+)$. Then the cyclic subgroup generated by $\bar{2}$ is the set $\{\bar{0},\bar{2},\bar{4}\}$, a proper subgroup of G. The set of multiples of $\bar{1}$ however is the whole group. That is $(\bar{1}) = G$. The reader should also verify that $(\bar{5}) = G$.

Example 4.7.5 Let $G = S_4$. Then the element (1 2 3 4) generates the cyclic group {(1 2 3 4), (1 3)(2 4), (1 4 3 2), (1)}.

Exercises

1. Show that S_4 contains cyclic subgroups of order 1, 2, 3, and 4, but of no larger order.
2. Show that $(\overline{Z}_m,+)$ is cyclic for all positive integers m. •

Since a cyclic group consists of the powers of a single element, and since by the law of exponents $a^n a^m = a^{n+m}$, the binary operation of a cyclic group behaves similarly to addition in Z. Exactly how far this analogy goes is investigated in the next several theorems.

Lemma 4.7.6 Let G be a cyclic group generated by a. Let e be the identity of G. Then $a^n = a^m$ for $n \neq m$ if and only if $a^x = e$ has a least positive solution, say d, and $n \equiv m \pmod{d}$.

Proof: Suppose $a^n = a^m$, $m \neq n$. Assuming $n < m$, we see that $a^{m-n} = e$ implies that $a^x = e$ has a positive solution and hence a least positive solution d. By the division algorithm, $m - n = qd + r$, $0 \leq r < d$. Then $e = a^{m-n} = a^{qd+r} = a^{qd}a^r = (a^d)^q a^r = e^q a^r = a^r$. Thus $a^r = e$. But since $0 \leq r < d$, we must have $r = 0$, for otherwise the choice of d as the smallest positive solution of $a^x = e$ is contradicted. Thus, $m - n = qd$, that is, $m \equiv n \pmod{d}$.

Conversely, suppose $m \equiv n \pmod{d}$, where d is the least positive solution to $a^x = e$. Then $m - n = kd$, for some integer k and

$$a^{m-n} = a^{kd} = (a^d)^k = e^k = e,$$

whence

$$a^m = a^n.$$

Theorem 4.7.7 Let G be a cyclic group generated by a, and let e denote the identity of G.

If $|G| = d$, then d is the least positive solution of $a^x = e$ and $G = \{a, a^2, \cdots, a^{d-1}, a^d = e\}$.

Conversely, if d is the least positive solution to $a^x = e$, then G is finite and $|G| = d$.

Proof: If G is finite, then there must be a repetition in the list $a, a^2, a^3, \cdots$. Thus, there are integers m and n, $m \neq n$, such that $a^m = a^n$. By Lemma 4.7.6, there is a least positive integer f satisfying $a^f = e$. The set of integers $\{0, 1, \cdots, f-1\}$ is a complete set of least positive residues modulo f. We may thus conclude:

i) If i and j are two distinct least positive residues, then $a^i \neq a^j$, for otherwise $i \equiv j \pmod{f}$ by Lemma 4.7.6. Hence the elements $e, a, a^2, \cdots, a^{f-1}$ are distinct.

ii) If m is any integer, then there exists a least positive residue $k \equiv m \pmod{f}$, and hence $a^k = a^m$. Thus, the set $\{a, a^2, \cdots, a^{f-1}, a^f = e\}$ contains all the elements of G.

Therefore, $|G| = f$ and so $f = d$; and d is the least positive solution of $a^x = e$.

Conversely, if d is the least positive solution of $a^x = e$, then by Lemma 4.7.6, $a^n = a^m$ if and only if $n \equiv m \pmod{d}$. It is now easy to see that $G = \{a, a^2, \cdots, a^{d-1}, a^d = e\}$ and $|G| = d$.

The close relation between cyclic groups and the arithmetic of residue classes is more than incidental.

Theorem 4.7.8 Let G be a cyclic group.

i) If G is finite of order d, then G is isomorphic to $(\overline{Z}_d, +)$, the additive group of residue classes modulo d.

ii) If G is infinite, then G is isomorphic to $(Z, +)$, the additive group of integers.

Proof: Exercise.

Definition 4.7.9 Let a be an element of the group G. The *order of a*, written $|a|$, is defined to be the order of the cyclic subgroup generated by a.

If the cyclic subgroup generated by a is finite, then the order of a is just the least positive integer satisfying $a^x = e$. Moreover, if $|a| = d$, then using Lemma 4.7.6, it is almost immediate that $a^m = e$ if and only if $d \mid m$. We leave this to Exercise 12.

Perhaps the reader has noticed that in the definition of cyclic group, care was taken to avoid talking about *the* generator of G. First, it is easy to see that if a is a generator of G, then a^{-1} is also a generator. Second, it can happen that G is generated by yet other elements. For instance, if G is the additive group $\{\overline{Z}_8, +\}$ of residue classes modulo 8, then G is generated not only by $\bar{1}$, but also by $\bar{3}$ or $\bar{5}$ or $\bar{7}$. Those elements of a cyclic group that can act as generators are completely described by the next theorem.

Theorem 4.7.10 Let G be a cyclic group generated by a.

i) If G is finite of order d, then a^k is a generator of G if and only if $(k,d) = 1$.

ii) If G is infinite, then a and a^{-1} are the only generators of G.

Proof: i) a^k is a generator of G if and only if $(a^k)^\ell = a$, for some integer ℓ. By Lemma 4.7.6, however, $(a^k)^\ell = a$ if and only if $k\ell \equiv 1 \pmod{d}$. But this equation, by Corollary 2.12.5, has a solution if and only if $(k,d) = 1$. Hence i) is proved.

ii) If a^k is a generator of G, then for some ℓ, $a^{k\ell} = a$. Hence, either $k\ell = 1$ or the equation $a^x = e$ has a positive solution. In the second case, G would be finite, a contradiction. Hence $k\ell = 1$ and $k = \pm 1$.

If we ask how many different elements of a cyclic group may be selected as generators, the theorem shows that this is equivalent to asking how many positive integers there are less than d and relatively prime to d. This was answered in Theorem 2.13.6, since $(d)\varphi$ (φ is the Euler φ-function) gives precisely this information.

Exercises

3. Prove Theorem 4.7.8, using the results of Theorem 4.7.7.
4. Let G and H be two cyclic groups of the same order. Prove that G and H are isomorphic.
5. Let G be the multiplicative group of residue classes modulo 7. (See Exercise 4, Section 4.2).
   i) Show that G is cyclic.
   ii) To what additive group of residue classes of integers is this group isomorphic? •

Theorem 4.7.11 If G is a cyclic group and if H is a subgroup of G, then H is cyclic.

Proof: Let G be generated by the element a. The elements of H form a subset of the powers of a. If $H = E$, then H is cyclic. Otherwise H contains a positive power of a. Let k be the least positive integer such that $a^k \in H$. Let $K = \{a^{k\ell} \mid \ell \in Z\}$. Then K is the cyclic subgroup of G generated by a^k, and $K \subseteq H$. We will show that $H = K$. Let a^s be an arbitrary element of H. By the division algorithm, there exist unique integers q and r such that

$$s = qk + r, \qquad 0 \leq r < k.$$

Then $a^s = a^{kq+r} = a^{kq}a^r$, whence $a^r = a^s(a^k)^{-q}$. Since a^s and a^k are in H, we have $a^r \in H$. But $0 \leq r < k$, and so by the choice of k, it follows that $r = 0$. Thus, $a^s = (a^k)^q \in K$.

Exercises

6. Let a and b be elements of a group G. Show that $|a| = |a^{-1}|$; $|a| = |g^{-1}ag|$ for all $g \in G$; and that $|ab| = |ba|$.

*7. Let G be a cyclic group of order n. Show that if $d \mid n$, then G contains one and only one subgroup of order d.

Hint: Consider $\overline{Z}_n$.

8. Let G be an abelian group and let $a,b \in G$ be elements of finite order with $(|a|, |b|) = 1$. Show that the order of ab is $|a|\,|b|$.

9. Let G be an abelian group of order pq, with $(p,q) = 1$. Show that if G contains elements a and b of orders p and q respectively, then G is cyclic.

*10. Let a be an element of a group G. Let $|a| = mn$, where m and n are integers. Show that if $b = a^m$, then $|b| = n$.

*11. Let G be an abelian group containing elements a and b of order m and n respectively. Show that there is $c \in G$, of order lcm$[m,n]$.

Hint: Let $m = p_1^{e_1} \cdots p_s^{e_s}$, $n = p_1^{f_1} \cdots p_s^{f_s}$, the p_i district primes, and $p_k^{e_k} < p_k^{f_k}$, $1 \leq k \leq t$, $p_k^{f_k} \leq p_k^{e_k}$, $t + 1 \leq k \leq s$. Let

$$m_1 = p_1^{e_1} \cdots p_t^{e_t}, \ n_1 = p_{t+1}^{f_{t+1}} \cdots p_s^{f_s}.$$

Consider a^{m_1} and b^{n_1}, and apply Exercise 8.

*12. Let a be an element of a group G and let $|a| = d$. Show $a^n = e$ if and only if $d \mid n$.

13. Show that the order of any subgroup of a finite cyclic group divides the order of the group. •

Note that by virtue of Exercise 4, we may speak of *the* cyclic group of order n, C_n, for any positive integer n with no ambiguity up to isomorphism.

In this section, we have thus far discussed groups generated by one element. We wish to extend this notion to sets of elements that generate a group.

Theorem 4.7.12 Let G be a group. Let $\{H_\alpha\}$ be a collection of subgroups of G. Then $\bigcap H_\alpha$ is a subgroup of G.

Proof: Exercise.

Now let G be a group and let A be a subset of G. Clearly there is at least one subgroup of G, namely G itself, which contains A. Thus, the following definition will define a group accordin g to Theorem 4.7.12.

Definition 4.7.13 Let G be a group and let A be a subset of G. Let $\{H_\alpha\}$ be the collection of all subgroups of G such that $A \subseteq H_\alpha$. Then $\bigcap H_\alpha$ is called the subgroup of G *generated* by A. A is called a set of *generators* of this subgroup. We denote this subgroup by (A).

Since any product of elements and inverses of elements in A is contained in any H_α containing A and since this set of products is a subgroup of G, clearly (A) is simply the set of all such products. (See Exercise 17). Thus (A) is the "smallest" subgroup of G containing the set A.

In case $A = \{a\}$, that is, A has exactly one element, then $(A) = (a)$, that is, (A) is the cyclic group generated by a.

It is not hard to see that a given group G may have different sets of generators. For example, if $G = (Z,+)$, then $A = \{1\}$ and $B = \{2,3\}$ will both be sets of generators of G. Also, any group G will have at least one set of generators, namely, the set G itself. Although this latter set of generators is usually of little interest, certain sets of generators will be of importance.

Definition 4.7.14 Let G be a group. A subset A of G is called an *irredundant* set of generators of G if $G = (A)$ and if whenever $B \subset A$, (B) is a proper subgroup of G.

Clearly, the set $\{2,3\}$ is an irredundant set of generators of $(Z,+)$ as is the set $\{1\}$. Thus two irredundant sets of generators need not have the same number of elements.

Theorem 4.7.15 Let G be a finite group. Then G has an irredundant set of generators.

Proof: Exercise.

Exercises

14. Prove Theorem 4.7.12.
15. Prove Theorem 4.7.15.
16. Let $A = \{a,b\}$ be a set of generators for the group G. Show that each

of the following is also a set of generators of G: $\{a^{-1},b\}$; $\{a,ab\}$; $\{ab,ab^{-1}a^{-1}\}$.

17. Let G be a group, $G = (A)$. Show that if $g \in G$, there exist elements $a_{i_1}, a_{i_2}, \cdots, a_{i_k}$ (with possible repetitions) of A such that

$$g = a_{i_1}^{\epsilon_1} a_{i_2}^{\epsilon_2} \cdots a_{i_k}^{\epsilon_k},$$

where each $\epsilon_j = 0, 1,$ or -1.

18. Let G be an infinite group, and suppose that $G = (A)$, where A is a finite subset of G. Show that if $G = (B)$ where B is infinite, then B is not irredundant.
19. Find irredundant sets of generators for S_3 and the Klein group.
20. Show that for any positive integer n, there is an irredundant set of generators of $(Z,+)$ containing n elements.
21. Show that the cycles $(1\ 2)$ and $(1\ 2 \cdots n)$ generate S_n.
22. Show that $\{r_1,h\}$ is an irredundant set of generators for D_4. In fact, show that every element of D_4 can be written $r_1^n h^m$, with $0 \le n \le 3$ and $0 \le m \le 1$.
23. Prove that a group which has only finitely many subgroups must be finite.[11]

*24. Let G be a group, and let $a,b \in G$. Suppose $a^{-(p-1)}ba^{p-1} = b$, with $|b| = p$, $|a| = q$, $(p - 1, q) = 1$. Show that $ab = ba$. Hint: Recall Exercise 5, Section 4.5. Use the fact that there exist r and s, $r > 0$, such that $1 = r(p - 1) + sq$. Show that $a^{-r(p-1)}ba^{r(p-1)} = b$, and then replace $r(p - 1)$ by $1 - sq$. Use the fact that $a^{sq} = e$.

4.8 COSETS AND LAGRANGE'S THEOREM

In this section we prove the famous theorem of Lagrange that asserts that the order of a subgroup A of a finite group G must divide the order of G. Aside from its own usefulness, this theorem can be taken as the starting point for a great many significant results in the theory of finite groups (see Sections 6.2 and 6.3).

The binary operation that is defined on the elements of a group can be extended to subsets of elements in the following way: If A and B are nonempty subsets of the group G, then the product AB is defined to be $\{ab \mid a \in A, b \in B\}$.

In general, little can be said about the set AB. For example, even if A and B are both subgroups of G, it still may not be true that the product AB is a subgroup of G.

[11] *American Mathematical Monthly*, Vol. 69, 1962, p. 566.

There are many special cases, however, in which the notion of a product of two sets is extremely important, in particular, when A consists of a single element and B is a subgroup.

Definition 4.8.1 Let G be a group. If $a \in G$ and H is a subgroup of G, we call the set $aH = \{ab \mid b \in H\}$ a *left coset of H* and we call the element a, a *representative* of aH. The set $Ha = \{ba \mid b \in H\}$ is called *a right coset of H*.

Example 4.8.2 Let $G = S_3$, the group of all permutations on the set $\{1,2,3\}$. Let $H = \{(1),(1\ 2)\}$. Then the left coset $(1\ 2\ 3)H = \{(1\ 2\ 3), (2\ 3)\}$ and the right coset $H(1\ 2\ 3) = \{(1\ 3), (1\ 2\ 3)\}$. Thus, $(1\ 2\ 3)H \neq H(1\ 2\ 3)$. Moreover, for any $g \in G$, $(1\ 2\ 3)H \neq Hg$. Thus, this example shows that the left coset gH need not be equal to the right coset Hg, and also that the left coset gH need not be the same as any right coset Hg'.

In the event $gH = Hg$, for all $g \in G$, we will refer to gH simply as a *coset* of H.

Exercises

1. Let G be the symmetric group S_3. Choose subgroups A of order two and B of order three and calculate the product AB. Is it a subgroup of G? Do the same for two subgroups of order two.
2. Let A and B be subgroups of a group G. Show that $AB = BA$ if and only if AB is a subgroup of G.

*3. Let A,B,C, be subsets of a group G. Prove that $(AB)C = A(BC)$.

*4. Let G be a finite group and let A and B be subsets of G with m and n elements respectively. Prove that if $|G| < m + n$, $G = AB$.

Hint: If $c \notin AB$, then consider $cB^{-1} \cap A$, where

$$B^{-1} = \{b^{-1} \mid b \in B\}.$$

5. In Example 4.8.2, show that $(1\ 2\ 3)H \neq Hg$, for all $g \in S_3$. ●

In Exercise 5 the reader should observe that a left coset may have more than one representative. The next theorem completely answers the question as to what elements are representatives of bH.

Theorem 4.8.3 Let H be a subgroup of G and let bH be a left coset of H. Then, if $g \in bH$, $gH = bH$, that is, every element in bH is a representative of bH.

Proof: Let $g \in bH$. Then $g = bh$, for some $h \in H$. Then, for any $h' \in H$, $gh' = bhh' = bh''$, where $h'' = hh' \in H$, since H is a subgroup of G. Thus, $gH \subseteq bH$. Similarly, since $b = gh^{-1}$, we can show that $bH \subseteq gH$. Thus, $bH = gH$.

It is easy to see that if H is a subgroup of a group G, then $G = \bigcup_{g \in G} gH$. We will now show that the set of cosets of H is a partition of G.

Theorem 4.8.4 Let H be a subgroup of the group G, and let aH and bH be two left cosets of H. Then, either $aH = bH$ or $aH \cap bH = \phi$. That is, the set of left cosets of H is a partition of G.

Proof: Suppose $aH \cap bH \neq \phi$. Then there exists an element $g \in G$ such that $g \in aH$ and $g \in bH$. By Theorem 4.8.3, $aH = gH = bH$. Since $G = \bigcup_{a \in G} aH$, the set of left cosets of H is a partition of G.

Theorem 4.8.5 ***Lagrange*** If G is a finite group of order n and if H is a subgroup of order m, then $m \mid n$.

Proof: It follows from Exercise 11, Section 4.2 that any left coset gH of H has the same number of elements as H. Thus, gH has m elements. Since G is finite, there are k distinct left cosets of H that are pairwise disjoint and that partition G, by Theorem 4.8.4. Then, since G is of order n, $n = |G| = km$ and $m \mid n$.

The number k which appears in the proof of Lagrange's theorem is just the number of distinct left cosets of H in G. We call this integer the *index* of H in G and we write $[G:H] = k$.

A parallel development of the theory for right cosets would also show that there are k right cosets of H in G, and hence the index could also be defined as the number of right cosets. If G is an infinite group and H is a subgroup of G, then we say that H is of *infinite index* in G if the set of cosets $\{gH \mid g \in G\}$ is an infinite set.

Exercises

*6. Let H be a subgroup of a finite group G. Show that

$$|G| = [G : H] \cdot |H|,$$

and thus the index of H in G divides the order of G.

7. Let G be a finite group, H a subgroup of G, and K a subgroup of H. Prove that $[G:K] = [G:H][H:K]$. ●

Corollary 4.8.6 The order of every element of a finite group G divides the order of G.

Proof: The order of a is equal to the number of elements in the cyclic subgroup generated by a. By Theorem 4.8.5, $|a| \mid |G|$.

Corollary 4.8.7 A group of order p, a prime, is cyclic and has no proper nontrivial subgroups.

Proof: Exercise.

The theorems of Euler and Fermat, (Corollary 2.14.2 and Theorem 2.14.3) can be proved as corollaries of Lagrange's Theorem.

Corollary 4.8.8 Let a be an integer and p a prime such that $p \nmid a$. Then $a^{p-1} \equiv 1 \pmod p$.

Proof: Let G be the multiplicative group of nonzero residue classes of integers modulo p. $|G| = p - 1$, and since $p \nmid a$, $\bar{a} \in G$. Thus, the order of $\bar{a}$ divides $p - 1$. By Exercise 12, Section 4.7, $(\bar{a})^{p-1} = \bar{1}$. But $(\bar{a})^{p-1} = \overline{a^{p-1}}$, whence $a^{p-1} \equiv 1 \pmod p$.

Corollary 4.8.9 If a is any integer and p is a prime, then $a^p \equiv a \pmod p$.

Proof: Exercise.

Exercises

8. Prove Corollary 4.8.7.
9. Prove Corollary 4.8.9.
*10. Let A and B be subgroups of a group G, $|A| = p$, a prime, and suppose $A \cap B \neq E$. Show that $A \subseteq B$.
11. Using Lagrange's Theorem prove Theorem 2.14.1.
12. Use Lagrange's Theorem to prove that the table given in Exercise 6, Section 4.3 is not the multiplication table of a group.

    Hint: Find the orders of the elements. •

As an application of Lagrange's Theorem we prove that there are precisely two nonisomorphic groups of order 4.

Theorem 4.8.10 Every group of order 4 is isomorphic either to the cyclic group of order 4 or to the group of symmetries of a nonsquare rectangle, the Klein group.

Proof: Let G be a group of order 4, $G = \{e,a,b,c\}$, where e is the identity. By Lagrange's Theorem, the elements a,b,c have either order 2 or order 4. If one of them has order 4, then G is cyclic of order 4.

Thus, suppose none of a,b,c has order 4, that is, each has order 2. Then $a^2 = b^2 = c^2 = e$.

Consider the product ab. If $ab = e$, then $b = a^{-1} = a$, since a has order 2, contradicting the fact that $b \neq a$. Thus, $ab \neq e$. If $ab = a$ then $b = e$, a contradiction. If $ab = b$ then $a = e$, a contradiction. Therefore, the only possibility left is $ab = c$ which must hold, since $ab \in G$.

At this stage, the multiplication table for G must appear as follows:

	e	a	b	c
e	e	a	b	c
a	a	e	c	
b	b		e	
c	c			e

Since every element of the group must appear in every row and column of its multiplication table, we must have $ac = b$. By filling in the remaining entries according to this property, we find in order that $bc = a$, $ba = c$, $ca = b$, and $cb = a$.

It is easy to establish that a group G with multiplication described above is isomorphic to the Klein group.

Exercises

13. Let G be a group and H a subgroup. Define the relation $\sim$ on G by: $a \sim b$ if and only if $a^{-1}b \in H$. Show that this is an equivalence relation on G.

14. Prove that the equivalence classes determined in Exercise 13 are precisely the left cosets of H, and hence the left cosets of H partition G.

†15. Show that there are exactly two groups of order 6 (up to isomorphism).

16. Let G be a group with no nontrivial proper subgroups. Show that $|G| = p$, a prime, or $|G| = 1$.

17. Let G be a group and H a subgroup of G. Show that there is a 1–1 map from the set $\{gH\}$ of left cosets of H onto the set $\{Hg\}$ of right cosets of H.

Hint: Consider $gH \to Hg^{-1}$.

18. Let G be a finite group of order n, and let H be a subset of G containing m elements. Suppose that $gH \cap g'H \neq \phi$ implies $gH = g'H$ for any g, g' in G. Then prove (a) $m \mid n$; (b) if $e \in G$ is the identity of G and $e \in H$, then H is a subgroup of G.[12]

*19. Prove the "Product Theorem": Let A and B be finite subgroups of the group G. Show that

$$|AB| = \frac{|A|\,|B|}{|A \cap B|}$$

where $|AB|$ is the number of elements in AB.

Hint: Observe that $C = A \cap B$ is a subgroup of B. Thus, there exist $b_1, b_2, \cdots, b_n$ in B such that $B = Cb_1 \cup \cdots \cup Cb_n$, where the Cb_i are the $n = |B| / |A \cap B|$ distinct right cosets of C in B. Then $AB = ACb_1 \cup \cdots \cup ACb_n$. Since $C = A \cap B$, $AC = A$. Thus, $AB = Ab_1 \cup \cdots \cup Ab_n$. If $Ab_i \cap Ab_j \neq \phi$, $i \neq j$, then $ab_i = a'b_j$, for some a, a' in A. Then $b_j b_i^{-1} = (a')^{-1}a \in A \cap B = C$, whence $Cb_j = Cb_i$, a contradiction. Thus, $Ab_i \cap Ab_j = \phi$, $i \neq j$. Thus, $|AB| = |Ab_1| + |Ab_2| + \cdots + |Ab_n|$, where $|Ab_i|$ is the number of elements in Ab_i. Now complete the proof.

[12] *American Mathematical Monthly*, Vol. 71 (1964), p. 793.

20. Let G be a group of order 20 and A and B subgroups of orders 4 and 5 respectively. Show that $G = AB$.

21. Let G be a group of order $p^\alpha m$ with p a prime and $(p,m) = 1$. Let A be a subgroup of order p^α and B a subgroup of order p^β, $0 < \beta \leq \alpha$, $B \not\subseteq A$. Show that AB is not a subgroup of G.

4.9 HOMOMORPHISMS AND NORMAL SUBGROUPS

If G and H are two groups that are isomorphic, then, as abstract algebraic systems, they are related in the strongest possible way, that is, there exists a function $f: G \to H$ that is 1–1, onto, and preserves products:

$$(g_1 g_2)f = (g_1 f)(g_2 f) \quad \text{for all} \quad g_1, g_2 \in G.$$

We have, however, already seen examples of groups that are related in a somewhat weaker manner. For example, there exists a mapping from the additive group of integers Z to the additive group $\overline{Z}_3$ of residue classes of integers modulo 3. The mapping here is defined by $af = \bar{a}$, where $\bar{a} \in \overline{Z}_3$, for all $a \in Z$. It is easy to show that this function preserves sums, is onto, but is not 1–1. There are, nevertheless, advantages in examining the range of such a function, for we may be able to discover certain aspects of the behavior of the domain group. In the case above, we gain some insight into the additive behavior of the remainders of integers upon division by 3.

Definition 4.9.1 Let f be a function from the group $(G,\circ)$ to the group $(H,*)$ such that

$$(a \circ b)f = (af) * (bf), \quad \text{for all} \quad a,b \in G.$$

Then f is called a *homomorphism* from G to H. The range of f in H is called a *homomorphic image* of G, or the *homomorphic image of G under f.*

Thus, in the example above, f is an onto function and $\overline{Z}_3$ is therefore a homomorphic image of Z.

The reader should note that an isomorphism is a special type of homomorphism.

Example 4.9.2 Let S_n be the symmetric group on n letters. Let $f: S_n \to \bar{Z}_2$ be defined by

$$gf = \begin{cases} \overline{0} \text{ if } g \text{ is an even permutation} \\ \overline{1} \text{ if } g \text{ is an odd permutation.} \end{cases}$$

Using the table in Section 4.4, we can easily verify that f is a homomorphism.

A homomorphism need not, of course, be an onto function. For example, if Z is the additive group of integers and $\overline{Z}_4$ the additive group of residue classes modulo 4, then the mapping $f: Z \to \overline{Z}_4$ defined by

$$uf = \overline{2}, \text{ if } u \text{ is odd}$$
$$uf = \overline{0}, \text{ if } u \text{ is even,}$$

is a homomorphism from Z to $\overline{Z}_4$, but it is not onto.

Exercises

1. Show that the function defined immediately above is a homomorphism, but not onto.
2. Find a homomorphism from Z to $\overline{Z}_6$ that is onto. Find four homomorphisms that are not onto. •

Theorem 4.9.3 Let f be a homomorphism from the group G to the group H. Then the range of f (Im f) is a subgroup of H. That is, the homomorphic image of a group is a group.

The proof of this theorem is facilitated by the following two lemmas.

Lemma 4.9.4 Let f be a homomorphism from the group G to the group H. Let e be the identity of G and e' the identity of H. Then $ef = e'$.

Proof: $(ef)(ef) = (ee)f = ef$, by the definition of a homomorphism. By Lemma 4.2.1, ef is the identity of H, that is, $ef = e'$.

Lemma 4.9.5 Let f be a homomorphism from the group G to the group H. Then, if $a \in G$, $a^{-1}f = (af)^{-1}$, that is, the image of the inverse of a is the inverse of the image of a.

Proof: Let e be the identity of G. Then $(a^{-1}f)(af) = (a^{-1}a)f = ef$, the identity of H by the previous lemma. Since inverses are unique,

$$(a^{-1})f = (af)^{-1}.$$

Proof of Theorem 4.9.3: By Theorem 4.6.3, to show that Im f is a subgroup of H we need only show that if $h_1, h_2 \in$ Im f, then $h_1 h_2^{-1} \in$ Im f. Let $a, b \in G$ have the property that

$$af = h_1, \qquad bf = h_2.$$

Then $h_1 h_2^{-1} = (af)(bf)^{-1} = (af)(b^{-1}f) = (ab^{-1})f \in$ Im f.

We note that since the image of a group G under a homomorphism f is again a group, then by suitably restricting the group H to its subgroup Im f, f may always be modified so that it is an onto mapping.

Exercises

*3. Let $f: G \rightarrow H$ be a homomorphism from the group G to the group H. Let $a \in G$. Show that for any integer n, $(a^n)f = (af)^n$.

*4. Let f be a homomorphism from G to H. Let A be a subgroup of G, and f' the restriction of f to A. Show that f' is a homomorphism from A to H, and hence the image of A under f is a subgroup of H. •

When a homomorphism f of the group G to the group H is not an isomorphism, f has the effect of "identifying" the elements of certain subsets of G. Thus, those elements of G that have the same image under f can be thought of as being "identified" by the mapping. A particularly important set of such elements are those that are mapped by f onto the identity of H.

Definition 4.9.6 Let f be a homomorphism from the group G to the group H. Let e' be the identity of H. Then the set $K = \{x \mid x \in G \text{ and } xf = e'\}$ is called the *kernel* of f. We often denote K by ker f.

Since $ef = e'$, $x \in \ker f$ if and only if $xf = ef$.

Example 4.9.7 Let $G = S_3$, the symmetric group on three letters and let $H = \{\overline{Z}_2, +\}$.

Define a map f from G onto H by

$$\begin{array}{ll} (1)\, f = \overline{0} & (1\,2\,3)\, f = \overline{0} \\ (1\,2)\, f = \overline{1} & (1\,3\,2)\, f = \overline{0} \\ (1\,3)\, f = \overline{1} & \\ (2\,3)\, f = \overline{1} & \end{array}$$

To show that f is a homomorphism, we need to verify that

$$(xy)f = xf + yf, \quad \text{for all} \quad x, y \in S_3.$$

We leave this to the reader.

Note that in this example $\ker f = \{(1), (1\,2\,3), (1\,3\,2)\}$. Moreover, the remaining elements of S_3 are "identified" in the sense that they all have the same image.

Exercise

5. Prove that if f is a homomorphism from S_3 to $(\overline{Z}_3, +)$ then $xf = \overline{0}$ for all $x \in S_3$. •

Theorem 4.9.8 Let f be a homomorphism from the group G to the group H. Then $\ker f$ is a subgroup of G.

Proof: It follows from Lemma 4.9.4 that $\ker f \neq \phi$. Let $a,b \in \ker f$. It is enough to show that $ab^{-1} \in \ker f$. Since $(ab^{-1})f = (af)(b^{-1}f) = (af)(bf)^{-1}$, and $af = bf = e'$, the identity of H,

$$(ab^{-1})f = e'(e')^{-1} = e'e' = e'.$$

Thus, $ab^{-1} \in \ker f$ and $\ker f$ is a subgroup of G.

Now suppose J is a set of elements of G all of which have the same image under f. Assume that this image is not e'. It is natural to ask if this set J of "identified" elements is also a subgroup of G. By examining Example 4.9.7, the reader may quickly convince himself that this is not the case. Sets such as J, however, bear a strong relation to $\ker f$.

Theorem 4.9.9 Let f be a homomorphism from the group G to the group H with $\ker f$ denoted by K. For any $r \in \operatorname{Im} f$, let $T_r = \{u \mid u \in G, uf = r\}$. Then

i) $vK = T_r$ for any $v \in T_r$,
ii) $Kv = T_r$ for any $v \in T_r$,
iii) $Kv = vK$ for $v \in G$ for $v \in G$, and
iv) $uf = vf$ if and only if $uK = vK$, for $u, v \in G$.

Proof:

i) Let $u \in T_r$. Then $r = uf = vf$. Hence $(vf)^{-1}(uf) = (v^{-1}f)(uf) = (v^{-1}u)f = e'$, the identity of H. Therefore $v^{-1}u \in K$ and $u \in vK$. Now let $vk \in vK$. Then $(vk)f = (vf)(kf) = vf$, which means that $vk \in T_r$. Therefore $T_r = vK$.

ii) In a similar manner to i) we can prove that $T_r = Kv$.

iii) Clearly, since for any $v \in G$, $v \in T_r$ for some $r \in \operatorname{Im} f$, it follows from i) and ii) that $vK = Kv$.

iv) If $uf = vf$, then $u,v \in T_r$ for some $r \in \operatorname{Im} f$. By i), $vK = T_r = uK$. Let $v \in T_r$. Then $vK = uK$ implies by i) that $vK = uK = T_r$ and hence $r = vf = uf$.

We see now that the "identification" that takes place in G as a result of the homomorphism f is precisely the decomposition of G into left cosets of the kernel K of f. In this case, however, we need not insist on left cosets, since, as we have shown, left cosets and right cosets coincide.

It is conceivable that a subgroup H of G other than K has the property $Hg = gH$ for all $g \in G$. Such subgroups are extremely important, as we shall soon see.

Definition 4.9.10 A subgroup N of the group G is called a *normal subgroup of G* (*N is normal in G*) if $gN = Ng$, for all $g \in G$. We denote this by $N \lhd G$.

Theorem 4.9.9 asserts, in part, that a kernel K of a homomorphism is normal. In the next section we prove that every normal subgroup is the kernel of some homomorphism.

Exercises

6. Let $f:G \rightarrow H$ be a homomorphism with kernel K. Prove without using Theorem 4.9.9 that $uK = vK$ implies $uf = vf$.
*7. Let G be a group and N a subgroup. Prove that the following statements are all equivalent.
   i) $N \lhd G$
   ii) $g^{-1}Ng \subseteq N$, for all $g \in G$.
   iii) $g^{-1}Ng = N$, for all $g \in G$.
*8. Let N be a subgroup of G. Prove $N \lhd G$ if and only if for each $a \in G$ and $n \in N$, there exists $n' \in N$ such that $an = n'a$.
9. Show that every subgroup of an abelian group G is normal in G.
10. Let H be a subgroup of a group G. Suppose $[G:H] = 2$. Show that $H \lhd G$.
11. Show that A_n is a normal subgroup of S_n.
12. Show by example that if $N \lhd G$, it is not necessarily true that $ah = ha$, for all $h \in N$, $a \in G$.
13. Let G be a cyclic group and let f be a homomorphism from G onto the group H. Show that H is cyclic.
14. Let G be a group and let A and B be normal subgroups of G. Show that $(A \cap B) \lhd G$.
*15. Let G be a group, with $A \lhd G$ and B a subgroup of G. Show that $AB = \{ab \mid a \in A, b \in B\}$ is a subgroup of G, and $A \lhd AB$.
*16. Let G be a group, with $A \lhd G$ and B a subgroup of G. Show that $(A \cap B) \lhd B$.
17. Find a normal subgroup N of order 2 in D_4. Find a homomorphism from D_4 onto the Klein group with N as kernel. ●

If f is a homomorphism from G onto H that is 1–1, then f is an isomorphism from G to H, as defined in Section 4.4. A simple criterion to tell when a homomorphism is an isomorphism is found in the following theorem.

Theorem 4.9.11 Let $f:G \rightarrow H$ be a homomorphism from the group G onto the group H. Then f is an isomorphism from G onto H if and only if $\ker f = E$.

Proof: Exercise.

Exercises

18. Prove Theorem 4.9.11.
19. Let G be a group, let $H \lhd G$, and let $K \lhd H$. Show by example that K need not be normal in G.

   Hint: Consider A_4 or D_4.

4.10 FACTOR GROUPS AND THE ISOMORPHISM THEOREMS

If N is a normal subgroup of a group G, then by definition, $aN = Na$, for all $a \in G$. This partial commutativity property allows us to define a binary operation on the set of cosets $\{aN \mid a \in G\}$ so that the collection of cosets and this binary operation form a group.

Definition 4.10.1 Let N be a normal subgroup of the group G. We define a binary operation on the set of cosets of N as follows:

$$aN \cdot bN = (ab)N.$$

To show that $\cdot$ is actually a binary operation, we must prove that the definition of multiplication is independent of the choice of coset representative, that is, if $aN = a'N$ and $bN = b'N$, then $(ab)N = aN \cdot bN = a'N \cdot b'N = (a'b')N$. Now if $aN = a'N$, then $a = a'n_1$, and if $bN = b'N$, then $b = b'n_2$ for some $n_1, n_2 \in N$. Therefore $(ab)N = (a'n_1b'n_2)N = (a'n_1b')N$ since $n_2N = N$. Now, by Exercise 8, Section 4.9, $n_1b' = b'n_1'$ for some $n_1' \in N$. Hence $(a'n_1b')N = (a'b'n_1')N = (a'b')N$, and the operation is well defined.

Theorem 4.10.2 Let N be a normal subgroup of the group G. Then the set of cosets $\{aN \mid a \in G\}$ together with the operation $aN \cdot bN = (ab)N$ is a group, and its order is $[G:N]$.

Proof: We have shown above that this operation is well defined. To show that it is associative consider the product: $aN \cdot (bN \cdot cN) = aN \cdot (bc)N = a(bc)N = (ab)cN = (abN) \cdot cN = (aN \cdot bN) \cdot cN$.

Since $aN \cdot eN = (ae)N = aN$, the coset $eN = N$ is a right identity.

Finally, since $(aN) \cdot (a^{-1}N) = (aa^{-1})N = eN$, $(aN)^{-1} = a^{-1}N$ and the set of cosets of N is a group.

The order of the group is clearly the number of cosets of N in G, that is, $[G:N]$.

Definition 4.10.3 Let N be a normal subgroup of G. The set of cosets of N together with the binary operation of Definition 4.10.1 is called the *quotient group of G with respect to the normal subgroup N*, or the *factor group of G with respect to N*, and is denoted by G/N. Frequently, "with respect to N" is replaced by "modulo N."

The technique of treating a set of elements as a new single element and of defining a binary operation on the set of the new elements is not unfamiliar. In fact, this is precisely what was done in forming the additive group of residue classes modulo m in Section 2.11. As the reader may verify, the set of residue classes modulo m is exactly the set of cosets in $(Z,+)$ of the normal subgroup (m) of all multiples of m. In the notation of Chapter 2 the zero element was denoted by $\bar{0}$. In coset notation, it is written $0 + (m)$ or simply (m). Similarly, $\bar{1}$ is now seen to be the same as $1 + (m)$, and in general, $\bar{a} = a + (m)$.

Example 4.10.4 If $G = S_3$, it is easy to verify that the subgroup $N = \{(1),(1\ 2\ 3),(1\ 3\ 2)\}$ is normal in G. Hence the cosets N and $(1\ 2)N$ are the elements of G/N. Since $(1\ 2)N\cdot(1\ 2)N = N$, the identity element of G/N, it follows that G/N is isomorphic to the cyclic group of order 2, C_2.

Example 4.10.5 Let S denote the set of all points in the plane: $S = \{(x,y) \mid x,y \text{ are real numbers}\}$. We define the operation $+$ in S as follows:

$$(x,y) + (x',y') = (x + x',y + y').$$

It is easy to show that $(S,+)$ is an abelian group. The group S should be familiar to the reader from his study of analytic geometry. The ordered pair (x,y) can be thought of as a vector in the plane with "tail" at the origin and "head" at the point (x,y). The definition of addition given above is exactly the same as the usual "parallelogram" definition of addition for vectors, illustrated in Figure 8.

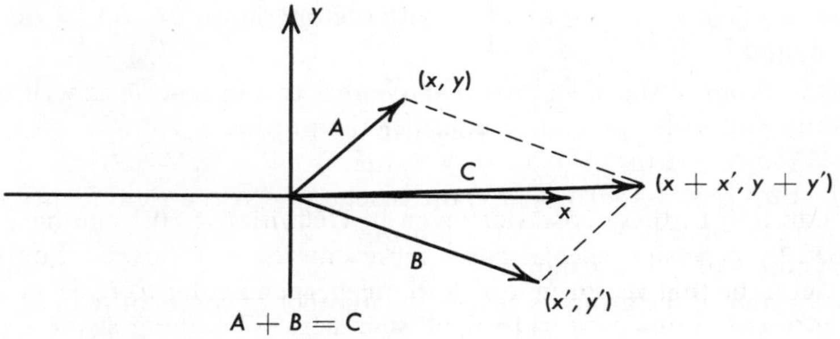

Figure 8

Now let $N = \{(rx_0,ry_0) \mid$ for fixed real numbers x_0,y_0 (not both 0) and all real numbers $r\}$. Then N represents the set of all "multiples" of the vector (x_0,y_0), all of which lie along the straight line L determined by (x_0,y_0) (Figure 9). N is easily seen to be a subgroup of S and since S is abelian, N is a normal subgroup of S. (What is N if $x_0 = y_0 = 0$?).

Let $\alpha \in S$, $\alpha \notin N$. Then $\alpha + N$ can be described geometrically. Since each vector in $\alpha + N$ is a sum of α and a vector in N, it will occur as the

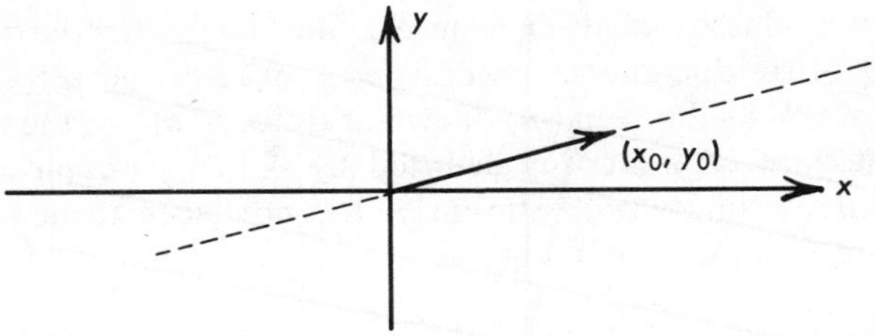

Figure 9

diagonal of a parallelogram with one edge along L, and the opposite edge through the point α and parallel to L (Figure 10).

If L' is the line through the point α and parallel to L, then the coset $\alpha + N$ will consist of exactly those vectors whose "heads" lie on the line L'. The set of all cosets of N can then be thought of as the set of lines in the plane parallel to L.

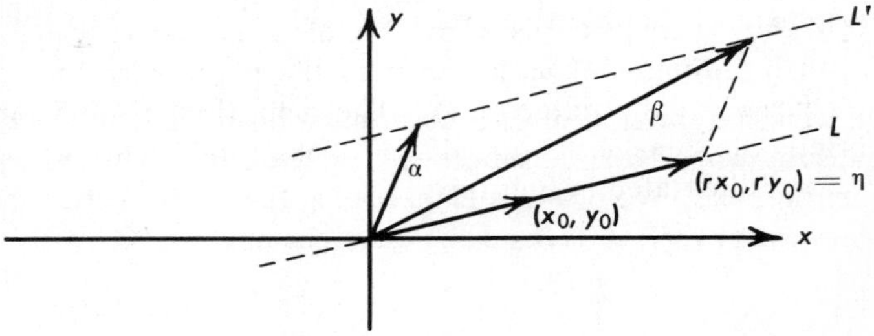

$\alpha + \eta = \beta \varepsilon \alpha + N$

Figure 10

The addition of these cosets as given in Definition 4.10.1 can be easily described by choosing special coset representives as follows: For each $\alpha + N$, let α' be that vector in $\alpha + N$ that is perpendicular to L. Since each coset represents a line parallel to L, all such α' will lie along a line, say P, perpendicular to all cosets. Hence since

$$(\alpha' + N) + (\beta' + N) = (\alpha' + \beta') + N,$$

the sum of two cosets is obtained by a translation from the origin along P by a length equal to the length of $\alpha' + \beta'$ in the direction of $\alpha' + \beta'$. (Figure 11).

This geometrical analysis allows us now to determine the group G/N. For, if d_i represents the perpendicular distance from the coset $\alpha_i + N$ to L,

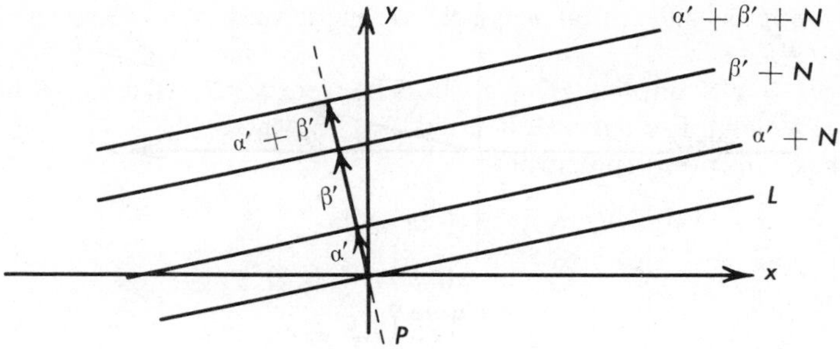

Figure 11

with the "upward" direction considered positive and the "downward" direction negative, the mapping:

$$d_i \to \alpha_i + N$$

is an isomorphism of the additive group of real numbers onto the group G/N.

We have seen that the notion of a homomorphism leads to the concept of a normal subgroup. Normal subgroups, on the other hand, allow us to form quotient groups. We now ask if there is a direct connection between the homomorphism $f: G \to H$, and the quotient group of G with respect to $\ker f$.

Theorem 4.10.6 First Isomorphism Theorem Let f be a homomorphism from the group G to the group H. Then $\ker f$ is normal in G and

$$G/\ker f \cong \operatorname{Im} f.$$

Conversely, let $N \lhd G$. Then there exists a homomorphism

$$h: G \xrightarrow{\text{onto}} G/N$$

with kernel N, defined by $gh = gN$. We call h the *natural homomorphism* from G to G/N.

Proof: Let $f: G \to H$ be a homomorphism, and denote $\ker f$ by K. Thus $K \lhd G$ and we may form $G/\ker f = G/K$. Now let

$$\nu: G/K \to \operatorname{Im} f$$

be defined by

$$(gK)\nu = gf, \quad \text{all } g \in G.$$

First, we must show that ν is well defined, that is, if $gK = g'K$, then $(gK)\nu = (g'K)\nu$.

Now $gK = g'K$ implies $gf = g'f$ by Theorem 4.9.9. Thus $(g'K)\nu = g'f = gf = (gK)\nu$, and so ν is well defined.

Next ν is a homomorphism, for

$$\begin{aligned}[(gK)(g'K)]\nu &= [(gg')K]\nu \\ &= (gg')f = (gf)(g'f) \\ &= (gK)\nu(g'K)\nu.\end{aligned}$$

Also ν is 1–1, for if

$$(gK)\nu = (g'K)\nu,$$

then $$gf = g'f,$$

whence $$gK = g'K \text{ by Theorem 4.9.9.}$$

Finally, ν is indeed an isomorphism from $G/K = G/\ker f$ onto $\operatorname{Im} f$.

Conversely, let $N \lhd G$ and form G/N. Define a mapping $h: G \to G/N$ by

$$gh = gN, \quad \text{for all } g \in G.$$

Then

$$(g_1g_2)h = (g_1g_2)N = (g_1N)(g_2N) = (g_1h)(g_2h).$$

Thus, h is a homomorphism, and h is clearly onto. Ker $h = \{g \mid gh = N$, the identity of $G/N\}$. Since $gh = gN$, $gh = N$ if and only if $gN = N$, that is, if and only if $g \in N$.

Thus, $\ker h = N$ and the proof is completed.

Example 4.10.7 Let $f: Z \to \overline{Z}_m$, with $m > 0$, $af = \bar{a}$. Then

$$\ker f = (m),$$

and $$Z/(m) \cong \overline{Z}_m.$$

The reader should note that the isomorphism ν of Theorem 4.10.6 is actually the identity function in this example, since $Z/(m)$ and $\overline{Z}_m$ are the same set and $[a + (m)]\nu = \bar{a} = a + (m)$.

Example 4.10.8 Let N be the normal subgroup of S_3 described in Example 4.10.4. As we have shown, $G/N \cong C_2$, the cyclic group of order 2. Then the mapping $f: G \to G/N$ defined by

$$gf = gN$$

is the homomorphism described in the converse portion of Theorem 4.10.6.

Example 4.10.9 Let G be the additive group of real numbers and H the set of points in the plane defined by

$$H = \{(\cos x, \sin x) \mid \text{all real numbers } x\}.$$

H is precisely the unit circle in the plane with center at the origin. We define a binary operation on H as follows:

$$(\cos x, \sin x)\cdot(\cos y, \sin y) = (\cos(x + y), \sin(x + y)).$$

The reader should verify that $(H, \cdot)$ is a group.

Now consider the following mapping from G to H:

$$xf = (\cos x, \sin x).$$

Clearly f is onto H and is a homomorphism, since $(x + y)f = (\cos(x + y), \sin(x + y)) = (\cos x, \sin x)\cdot(\cos y, \sin y) = (xf)\cdot(yf)$.

By Theorem 4.10.6, G/N can be thought of as the set of real numbers where two elements are identified if they differ by an integral multiple of 2π. The mapping f has the effect of "wrapping" the real line around the unit circle.

Theorem 4.10.6 shows that any homomorphic image of a group G can be constructed from G, that is, if f is a homomorphism from G onto the group H, then H is isomorphic to a factor group of G.

If N is a normal subgroup of the group G, then we prove in Theorem 4.10.11 that the subgroups and normal subgroups of G which contain N are in 1–1 correspondence with those of the subgroups and normal subgroups of G/N.

Lemma 4.10.10 Let $f: G \xrightarrow{\text{onto}} H$ be a homomorphism and let M be a subgroup of H. Then the preimage N of M is a subgroup of G containing $\ker f$. Further if $M \lhd H$, then $N \lhd G$.

Proof: By definition, $N = \{g \mid g \in G \text{ and } gf \in M\} \neq \phi$. If $g_1, g_2 \in N$, then $(g_1g_2^{-1})f = (g_1f)(g_2^{-1}f) = (g_1f)(g_2f)^{-1} \in M$, since M is a group. Thus $g_1g_2^{-1} \in N$ and N is a subgroup of G. Clearly $\ker f \subseteq N$.

Now consider $g^{-1}ag$ for $a \in N$ and $g \in G$ and assume $M \lhd H$. Then $(g^{-1}ag)f = (gf)^{-1}(af)(gf) \in M$, since $af \in M$ and $M \lhd H$. Therefore $g^{-1}ag \in N$ and $N \lhd G$.

Theorem 4.10.11 Let G be a group with normal subgroup N. Let $f: G \to G/N$ be defined by

$$gf = gN.$$

Then f induces a 1–1 correspondence $\tilde{f}$ between those subgroups of G that contain N and the subgroups of G/N. The function $\tilde{f}$ is defined by $H\tilde{f} = (H)f$, the image of H under f. Further, $\tilde{f}$ induces a 1–1 correspondence between those normal subgroups of G containing N and the normal subgroups of G/N.

Proof: It follows from Theorem 4.10.6 that the function f is a homomorphism. By Exercise 4, Section 4.9, if A is a subgroup of G containing N, then Af is a subgroup of G/N.

Let A_1 and A_2 be distinct subgroups of G containing N. For each $a \in A_1$, $aN \in (A_1)\tilde{f}$ and we may assume that there exists $a \in A_1$ such that $a \notin A_2$. Now suppose that $aN \in (A_2)\tilde{f}$. Then there exists $b \in A_2$ such that $bN = aN$, that is $a \in bN$. But since $N \subseteq A_2$, $bN \subseteq A_2$ whence $a \in A_2$, a contradiction. Hence if $A_1 \neq A_2$, then $(A_1)\tilde{f} \neq (A_2)\tilde{f}$, and $\tilde{f}$ is 1–1.

Next, we show that $\tilde{f}$ is onto. Let $\overline{A}$ be a subgroup of G/N, and let A be the preimage of $\overline{A}$, that is, A is the set of elements of G contained in those cosets aN that are the elements of $\overline{A}$. By Lemma 4.10.10, A is a subgroup of G containing N whose image under f is $\overline{A}$.

To complete the proof of the theorem it remains to show that $\tilde{f}$, restricted to the normal subgroups of G containing N, is a 1–1 correspondence between the normal subgroups of G containing N and the normal subgroups of G/N. We leave this as an exercise.

We shall prove two additional isomorphism theorems that follow from Theorem 4.10.6. These theorems, which show relationships among quotient groups and normal subgroups of G, will have important applications in Chapter 6.

Theorem 4.10.12 ***Second Isomorphism Theorem*** Let G be a group, $A \lhd G$, and B a subgroup of G. Then $A \cap B \lhd B$ and $AB/A \simeq B/A \cap B$.

Proof: By Exercises 15 and 16 of Section 4.9, AB is a group, $A \lhd AB$, and $A \cap B \lhd B$. Thus the factor groups indicated in the statement of the theorem make sense. Now let $f: B \to AB/A$ be defined by

$$bf = bA, \quad \text{for all } b \in B.$$

Clearly f is a function. Also, f is onto, for if $(ab)A$ is any element of AB/A, then, since $A \lhd G$, there is an element $a' \in A$ such that $ab = ba'$, whence $(ab)A = (ba')A = b(a'A) = bA$. Thus $bf = bA = (ab)A$ and f is onto.

To show that f is a homomorphism, we see that $(b_1b_2)f = (b_1b_2)A = (b_1A)(b_2A) = (b_1f)(b_2f)$.

Now $\ker f = \{b \in B \mid bf = A\}$, since A is the identity element of AB/A. Since $bf = bA$, $\ker f = \{b \mid b \in B, b \in A\}$, that is $\ker f = A \cap B$. By Theorem 4.10.6, $B/(A \cap B) \simeq AB/A$.

Theorem 4.10.13 ***Third Isomorphism Theorem*** Let G be a group and let $H \lhd G$, $K \lhd G$, and K a subgroup of H. Then $H/K \lhd G/K$ and

$$(G/K)/(H/K) \simeq G/H.$$

Proof: Let $f: G/K \to G/H$ be defined by

$$(gK)f = gH, \text{ for all } g \in G.$$

We first show that f is a function. Let $g_1K = g_2K$. Then $(g_1K)f = g_1H$ and $(g_2K)f = g_2H$. But since $g_1K = g_2K$, $g_2^{-1}g_1 \in K$, whence $g_2^{-1}g_1 \in H$, and so $g_1H = g_2H$. Clearly f is onto G/H, and since

$$(g_1K \cdot g_2K)f = [(g_1g_2)K]f = (g_1g_2)H = (g_1H)(g_2H) = (g_1K)f \cdot (g_2K)f,$$

f is a homomorphism.

The kernel of f is the set $\{gK \mid gH = H\}$, that is, $\ker f = \{gK \mid g \in H\}$. But since K is a normal subgroup of H, $\ker f = H/K$. Thus $H/K \lhd G/K$ and, by Theorem 4.10.6, $G/H \simeq (G/K)/(H/K)$.

Example 4.10.14 Consider D_4 in Example 4.1.8, the group of symmetries of a square. The reader can easily verify that the subgroups $N = \{e, r_1, r_2, r_3\}$ and $M = \{e, r_2\}$ are the only proper nontrivial normal subgroups of G. $B = \{e, d_1\}$ is a subgroup of D_4 which is not normal. $NB/N \simeq B/(N \cap B)$ by Theorem 4.10.12. But $N \cap B = E$ and hence $NB/N \simeq B$. Also $D_4/N \simeq D_4/M/N/M$ by Theorem 4.10.13. The reader should show that D_4/M is isomorphic to the Klein group and hence that every subgroup of D_4/M is normal in D_4/M. Hence, by Lemma 4.10.10, every subgroup of D_4 that contains M is normal in D_4.

Exercises

1. Complete the proof of Theorem 4.10.11.

*2. Let G be a finite group and let N be a normal subgroup of G. Show that for every $a \in G$ the order of aN in G/N divides the order of a in G.

3. Let G be an abelian group of order pq, p and q distinct primes. Show that G is cyclic.

   Hint: Find an element of order p or q, say a. Then consider $G/(a)$ and recall Exercise 9, Section 4.7.

4. Let m, n be integers such that $m \mid n$. Prove that

$$Z/(n)\big/(m)/(n) \simeq \overline{Z}_m.$$

5. Let G be a finite group such that $G = AB$ and $A \lhd G$. Show that if $G/A \cong B$, then $A \cap B = E$.
6. Let N be a subgroup of the group G. Suppose the set $\{aN \mid a \in G\}$ is a group with respect to the binary operation $aN \cdot bN = abN$. Show that $N \lhd G$.
7. Let $f: G \to H$ be a homomorphism with H abelian. Let N be a subgroup of G which contains $\ker f$. Show $N \lhd G$.

4.11. PERMUTATION GROUPS AND CAYLEY'S THEOREM

In this section we shall show that a study of groups of permutations is in fact no less than a study of all abstract groups. This idea is made precise in the famous theorem of Cayley. Several of the more elementary results in this section are simply restatements in group-theoretical terminology of theorems proved in Chapter 3.

Theorem 4.11.1 The set of all permutations on the nonempty set X is a group with respect to the operation of composition of permutations.

Proof: The proof has been given in Example 4.1.10.

Definition 4.11.2 A group G is called a *permutation group* if G is a subgroup of the group of all permutations on a fixed set X.

Definition 4.11.3 The group S_n of permutations on the set $\{1,2,\cdots,n\}$ is called the *symmetric group on n letters.*[13]

In Section 3.4 we discussed the subset A_n of S_n, in which A_n consists of all even permutations on n letters.

Theorem 4.11.4 If $n \geq 2$, A_n is a subgroup of S_n, and $|A_n| = n!/2$. (A_n is called the *alternating group on n letters.*)

Proof: Exercise.

Theorem 4.11.5 Cayley Let G be a group. Then the group $(G,\circ)$ is isomorphic to a permutation group on the set G.

Before giving the formal proof of Cayley's Theorem, let us look briefly at the case in which G is finite, say $G = \{g_1,\cdots,g_n\}$. Then $Gg = \{g_1g,$

[13]We have defined S_n as the set of all permutations on the set of integers $X_n = \{1,\cdots,n\}$. If we consider the set of all permutations on the set $Y_n = \{\alpha_1,\cdots,\alpha_n\}$, $\alpha_i \neq \alpha_j$ for $i \neq j$, we get a group T_n isomorphic to S_n, but not equal to it (see Exercise 4, Section 4.4). This distinction, however, between the elements being permuted is not important for our purposes, hence we will consider the group S_n as the set of all permutations on any set of n distinct elements.

$\cdots, g_n g\} = G$, so that multiplication of G on the right permutes the elements of G. The elements of the permutation group in Cayley's Theorem will be precisely the permutations effected by these right multiplications.

Proof of Cayley's Theorem: To each element $g \in G$, we associate the function π_g on the set G defined by: $x\pi_g = xg$, for all $x \in G$. It is easy to show that π_g is a 1–1 map from G onto G, and is hence a permutation, even if G is infinite.

Now let f be a map from the group G to the group of permutations on the set G defined by $gf = \pi_g$. Clearly f is a function and we must show that the set $T = \{\pi_g \mid g \in G\}$ is a group and that f is an isomorphism from G onto T.

i) We first show that f is a homomorphism into the group of all permutations on the elements of G. Let x be an element of G. Then

$$x[(g_1g_2)f] = x\pi_{g_1g_2} = xg_1g_2 = (xg_1)g_2 = (x\pi_{g_1})g_2$$
$$= (x\pi_{g_1})\pi_{g_2} = x(\pi_{g_1}\pi_{g_2}).$$

Thus

$$(g_1g_2)f = \pi_{g_1}\pi_{g_2} = (g_1f)(g_2f).$$

Hence f is a homomorphism and, since $T = \operatorname{Im} f$, T is a group by Theorem 4.9.3.

ii) To show that f is an isomorphism from G onto T, let $g \in \ker f$. Hence $x\pi_g = xg = x$ for all $x \in G$. Therefore $g = e$ and f is an isomorphism by Theorem 4.9.11.

If G is a finite group, then one can obtain the permutation used in the proof of Cayley's Theorem by examining the multiplication table of G. The permutations are given by comparing the extreme left column of elements with each column in the table. For example, let G be the Klein group. Then $G = \{e = a_1, a_2, a_3, a_4\}$ and its multiplication table is

	a_1	a_2	a_3	a_4
a_1	a_1	a_2	a_3	a_4
a_2	a_2	a_1	a_4	a_3
a_3	a_3	a_4	a_1	a_2
a_4	a_4	a_3	a_2	a_1

Then

$$\pi_{a_1} = (a_1),$$

$$\pi_{a_2} = (a_1a_2)(a_3a_4), \quad \text{that is,} \quad a_1\pi_{a_2} = a_2,$$

$$a_2\pi_{a_2} = a_1, \quad a_3\pi_{a_2} = a_4, \quad a_4\pi_{a_2} = a_3$$

$$\pi_{a_3} = (a_1a_3)(a_2a_4),$$

and $$\pi_{a_4} = (a_1a_4)(a_2a_3).$$

Replacing each element by its subscript, we have an isomorphism from G onto a subgroup of S_4, namely $\{(1), (1\ 2)(3\ 4), (1\ 3)(2\ 4), (1\ 4)(2\ 3)\}$.

Exercises

1. Do Exercises 5, 7, and 8, Section 3.2, using properties of groups.
2. Let C_n be a cyclic group of order n. Find a permutation group isomorphic to C_n. What is the smallest integer r such that C_n is isomorphic to a subgroup of S_r?
3. Prove Theorem 4.11.4.
4. Suppose that in the proof of Cayley's Theorem we defined a permutation Γ_g on G by $x\Gamma_g = gx$, all $x \in G$. Does the proof of Theorem 4.11.5 still work? Explain.
5. Show that the group of symmetries of an equilateral triangle is isomorphic to a permutation group on three letters and also to a permutation group on six letters.
6. Let $f_n: Z \to Z$ be defined by: $xf_n = x + n$ for all $x \in Z$. Show that $\{f_n \mid n \in Z\}$ is a group isomorphic to Z.

†7. Show that any finite group G is isomorphic to a subgroup of A_n for some n. ●

As we have seen in the illustration above, the proof of Cayley's Theorem provides us with a technique for constructing a group of permutations isomorphic to a given group G. One disadvantage of this technique is that it tends to be relatively inefficient. For, if we are given the group S_3 in terms of its multiplication table, for example, without knowing that it is the group of permutations on *three* symbols, an application of this construction will provide us with a group of permutations on *six* symbols that is isomorphic to S_3. The next theorem and corollary give a modification which in many cases helps to reduce the number of symbols that must be considered. This is accomplished by mapping the group G onto a set of permutations on the right cosets of a subgroup of G.

Theorem 4.11.6 Let H be a subgroup of the group G, and let $C = \{Hg \mid g \in G\}$. Let T be the set of permutations π_g on C defined by: $(Hx)\pi_g = Hxg$. Then T is a permutation group and the mapping $f: G \to T$ defined by $gf = \pi_g$ is a homomorphism whose kernel is contained in H.

Proof: As in the proof of Cayley's Theorem, we must verify that f preserves the group operation.

Let

$$(g_1g_2)f = \pi_{g_1g_2}.$$

Then

$$(Hx)\pi_{g_1g_2} = Hxg_1g_2 = [(Hx)\pi_{g_1}]g_2 = (Hx)\pi_{g_1}\pi_{g_2}.$$

Hence

$$(g_1g_2)f = \pi_{g_1g_2} = \pi_{g_1}\pi_{g_2} = (g_1)f(g_2)f.$$

Now let $g \in \ker f$. Then $(Hx)\pi_g = Hxg = Hx$; for all $x \in G$. Hence, if $x = e$, then $g \in H$, and $\ker f \subseteq H$.

Corollary 4.11.7 Let H be a subgroup of G of index n and assume that no nontrivial normal subgroup of G is contained in H. Then G is isomorphic to a subgroup of S_n.

Proof: Let f be the homomorphism given in Theorem 4.11.6. Then since $\ker f$ is a normal subgroup of G contained in H, $\ker f = E$ and f is an isomorphism onto a group of permutations on the n right cosets of H.

Exercises

8. Let H be a subgroup of order 2 in S_3. Show that S_3 is isomorphic to a group of permutations on the right cosets of H. Suppose H is a subgroup of order 3. What can you conclude about H in the light of Corollary 4.11.7?

†9. Let H be a subgroup of order 7 and index 4 in a group G. Show that H is normal in G.

†10. Show that if a group G contains a proper subgroup of finite index, it contains a proper normal subgroup of finite index.

†11. Let G be a group of order pn, p prime and $p > n$. Let H be a subgroup of G of order p. Show that $H \lhd G$.

4.12. *AUTOMORPHISMS*

A particularly important class of homomorphisms are the isomorphisms from a group G onto itself. Such a mapping is a permutation on the elements of G as well as a homomorphism. In this section we will study some of the properties of these mappings and show how they are used to investigate the structure of a group.

Definition 4.12.1 Let f be an isomorphism from G onto G. Then f is called an *automorphism* of G.

Theorem 4.12.2 Let G be a group and $a \in G$. Then the function f, defined by $gf = a^{-1}ga$ for all $g \in G$, is an automorphism of G.

Proof: To show that f is onto, let $h \in G$, and let $h' = aha^{-1}$. Then $h'f = a^{-1}h'a = a^{-1}(aha^{-1})a = h$, and therefore f is onto. Since $g^{-1}ag = g^{-1}bg$ implies $a = b$, f is clearly 1–1.

It remains to show only that f is a homomorphism. If $u, v \in G$, then $uf = a^{-1}ua$, $vf = a^{-1}va$, and $(uv)f = a^{-1}uva$. But $a^{-1}uva = a^{-1}u(aa^{-1})va = (a^{-1}ua)(a^{-1}va) = (uf)(vf)$. Hence $(uv)f = (uf)(vf)$, and f is a homomorphism.

Definition 4.12.3 Let G be a group and let a be a fixed element of G. Then the automorphism f, defined by $gf = a^{-1}ga$ for all $g \in G$, is called the *inner automorphism* determined by a. Any automorphism that is not equal to some inner automorphism is called an *outer automorphism.* The element $a^{-1}ga$ is called a *conjugate* of g, and the function f is also called *conjugation by a.* The elements a and b are called *conjugate* if there exists $g \in G$ such that $b = g^{-1}ag$.

Exercises

1. Let G be a group. Show that the identity function on G is an inner automorphism.
2. Show that if the oniy inner automorphism of a group G is the identity function, then G is abelian, and conversely.
3. Find an outer automorphism on the
   a) cyclic group of order 3
   b) cyclic group of order 6.
4. Show that the only automorphism of C_2 is the identity automorphism.
5. Let f be a function on the group G defined by $gf = g^{-1}$ for all $g \in G$. Show that f is an automorphism if and only if G is abelian.
6. Find the number of inner automorphisms and outer automorphisms of each of the following groups:
   i) Klein group
   ii) $(\overline{Z}_5, +)$
   iii) $(\overline{Z}_m, +)$
   iv) S_3.
7. Let G be a group containing an element a not of order 2. Prove that G has an automorphism different from the identity automorphism.
   Hint: In the abelian case, consider Exercise 5. ●

The notion of inner automorphism as a function defined on elements of G can be extended in a natural way to a function on sets of elements as follows:

Definition 4.12.4 Let f be the inner automorphism on G determined by $a \in G$, and let S be a subset of elements of G. Then

$$a^{-1}Sa = \{a^{-1}sa \mid s \in S\}.$$

If S is a subgroup of G, then $a^{-1}Sa$ is called a *subgroup conjugate to S*, or simply a *conjugate of S*.

Theorem 4.12.5 Let S be a subgroup of the group G. Then $a^{-1}Sa$ is a subgroup of G isomorphic to S.

Proof: Let $f: G \to G$ be defined by $gf = a^{-1}ga$. Then, by Theorem 4.12.2, f is an automorphism. Thus f restricted to S is an isomorphism.

It follows directly from the definition of automorphism that the identity element of a group G is invariant under any automorphism, that is, $ef = e$ for any automorphism f. It is also easy to describe those elements of G that are invariant under any inner automorphism of G.

Definition 4.12.6 An element $g \in G$ is called *central* in G if $a^{-1}ga = g$, or equivalently $ga = ag$, for all $a \in G$. The set of such elements is called the *center* of G, and is denoted by $C(G)$.

Exercises

8. Show that the center of a group G is a normal subgroup of G.
*9. Show that if $G/C(G)$ is cyclic, then G is abelian.
10. Let f_a and f_b be the inner automorphisms defined by $gf_a = a^{-1}ga$, $gf_b = b^{-1}gb$. Show that the inner automorphism $f_a = f_b$ if and only if $a \in bC(G)$. ●

If we attempt to extend the notion of a central element from elements to subgroups, we are led to investigate those subgroups N of G with the property that $a^{-1}Na = N$ for all $a \in G$. As we have already seen in Section 4.9, this is precisely the definition of a normal subgroup. It is for this reason that normal subgroups are sometimes called invariant subgroups.

Since an automorphism on a group G is a permutation on G, automorphisms may be multiplied as permutations.

Theorem 4.12.7 Let $A(G)$ be the set of all automorphisms on G and $I(G)$ the set of all inner automorphisms. Then $A(G)$ is a group with respect to permutation multiplication and $I(G)$ is a normal subgroup of $A(G)$.

Proof: We leave the proof of the fact that $A(G)$ and $I(G)$ are groups as an exercise, but give the proof that $I(G) \lhd A(G)$.

Let $f_a \in I(G)$ be defined by

$$gf_a = a^{-1}ga \quad \text{for all} \quad g \in G.$$

Let τ be an arbitrary element of $A(G)$. We must show that $\tau^{-1}f_a\tau \in I(G)$. Consider

$$g(\tau^{-1}f_a\tau) \quad \text{for any} \quad g \in G.$$

Then

$$g(\tau^{-1}f_a\tau) = (g\tau^{-1})f_a\tau = [a^{-1}(g\tau^{-1})a]\tau.$$

Since τ is a homomorphism

$$[a^{-1}(g\tau^{-1})a]\tau = (a^{-1}\tau)[(g\tau^{-1})\tau](a\tau) = (a\tau)^{-1}g(a\tau).$$

Hence

$$\tau^{-1}f_a\tau = f_{a\tau} \in I(A).$$

Definition 4.12.8 The set of all automorphisms on a group G, $A(G)$, together with permutation multiplication, is called the *automorphism group of G*, and $I(G)$ is called the *inner automorphism group of G*.

Exercises

11. Complete the proof of Theorem 4.12.7.
12. Show that $G/C(G) \simeq I(G)$.

    Hint: Use the first isomorphism theorem.
13. Express all automorphisms on S_3 as permutations. How many symbols are needed to define these permutations? To what group is $A(S_3)$ isomorphic? •

The group of inner automorphisms $I(G)$ has the effect of inducing an equivalence relation and hence a partition on the group G, as is shown below.

Theorem 4.12.9 Let G be a group. Let R be the relation of conjugacy defined on G as follows: Given $a,b \in G$, $a\,R\,b$ if there exists $g \in G$ such that $a = g^{-1}bg$. Then R is an equivalence relation on G.

Proof: For any $a \in G$, $a = e^{-1}ae$, where e is the identity of G. Thus, aRa.

Now suppose aRb. Then $a = g^{-1}bg$ for some $g \in G$, whence

$$b = (g^{-1})^{-1}ag^{-1} \text{ and so } bRa.$$

Lastly, suppose aRb and bRc, that is, $a = g_1^{-1}bg_1$ and $b = g_2^{-1}cg_2$, for some $g_1,g_2 \in G$. Then

$$a = g_1^{-1}(g_2^{-1}cg_2)g_1 = (g_2g_1)^{-1}c(g_2g_1), \quad \text{and so} \quad aRc.$$

Definition 4.12.10 Let G be a group. The equivalence classes determined by the relation of conjugacy are called the *conjugate classes* of G.

These conjugate classes have many interesting and useful properties. For example, unlike the case of a partition into left cosets, the number of elements in each class is not always the same, for the identity element is always in a class by itself, as is any central element. But if an element is not central, then its conjugate class has at least two members. Finally, we note that if A is a conjugate class, and $a \in A$, then $A = \{g^{-1}ag \mid g \in G\}$.

Definition 4.12.11 Let G be a finite group of order α. Let the conjugate classes of G be $\{A_i\}$, $i = 1,\cdots,n$, and let A_i have α_i elements. Then the expression: $\alpha = |G| = \alpha_1 + \alpha_2 + \cdots + \alpha_n$ is called the *class equation of* G.

Definition 4.12.12 Let g be an element of the group G. Then the set $C_G(g) = \{x \mid x^{-1}gx = g, x \in G\}$ is called the *centralizer* of g in G. If A is a subgroup of G, then the set $N_G(A) = \{x \mid x \in G, x^{-1}Ax = A\}$ is called the *normalizer* of A in G.

We note that an element $g \in G$ is central if and only if $C_G(g) = G$ and that a subgroup $A \subseteq G$ is normal in G if and only if $N_G(A) = G$.

Exercises

*14. Show that $C_G(g)$ is a subgroup of G for any $g \in G$.

15. Show that $N_G(A)$ is a subgroup of G for any subgroup A of G, and show that $A \lhd N_G(A)$.

16. Let A be a subgroup of a group G. Show that if $A \lhd B$, a subgroup of G, then $B \subseteq N_G(A)$. •

Theorem 4.12.13 Let G be a finite group and let α_i be the number of elements in the conjugate class A_i of G. If $a \in A_i$, then $\alpha_i = [G:C_G(a)]$.

Proof: We will show there exists as 1–1 correspondence between the set A_i and the set of right cosets $\{C_G(a)g \mid g \in G\}$. For $g_1^{-1}ag_1 = g_2^{-1}ag_2$ if and only if $g_2g_1^{-1}ag_1g_2^{-1} = a$ if and only if $g_1g_2^{-1} \in C_G(a)$ if and only if $C_G(a)g_1 = C_G(a)g_2$. Hence the mapping f defined by $(g^{-1}ag)f = C_G(a)g$ is 1–1 and onto.

Corollary 4.12.14 Let G be a finite group with class equation $|G| = \alpha_1 + \cdots + \alpha_k$. Then $\alpha_i \mid |G|$ for $i = 1,2,\cdots,k$.

Proof: It follows from the theorem that α_i is the index of the centralizer of some element of G, and hence by Lagrange's Theorem, $\alpha_i \mid |G|$.

We now give two important theorems about finite groups that follow readily from Corollary 4.12.14.

Theorem 4.12.15 Let G be a finite group, $|G| = p^n$, $n > 0$, p a prime. Then G has a nontrivial center, of order at least p.

Proof: Let $|G| = p^n = \alpha_1 + \cdots + \alpha_k$ be the class equation of G. By Corollary 4.12.14, $\alpha_i \mid |G|$. If $\alpha_i > 1$, then, since p is a prime, $p \mid \alpha_i$. Assume that e is the only central element of G. Then for precisely one α_i, say α_1, $\alpha_1 = 1$. Thus $p \mid \alpha_i$, for $i \geq 2$. But then, since $p \mid |G|$, $p \mid [|G| - (\alpha_2 + \cdots + \alpha_k)]$. Since $\alpha_1 = |G| - (\alpha_2 + \cdots + \alpha_k), p \mid \alpha_1$, a contradiction. Hence the center of G contains more than one element, and since $C(G)$ is a subgroup, $|C(G)| \geq p$.

Corollary 4.12.16 Let G be a group of order p^2, p a prime. Then G is abelian.

Proof: Since $|G| = p^2, p$ a prime, by Theorem 4.12.15, G contains a nontrivial center $C(G)$. Since $C(G) \lhd G$, consider $G/C(G)$. Since $C(G)$ is nontrivial $|G/C(G)| = p$ or 1. In either case, $G/C(G)$ is cyclic, and hence by Exercise 9, Section 4.12, G is abelian, that is, $C(G) = G$.

The next theorem provides information about the subgroups of a finite group, in terms of the primes that divide its order. As we shall see in Chapter 6, this is a special case of the first Sylow theorem.

Theorem 4.12.17 Let G be a finite abelian group. If p is a prime and $p \mid |G|$, then G contains an element of order p.

We use a technique of proof in this and the following theorem that is an application of the law of well ordering and is particularly suited for finite groups. The argument goes as follows: If the theorem in question is not true, then the set of groups for which it is false is nonempty; hence the set of orders of these groups is a nonempty set of positive integers. Let n be the least such and let G be one of the groups of order n for which the theorem is false. G is therefore called a *minimal counterexample.* It must then be shown that G, in fact, does not exist and hence the set of orders is empty and therefore the set of groups for which the theorem fails is empty. The chief tool for accomplishing this is the fact that if A is a proper subgroup of G or if G/N is a proper factor group of G, then the theorem is true for A and for G/N since $|A| < |G|$, $|G/N| < |G|$ and G is a group of minimal order for which the theorem is false. That the theorem holds for all proper subgroups and factor groups of G is then used to bring about a contradiction.

Proof: Let G be a minimal counterexample. That is, $p \mid |G|$ for some prime p, but G contains no element of order p. Further, if G' is any other group with these properties, then $|G| \leq |G'|$.

Let $g \in G, g \neq e$. If $|g| = pm$, then $|g^m| = p$, by Exercise 10, Section 4.7, a contradiction. Hence, assume that every element of G has order relatively prime to p.

Then, for any $g \neq e$, (g) is a proper subgroup of G since otherwise G would be cyclic and $|G| = |g|$. But $p \mid |G|$ and $p \nmid |g|$, so G is not cyclic.

Since G is abelian, (g) is normal and we consider $G/(g)$. Now $E \subset (g)$ and $|g| > 1$, whence $|G/(g)| < |G|$. Since $|G/(g)|\,|(g)| = |G|$, it follows that $p \mid |G/(g)|$. Since G is a minimal counterexample, $G/(g)$ contains an element $h(g)$ of order p. But by Exercise 2, Section 4.10 the order of a coset as an element in the quotient group divides the order of any representative in the full group. Hence $p \mid |h|$. This implies that G has an element of order p, a contradiction. Hence G is not a minimal counterexample and the theorem is proved.

Theorem 4.12.18 Cauchy Let G be a finite group.
If $p \mid |G|$, p a prime, then G contains an element of order p.

Proof: Let G be a minimal counterexample. Thus, $|G|$ is divisible by p, but G does not contain an element of order p. Now, if $p \mid |H|$, H a proper subgroup of G, then H contains an element of order p, and this element is also an element of G. Therefore, all proper subgroups of G have orders not divisible by p.

We now consider the class equation of G:

$$|G| = \alpha_1 + \alpha_2 + \cdots + \alpha_k.$$

If $\alpha_i > 1$ then α_i is the index of a proper subgroup C_i of G. As we have seen above, $p \nmid |C_i|$ and hence $p \mid [G:C_i] = \alpha_i$ for all $\alpha_i > 1$. Therefore, since $p \mid |G|$, $p \mid \alpha'$ where α' is the number of α_j's such that $\alpha_j = 1$. But α' is precisely the order of $C(G)$, the center of G, and, by assumption, p does not divide the order of any proper subgroup of G. Therefore, $C(G) = G$ and G is abelian. Hence, by Theorem 4.12.17, G contains an element of order p, a contradiction. This completes the proof of the theorem.

Corollary 4.12.19 Let G be a finite group each of whose elements different from e has order a power of a fixed prime p. Then $|G| = p^\alpha$.

Proof: Exercise.

Exercises

†17. Let G be a finite abelian group and let $G = \{a_1, \cdots, a_n\}$, where each a_j has order $\alpha_j \geq 1$, $j = 1, 2, \cdots, n$. Show that there exists an integer m such that any element of G is equal to precisely m expressions of the form $a_1^{\beta_1} a_2^{\beta_2} \cdots a_n^{\beta_n}$, $0 \leq \beta_i < \alpha_i$.

18. Using Exercise 17, give another proof of Theorem 4.12.17.
Hint: Express $m \cdot |G|$ in terms of the α_i.

19. Let A be a subgroup of the finite group G. Show that $[G:N_G(A)]$ is the number of distinct subgroups conjugate to A.

20. Let G be a finite group with precisely two conjugate classes. Show that $|G| = 2$.

21. Let the group G contain an element a having exactly two conjugates. Show that G has a proper normal subgroup $N \neq E$.
22. Prove Corollary 4.12.19.

4.13 DIRECT PRODUCTS

We have seen in Section 1.6 that it is possible to form a "larger" set from two given ones, say A and B, by forming the Cartesian product $A \times B$. We say that A and B are "embedded" in $A \times B$ in the sense that the set $A_1 = \{(a, b_1) \mid \text{all } a \in A \text{ and some fixed } b_1 \in B\} \subseteq A \times B$ "looks" very much like A and can, of course, be put into 1–1 correspondence with A. In a similar manner, B is "embedded" in $A \times B$.

On the other hand, there are many familiar sets that can be considered to be the Cartesian product of "smaller" sets. For example, if K is the set of real numbers, the set of points in the Euclidean plane can be thought of as the set of all ordered pairs $\{(x, y) \mid x, y \in K\} = K \times K$. The "smaller" set in this case is the set K of real numbers. The "embedding" of K in $K \times K$ is given, for example, by the set $\{(x,0) \mid \text{all } x \in K\}$.

In this section we shall show that if, instead of considering sets A and B, we consider groups G and H, then it is possible to define a new, "larger" group $G \times H$ in such a way that G and H are "embedded" as groups in $G \times H$. Also, we shall start with a group G and show when it is possible to write G in the form $H_1 \times H_2$, where H_1 and H_2 are subgroups of G.

Definition 4.13.1 Let $(G, \cdot)$ and $(H, *)$ be groups. Let $(G \times H, \circ)$ be the set $G \times H = \{(g,h) \mid g \in G,\ h \in H\}$ together with the binary operation $(g_1,h_1) \circ (g_2,h_2) = (g_1 \cdot g_2,\ h_1 * h_2)$. Then $(G \times H, \circ)$ is called the *direct product* of G and H and is denoted by $G \times H$.

Definition 4.13.2 A group G is said to be *embedded* in a group G' if there is an isomorphism from G onto a subgroup of G'.

We shall now show that $G \times H$ is a group in which G and H are embedded.

Theorem 4.13.3 The direct product $G \times H$ of groups G and H is a group. Furthermore, $G \times H$ contains subgroups G' and H' that are isomorphic to G and H respectively.

Proof: We first show that the operation $\circ$ is a binary operation on $G \times H$. This amounts to showing that for any two elements (g_1,h_1) and (g_2,h_2) of $G \times H$, the definition of $\circ$ leads to precisely one element (g_3,h_3) of $G \times H$. The details are left to the reader.

The associtivity of this binary operation follows from the associativity of $\cdot$ and $*$, for, $((g_1,h_1) \circ (g_2,h_2)) \circ (g_3,h_3) = (g_1 \cdot g_2,\ h_1 * h_2) \circ (g_3,h_3)$

$$= ((g_1 \cdot g_2) \cdot g_3,\ (h_1 * h_2) * h_3) \ = \ (g_1 \cdot (g_2 \cdot g_3),\ h_1 * (h_2 * h_3))$$
$$= (g_1,h_1) \circ (g_2 \cdot g_3,\ h_2 * h_3) = (g_1,h_1) \circ ((g_2,h_2) \circ (g_3,h_3)).$$

Finally, if e is the identity of G and e' the identity of H, then (e,e') is the identity of $G \times H$ and (g^{-1},h^{-1}) is the inverse of the element (g,h) of $G \times H$.

To show that $G \times H$ contains subgroups $G' \cong G$ and $H' \cong H$, let $G' = \{(g,e') \mid \text{all } g \in G\}$, and $H' = \{(e,h) \mid \text{all } h \in H\}$. We leave the verification of the isomorphisms as an exercise.

Exercises

1. Complete the proof of Theorem 4.13.3.
2. Let G' and H' be the subgroups of $G \times H$ defined in the proof of Theorem 4.13.3. Show that $g'h' = h'g'$, for all $g' \in G'$, $h' \in H'$. Show also that $G' \cap H'$ is the trivial subgroup of $G \times H$.

*3. Let G and H be finite groups. What is the order of $G \times H$ in terms of the orders of G and H.

4. Show that the subgroups G' and H' defined in the proof of Theorem 4.13.3 above are *normal* subgroups of $G \times H$. Show also that $H \cong (G \times H)/G'$ and $G \cong (G \times H)/H'$.
5. Let G be the cyclic group of order 2 and H the cyclic group of order 3. Form $G \times H$. To what familiar group is it isomorphic?
6. Let G and H be abelian groups. Show that $G \times H$ is abelian.

*7. Let $G = (\bar{Z}_m,+)$ and $H = (\bar{Z}_n,+)$. Show that if $(m,n) = 1$, then $G \times H$ is cyclic.

8. Let G and H be finite cyclic groups. Find necessary and sufficient conditions for $G \times H$ to be cyclic.

*9. Let G be a cyclic group of order p^α, p a prime. Show that if $G \cong A \times B$, then either $|A| = 1$ or $|B| = 1$. That is, a cyclic group of prime power order can be represented as a direct product only in a trivial way.

10. Let $R \subseteq G \times H$. Define the projection of R to G as $R\pi_1 = \{g \mid g \in G$ such that $(g,h) \in R$ for some $h \in H\}$ and define the projection of R to H as $R\pi_2 = \{h \mid h \in H$ such that $(g,h) \in R$ for some $g \in G\}$. Show that if R is a subgroup of $G \times H$, then $R\pi_1$ and $R\pi_2$ are subgroups of G and H, respectively. Also, show that if $R \lhd G \times H$, then $R\pi_1 \lhd G$ and $R\pi_2 \lhd H$.
11. Let $G \cong A \times B$. Prove that if $A \cong C$, then $G \cong C \times B$. •

Although the direct product was defined for a pair of groups G and H, it is not difficult to see how the definition may be extended to three groups, or to any finite number of groups. That is, if G, H, and K are groups, we can form $(G \times H) \times K$ or $G \times (H \times K)$. As we shall show, these direct products are isomorphic. Thus we can write $G \times H \times K$ with no ambiguity up to isomorphism. The elements of $G \times H \times K$ may be considered to be the ordered triples (g,h,k) for $g \in G, h \in H, k \in K$.

Theorem 4.13.4 Let G, H, K be groups. Then $(G \times H) \times K \cong G \times (H \times K)$.

Proof: Exercise.

Exercises

12. Prove Theorem 4.13.4.
13. Generalize Theorem 4.13.4 to an arbitrary finite set of groups. •

If G is a group, then it is very useful to know if G is isomorphic to a direct product of "smaller" groups. The next theorem provides a necessary and sufficient condition for determining when this is the case. We first prove a lemma.

Lemma 4.13.5 Let A and B be normal subgroups of a group G such that $A \cap B = E$. Then $ab = ba$ for all $a \in A$ and all $b \in B$.

Proof: Let $a \in A$ and $b \in B$. Then $ab = bac$ for some $c \in G$, and it suffices to show that $c = e$. Since $c = a^{-1}b^{-1}ab = (a^{-1}b^{-1}a)b$ and since $B \lhd G$, $a^{-1}b^{-1}a \in B$ and therefore $c = a^{-1}b^{-1}ab \in B$. On the other hand, $a^{-1}b^{-1}ab = a^{-1}(b^{-1}ab)$ and, since $A \lhd G$, $b^{-1}ab \in A$ and, therefore, $c = a^{-1}b^{-1}ab \in A$. Therefore, $c \in A \cap B$ and $c = e$. Hence $ab = ba$.

Theorem 4.13.6 Let A and B be normal subgroups of G such that
i) $AB = G$
ii) $A \cap B = E$. Then

$$G \cong A \times B.$$

Proof: Let f be the mapping from $A \times B$ to G defined as follows:

$$(a,b)f = ab.$$

It follows from i) that f is a function from $A \times B$ onto G.

Now $((a_1,b_1) \circ (a_2,b_2))f = (a_1a_2, b_1b_2)f = a_1a_2b_1b_2$. But, by Lemma 4.13.5, $a_2b_1 = b_1a_2$; hence $a_1a_2b_1b_2 = a_1b_1a_2b_2 = (a_1,b_1)f(a_2,b_2)f$. Thus f is a homomorphism.

To complete the proof we show that ker f is trivial and therefore f is an isomorphism.

Let $(a,b)f = ab = e$. Then $a = b^{-1}$ and $a \in A \cap B$. Hence $a = e = b$ and (a,b) is the identity of $A \times B$.

Whenever it is possible to find normal subgroups A and B of a group G satisfying the hypotheses of Theorem 4.13.6, that is $G \cong A \times B$, we shall say that G is an *internal direct product* of its subgroups A and B and we shall write $G = A \dot{\times} B$.

The criterion of Theorem 4.13.6 can be put in a slightly altered form that proves very useful in certain cases.

Theorem 4.13.7 Let A and B be subgroups of a group G such that i) $ab = ba$, for all $a \in A$, $b \in B$ and ii) for each $g \in G$, there are unique elements $a \in A$ and $b \in B$ such that $g = ab$. Then $G = A \dot{\times} B$.

Proof: It follows immediately that $G = AB$. We now show that $A \lhd G$ and $B \lhd G$. Let $a \in A$ and $g \in G$. Then $g = a_1 b_1$ for some $a_1 \in A$ and $b_1 \in B$. Hence $g^{-1}ag = b_1^{-1}a_1^{-1}aa_1b_1 = a_1^{-1}aa_1$ since $a'b' = b'a'$ for all $a' \in A$ and $b' \in B$. Since $a_1^{-1}aa_1 \in A$, $g^{-1}ag \in A$ and $A \lhd G$. Similarly, $B \lhd G$.

Finally suppose that $g \in A \cap B$. Then $g \in A$ and $g \in B$. Since $g = a_1 b_1$, for unique elements a_1 of A and b_1 of B, $b_1 = a_1^{-1}g \in A$ and $a_1 = gb_1^{-1} \in B$. Thus, $g = a_1 b_1 = a_2$ for some $a_2 \in A$ and $g = a_1 b_1 = b_2$ for some $b_2 \in B$. But then

$$g = a_1 b_1 = a_2 e \quad \text{and} \quad g = a_1 b_1 = e b_2.$$

By the unique representation for g in the form ab, $a \in A$, $b \in B$, $a_1 = a_2$, $b_1 = e$, and $a_1 = e$, $b_1 = b_2$. Thus, $g = ee = e$. That is, $A \cap B = E$. By Theorem 4.13.6, $G = A \dot{\times} B$.

Exercise

14. Show that if the condition $ab = ba$ is removed, Theorem 4.13.7 is false.

Hint: Consider S_3. •

If G is a group containing subgroups A and B fulfilling the conditions of Theorem 4.13.7, $G = A \dot{\times} B$. If the subgroup A contains subgroups A_1, A_2 also fulfilling the conditions of the theorem with respect to A, $A = A_1 \dot{\times} A_2$, and $G = (A_1 \dot{\times} A_2) \dot{\times} B$ (Exercise 10, Section 4.13). As we have seen, the operation of direct product is associative, and we can generalize the statement of Theorem 4.13.6 in the following manner.

Theorem 4.13.8 Let $A_1, \cdots, A_n$ be normal subgroups of a group G, satisfying:

i) $G = A_1 \cdots A_n$

ii) $A_i \cap \hat{A}_i = E$ where $\hat{A}_i = A_1 \cdots A_{i-1} A_{i+1} \cdots A_n$, $i = 1, \cdots, n$. Then $G = A_1 \dot{\times} \cdots \dot{\times} A_n$.

Proof: Exercise.

We conclude this section with several theorems about finite abelian groups of some special types.

Theorem 4.13.9 Let $G \neq E$ be a finite abelian group all of whose elements different from e have order p a prime. Then, for some integer $n \geq 1$, $G \cong A_1 \times \cdots \times A_n$ where $A_i \cong C_p$, the cyclic group of order p, for $i = 1, \cdots, n$, and $|G| = p^n$.

Proof: Let $\{a_1, a_2, \cdots, a_n\}$ be an irredundant set of generators of G. Now let $A_i = (a_i)$, and $\hat{A}_i = A_1 \cdots A_{i-1}A_{i+1} \cdots A_n$ for $i = 1, \cdots, n$. Clearly, $|a_i| = p$, hence $A_i \cong C_p$ for all i. Also, $G = A_1 \cdots A_n$, since this product of subgroups is a subgroup and contains the set of generators $\{a_1, \cdots, a_n\}$. If $A_i \cap \hat{A}_i \neq E$, then $A_i \subseteq \hat{A}_i$, and $\{a_1, \cdots, a_n\}$ is not irredundant (see Exercise 10, Section 4.8). Therefore, $A_i \cap \hat{A}_i = E$ for all i and, by Theorem 4.13.8, $G = A_1 \dot{\times} \cdots \dot{\times} A_n$. Clearly, $|G| = p^n$.

Theorem 4.13.10 Let G be a group of order p^2, p a prime. Then either $G \cong C_{p^2}$, the cyclic group of order p^2 or $G \cong C_p \times C_p$, the direct product of a cyclic group of order p with itself.

Proof: By Lagrange's theorem each element $g \in G$, $g \neq e$, has order p or p^2. If G contains an element of order p^2, then G is cyclic and hence isomorphic to C_{p^2}. Otherwise, every element of G different from e has order p. Since G is abelian by Corollary 4.12.16, $G \cong C_p \times C_p$ by Theorem 4.13.9.

Exercises

15. Prove Theorem 4.13.8.

*16. Let $N_1, \cdots, N_r$ be normal subgroups of a group G and assume that $G = N_1 N_2 \cdots N_r$. Show that $G = N_1 \dot{\times} N_2 \dot{\times} \cdots \dot{\times} N_r$ if and only if whenever $a_1 a_2 \cdots a_r = e$ for $a_i \in N_i$, then $a_i = e$ for $i = 1, \cdots, r$.

*17. Show that there exists exactly one group of order 8 all of whose elements have order 2.

18. Let G be a direct product of its subgroups A and B. Prove that $G/A \cong B$, and $G/B \cong A$.

19. Let G be a finite group, $|G| > 2$. Show that G has a nonidentity automorphism (see Exercise 7, Section 4.12).

4.14 CLASSIFICATION OF GROUPS OF SMALL ORDER

It has been said that the main problem in the theory of finite groups is to determine all groups of an arbitrary order n. In one sense this problem is solved, since for each order n one can, in a finite number of steps, enumerate all possible $n \times n$ multiplication tables and exhaustively check for isomorphic pairs. This solution has two serious defects. First, the effort involved in enumerating all multiplication tables and testing for isomorphic pairs becomes astronomical for even moderately large n. Secondly, the multiplication table of a group presents the important properties of a group in an extremely inconvenient form. The important results in the theory of groups give us information concerning specific properties for large classes of groups. Our work up-to-now has given us sufficient tools to completely classify groups of relatively small order without recourse to an exhaustive search of possible multiplication tables. We now give (with some gaps to be filled in by the reader) the complete classification of all finite groups of order ≤ 9.

I. $|G| = 1$. Then $G \simeq E$, the group with one element.

II. $|G| = 2$. Then $G \simeq C_2$.

III. $|G| = 3$. Then $G \simeq C_3$.

IV. $|G| = 4$. By Theorem 4.8.10 or by Theorem 4.13.10, either $G \simeq C_4$ or $G \simeq C_2 \times C_2$. Clearly these groups are not isomorphic.

V. $|G| = 5$. Then $G \simeq C_5$.

VI. $|G| = 6$. By Exercise 15, Section 4.8, either $G \simeq C_6$ or $G \simeq S_3$. (In the event the reader has not yet completed this exercise, he should again attempt it following our discussion of case VIII). Since C_6 is abelian and S_3 is not abelian, these groups are not isomorphic.

VII. $|G| = 7$. Then $G \simeq C_7$.

VIII. $|G| = 8$.

A. If G is abelian there are three possibilities:

i) G has an element of order 8.

ii) G has no element of order 8, but G does have an element of order 4.

iii) Every nonidentity element of G has order 2.

i) Clearly $G \simeq C_8$.

ii) Let $a \in G$, a of order 4. Then, since $(a) \subset G$, there is an element $b \in G$, $b \notin (a)$. If $b^2 = e$, then $G = (a)(b)$ and $(a) \cap (b) = E$. Thus $G \simeq C_4 \times C_2$ by Theorem 4.13.6.

If $b^2 \neq e$, then $b^2 \in (a)$, for otherwise $|(b)| = 4$ and $(a) \cap (b) = E$ and $|G| \geq 16$. Hence $b^2 \in (a)$ and since $|b^2| = 2$, $b^2 = a^2$. Now let $c = ba^{-1}$. Clearly $c \notin (a)$, and $c^2 = b^2a^{-2} = e$. Thus $G = (a)(c) \simeq C_4 \times C_2$.

iii) By Theorem 4.13.9, $G \simeq C_2 \times C_2 \times C_2$.

We leave it to the reader to verify that no two of these three groups are isomorphic.

B. G is nonabelian.

We first note that G can have no element of order 8, for if it did, this would imply $G \simeq C_8$ an abelian group. Also, not every element of G, $g \neq e$, can have order 2. For if this were the case, G would be abelian by Exercise 7, Section 4.2.

Thus, G has an element of order 4, but none of order 8. Let $a \in G$, a of order 4. Then $[G:(a)] = 2$ and (a) is normal in G. Hence $G/(a)$ has order 2, and so there exists an element $b \in G$, $b \notin (a)$ and $b^2 \in (a)$. If $b^2 = a$, then, since a has order 4, b would have order 8, a contradiction. Similarly, $b^2 \neq a^3$. Hence i) $b^2 = e$ or ii) $b^2 = a^2$.

i) $b^2 = e$. In this case, we may express all the elements of G in terms of a and b, as follows: $a, a^2, a^3, a^4 = e, ab, a^2b, a^3b, a^4b = b$. It is easy to see that these are all distinct. To show that the product of any two of these elements is one of the list, we need only determine the product ba.

Since $b \notin (a)$, $ba \notin (a)$. If $ba = b$ then $a = e$, a contradiction. If $ba = ab$ then G is abelian, another contradiction. If $ba = a^2b$ then $bab^{-1} = a^2$. But bab^{-1} has order 4 while a^2 has order 2, again a contradiction. Thus, the only possibility that can hold is $ba = a^3b$.

Hence G has two generators, a and b, and $a^4 = e$, $b^2 = e$, and $ba = a^3b$. The group D_4 contains the generators r_1 and h that respectively satisfy the properties of a and b above. The mapping $f: D_4 \to G$ defined by

$$(r_1{}^n h^m)f = a^n b^m$$

(see Exercise 22, Section 4.7) can be shown to be an isomorphism. We leave this for the reader.

ii) $b^2 = a^2$. Again

$$G = \{e,a,a^2,a^3,b,ab,a^2b,a^3b\}.$$

As in i) we must determine the product ba. Exactly as in i), we find that we must have $ba = a^3b$. We now know that G is generated by a and b, where $b^2 = a^2$, $a^4 = e$, $ba = a^3b$. These relations are sufficient to determine a multiplication table for the group G. From the table, writing the elements in the order $e,a,a^2,a^3,b,ab,a^2b,a^3b$, we can find a permutation group that is isomorphic to G, as we did in the example in Section 4.11. Indeed, as in the proof of Cayley's theorem, a corresponds to $(1\ 2\ 3\ 4)(5\ 8\ 7\ 6)$ and b to $(1\ 5\ 3\ 7)(2\ 6\ 4\ 8)$. The group generated by $(1\ 2\ 3\ 4)(5\ 8\ 7\ 6)$ and $(1\ 5\ 3\ 7)(2\ 6\ 4\ 8)$ is a group of order 8 isomorphic to G. This group is called the *quaternion group* and in the exercises the reader will show that it is not isomorphic to D_4.

To summarize, we have displayed five nonisomorphic groups of order 8 and have proved that any group of order 8 is isomorphic to one of these. They are

1. C_8
2. $C_4 \times C_2$
3. $C_2 \times C_2 \times C_2$
4. Group of symmetries of the square, D_4.
5. Quaternion group—consisting of the elements e,a,a^2,a^3,b,ab,a^2b, a^3b, in which the product of elements can be computed from $a^4 = b^4 = e$, $a^2 = b^2$, $ba = a^3b$.

IX. $|G| = 9$.

By Theorem 4.13.10, either $G \simeq C_9$ or $G \simeq C_3 \times C_3$. These groups are clearly nonisomorphic.

Exercises

1. Show that no two of the groups C_8, $C_4 \times C_2$ and $C_2 \times C_2 \times C_2$ are isomorphic.
2. Show that D_4 is not isomorphic to the quaternion group.

   Hint: Show that the quaternion group contains only one element of order 2.
3. Let $G = \{1, -1, i, -i, j, -j, k, -k\}$, with $-1, 1 \in Z$; the remaining symbols are distinct and satisfy:

$$ij = k, \quad jk = i, \quad ki = j$$

$$i^2 = j^2 = k^2 = -1$$

$$(-a)b = a(-b) = -(ab) = ba \text{ for all } a, b \in G$$

$$-a = (-1)a = a(-1).$$

   Show that G is isomorphic to the group of quaternions.
4. Classify the groups of order 10.

CHAPTER 5

The Theory of Rings

In our study of groups we have referred to properties of the integers Z, both for purposes of illustration and to aid in proving several theorems. As a source of examples we considered additive properties of the set Z and multiplicative properties of $\overline{Z}_p - \{\overline{0}\}$, for any prime p. Some of the most important properties of the integers, however, are those that simultaneously involve the operations of addition and multiplication: for example, the division algorithm.

The integers are one example of an algebraic system involving two binary operations that are "intertwined" in some way. For Z, this intertwining takes the form of the distributive law: $a(b + c) = ab + ac$. Many other familiar number systems also satisfy this general description: the rational numbers and the real numbers, for example.

In this chapter we shall study an abstract algebraic system, known as a *ring*, that involves two binary operations and that includes the integers, rational numbers, and real numbers as special cases. As with the concept of a group, that of a ring is basic in the study of mathematics.

5.1 DEFINITION OF RING AND EXAMPLES

Definition 5.1.1 Let R be a nonempty set and let $+$ and $\cdot$ denote two binary operations on R, which we refer to as "addition" and "multiplication," respectively. Then $(R, +, \cdot)$ is called a *ring* if the following conditions hold:

i) $(R, +)$ is a commutative group.
ii) $\cdot$ is associative. That is, $(a \cdot b) \cdot c = a \cdot (b \cdot c)$ for all $a,b,c \in R$.
iii) $a \cdot (b + c) = (a \cdot b) + (a \cdot c)$ (left distributive law) and
$(a + b) \cdot c = (a \cdot c) + (b \cdot c)$ (right distributive law) for all $a,b,c \in R$

When no ambiguity exists we shall refer to the ring $(R, +, \cdot)$ simply as R. As with groups, we shall usually drop the dot notation for products and write ab for $a \cdot b$. The identity of $(R,+)$ is denoted by 0 and is called the *zero* of the ring R. If there exists an element e in R such that for all a in R, $ea = ae = a$, then e is called a *multiplicative identity* of R.

We now proceed to some examples of rings.

Example 5.1.2 $(Z,+,\cdot)$, the ring of integers, with the usual interpretation of + and $\cdot$

Example 5.1.3 $(W,+,\cdot)$, the ring of even integers with the usual interpretation of + and $\cdot$. This ring has no multiplicative identity.

Example 5.1.4 $(\overline{Z}_m,+,\cdot)$, the ring of residue classes modulo m, with + and $\cdot$ as defined in Definition 2.11.1.

Example 5.1.5 $(Q,+,\cdot)$, the ring of rational numbers,[14] that is, real numbers of the form $p/q, p,q \in Z, q \neq 0$, with the usual interpretation of + and $\cdot$.

Example 5.1.6 $(K,+,\cdot)$, the ring of real numbers, with the usual interpretation of + and $\cdot$.

Example 5.1.7 Let S be a set, and let $\mathcal{S}$ be the collection of all subsets of S. For any $A,B \in \mathcal{S}$ we define + and $\cdot$ as follows:

$$A + B = (A \cup B) - (A \cap B),$$

$$A \cdot B = A \cap B.$$

It can then be shown that $(\mathcal{S},+,\cdot)$ is a ring with ϕ serving as the identity of $(\mathcal{S},+)$. The set $S \in \mathcal{S}$ is a multiplicative identity of the ring $\mathcal{S}$.

Example 5.1.8 Let $R = \{(a,b) \mid a,b \in Z\}$. For (a,b) and (c,d) in R we define an addition and multiplication on R as follows:

$$(a,b) + (c,d) = (a + c, b + d)$$

$$(a,b)\cdot(c,d) = (ac + bd, ad + bc).$$

The reader should note that $(R,+)$ is simply the additive group $Z \times Z$.

Example 5.1.9 Let H be the set of formal elements of the form: $a_0 + a_1 i + a_2 j + a_3 k$, where a_0, a_1, a_2, and a_3 are real numbers. Two ele-

[14]Although we often discuss the rational and real number systems for purposes of illustration, the formal development in this chapter does not depend on a complete definition of these number systems.

ments, $a_0 + a_1 i + a_2 j + a_3 k$ and $b_0 + b_1 i + b_2 j + b_3 k$, are said to be equal if $a_0 = b_0$, $a_1 = b_1$, $a_2 = b_2$, and $a_3 = b_3$. We define addition and multiplication on H as follows:

$$(a_0 + a_1 i + a_2 j + a_3 k) + (b_0 + b_1 i + b_2 j + b_3 k)$$
$$= (a_0 + b_0) + (a_1 + b_1)i + (a_2 + b_2)j + (a_3 + b_3)k.$$
$$(a_0 + a_1 i + a_2 j + a_3 k) \cdot (b_0 + b_1 i + b_2 j + b_3 k)$$
$$= (a_0 b_0 - a_1 b_1 - a_2 b_2 - a_3 b_3) + (a_0 b_1 + a_1 b_0 + a_2 b_3 - a_3 b_2)i$$
$$+ (a_0 b_2 + a_2 b_0 + a_3 b_1 - a_1 b_3)j + (a_0 b_3 + a_3 b_0 + a_1 b_2 - a_2 b_1)k.$$

Then $(H,+,\cdot)$, called the ring of *real quaternions*, is a ring with zero element $0 + 0i + 0j + 0k$, which we shall write as 0, and the element $1 + 0i + 0j + 0k$ is a multiplicative identity, which we shall write as 1.

The ring H is our first example of a noncommutative ring, that is, a ring in which $\cdot$ is not a commutative operation.

The definition of multiplication in H could also be given in another way. We compute the product of two quaternions by first multiplying according to the distributive laws and associative laws and then using the rules for i,j,k given in Exercise 3, Section 4.14, together with the condition that $ax = xa$ for $x = i,j,k$ and all real numbers a. For example, $(0 + i + j + 0k)(2 + 0i + j + 0k) = 0\cdot 2 + 0(0i) + 0j + 0(0k) + i2 + i(0i) + ij + i(0k) + j\cdot 2 + j(0i) + jj + j(0k) + (0k)2 + (0k)(0i) + (0k)j + (0k)(0k)$
$= i2 + ij + j2 + jj$
$= 2i + k + 2j - 1$
$= -1 + 2i + 2j + k.$

Example 5.1.10 Let $(G,\cdot)$ be a finite group written multiplicatively, $G = \{g_1, g_2, \cdots, g_n\}$. Let R be a ring and let $R(G)$ denote the set of all n-tuples

$$(a_1, a_2, \cdots, a_n), \quad a_i \in R.$$

We define $+$ and $\cdot$ in $R(G)$ as follows:

$$(a_1, a_2, \cdots, a_n) + (b_1, b_2, \cdots, b_n) = (a_1 + b_1, a_2 + b_2, \cdots, a_n + b_n)$$
$$(a_1, a_2, \cdots, a_n)\cdot(b_1, b_2, \cdots, b_n) = (c_1, c_2, \cdots, c_n),$$

where $c_j = \Sigma a_k b_\ell$, the sum being taken over all pairs $a_k b_\ell$ such that $g_k g_\ell = g_j$ in the group G.

Then $R(G)$ is a ring called the *group ring of G over R*.

The n-tuple $(a_1, a_2, \cdots, a_n)$ is often written as the formal sum

$$\sum_{i=1}^{n} a_i g_i.$$

Thus, the product $\left(\sum_{i=1}^{n} a_i g_i\right)\left(\sum_{j=1}^{n} b_j g_j\right)$ is obtained by multiplying these sums, using the convention that $(a_j g_j)(a_k g_k) = (a_j a_k)(g_\ell)$ in G. For example, if $G = \{e,a\}$, $a^2 = e$, then in $R(G)$ $(r_1 e + r_2 a)(s_1 e + s_2 a) = (r_1 e)(s_1 e) + (r_2 a)(s_1 e) + (r_1 e)(s_2 a) + (r_2 a)(s_2 a) = (r_1 s_1 + r_2 s_2)e + (r_2 s_1 + r_1 s_2)a$. This is precisely the ring of Example 5.1.8.

Example 5.1.11 Let K denote the set of all real numbers, and let F denote the set of all functions $f: K \to K$ such that f is continuous on K. For $f,g \in K$ we define $+$ and $\cdot$ as follows:

$$x(f + g) = xf + xg$$

$$x(f \cdot g) = (xf)(xg).$$

(Note that $f \cdot g$ is not the composite function $f \circ g$). Then $(F, +, \cdot)$ forms a ring whose zero element is the function $\theta, x\theta = 0$ for all $x \in K$. The additive inverse of f is the function g defined by $xg = -(xf)$.

Example 5.1.12 Let $(G, +)$ be any abelian group written additively, with identity element 0. We define a multiplication on G as follows:

$$g_1 \cdot g_2 = 0, \quad \text{all } g_1, g_2 \in G.$$

Then $(G, +, \cdot)$ is a ring.

Example 5.1.13 A two by two "array" of real numbers,

$$\begin{bmatrix} a_{11} & a_{12} \\ a_{21} & a_{22} \end{bmatrix}$$

is called a 2×2 *matrix* over the set of real numbers K. Let

$$K_2 = \left\{ \begin{bmatrix} a_{11} & a_{12} \\ a_{21} & a_{22} \end{bmatrix} \middle| \, a_{ij} \in K \right\}.$$

We define addition and multiplication of matrices as follows:

$$\begin{bmatrix} a_{11} & a_{12} \\ a_{21} & a_{22} \end{bmatrix} + \begin{bmatrix} b_{11} & b_{12} \\ b_{21} & b_{22} \end{bmatrix} = \begin{bmatrix} a_{11} + b_{11} & a_{12} + b_{12} \\ a_{21} + b_{21} & a_{22} + b_{22} \end{bmatrix}$$

$$\begin{bmatrix} a_{11} & a_{12} \\ a_{21} & a_{22} \end{bmatrix} \cdot \begin{bmatrix} b_{11} & b_{12} \\ b_{21} & b_{22} \end{bmatrix} = \begin{bmatrix} c_{11} & c_{12} \\ c_{21} & c_{22} \end{bmatrix}$$

where $c_{ij} = \sum_{\ell=1}^{2} a_{i\ell} b_{\ell j}$. Then $(K_2, +, \cdot)$ is a ring.

Exercises

1. Show that the multiplication in Example 5.1.7 is associative.
2. Show that the multiplications in Examples 5.1.8, 5.1.9, 5.1.10, and 5.1.13 are associative.
3. Prove the distributive laws in the rings of Examples 5.1.8, 5.1.9, 5.1.10, and 5.1.13.
4. Find quaternions q_1 and q_2 such that $q_1 \cdot q_2 \neq q_2 \cdot q_1$.
5. Let q be a quaternion $\neq 0$. Show that there exists a quaternion q' such that $q \cdot q' = 1$.
6. Prove that in a ring R, $(a + b + c)d = ad + bd + cd$ for all $a,b,c,d \in R$.
7. Give two examples of a ring R with a finite number of elements containing a pair of elements a,b such that $ab \neq ba$.

   Hint:
   i) In Example 5.1.10 let $R = \overline{Z}_m$.
   ii) In Example 5.1.13 replace K by $\overline{Z}_m$.
8. In Example 5.1.9 replace the real numbers by $\overline{Z}_2$ and show that the resulting ring is commutative. Find a nonzero element in this ring that does not have a multiplicative inverse.

5.2 *ISOMORPHISM OF RINGS*

In Chapter 4 we discussed what it means for two groups to be abstractly identical, that is, isomorphic. In this section we extend this notion to rings, noting the fact that here we must have a single one-to-one correspondence that preserves both operations.

Definition 5.2.1 Let $(R_1, +, \cdot)$ and $(R_2, \oplus, \odot)$ be two rings. Then R_1 and R_2 are *ring isomorphic* (or, simply, *isomorphic*) if there is a 1–1 function f from R_1 onto R_2 such that

$$(a + b)f = af \oplus bf \quad \text{and}$$

$$(a \cdot b)f = af \odot bf \quad \text{for all } a,b \in R.$$

The function f is called a *ring isomorphism*, and we write $R_1 \cong R_2$.

To illustrate, let $\overline{Z}_m$ be the ring of residue classes modulo m (Example 5.1.4). Let $Z_m = \{0,1,\cdots,m - 1\}$, the set of least positive residues modulo m. We define addition $\oplus$ and multiplication $\odot$ on Z_m as follows: $a \oplus b = c$, the least positive residue congruent to $a + b$ modulo m. Similarly $a \odot b = d$, the least positive residue congruent to ab. Then it is easy to see that $(Z_m, \oplus, \odot)$ is a ring and that this ring is isomorphic to $(\overline{Z}_m, +, \cdot)$.

The function that establishes the isomorphism is $f: Z_m \to \overline{Z}_m$ defined by $af = \bar{a}$. Thus, abstractly, these two rings are indistinguishable. In the sequel we shall usually work with the ring $(Z_m, \oplus, \odot)$, replacing $\oplus$ and $\odot$ by the more usual + and $\cdot$. If the rings $(R_1, +, \cdot)$ and $(R_2, \oplus, \odot)$ are isomorphic, then the groups $(R_1, +)$ and $(R_2, \oplus)$ are isomorphic as groups. The converse of this statement is not true, that is, there exist pairs of rings with isomorphic additive groups but that are not isomorphic as rings. The following example shows such a pair.

Example 5.2.2 Let $R_1 = (Z, +, \cdot)$ be the ring of integers with the usual addition and multiplication. Let $R_2 = (Z, +, \odot)$ be the ring of integers with the usual addition but with $\odot$ defined by: $a \odot b = 0$ for all $a, b \in Z$. Clearly, R_1 and R_2 are isomorphic as additive groups. Now suppose there is a function $f: R_1 \to R_2$ satisfying the requirements of Definition 5.2.1 for R_1 and R_2. Then, for any a in R_1, $af = (a \cdot 1)f = af \odot 1f = 0$. Hence, f is not onto and therefore the ring R_1 is not isomorphic to the ring R_2.

Exercises

1. Let $R = \{e, f, g, h\}$. Define + and $\cdot$ on R as follows:

+	e	f	g	h
e	e	f	g	h
f	f	e	h	g
g	g	h	e	f
h	h	g	f	e

$\cdot$	e	f	g	h
e	e	e	e	e
f	e	f	e	f
g	e	e	g	g
h	e	f	g	h

Show that $(R, +, \cdot)$ is a ring. Can you find any proper subsets of R that form a ring with respect to + and $\cdot$?

2. Let $S = \{a, b, c, d\}$. Define $\oplus$ and $\odot$ on S, as follows:

$\oplus$	a	b	c	d
a	a	b	c	d
b	b	a	d	c
c	c	d	a	b
d	d	c	b	a

$\odot$	a	b	c	d
a	a	a	a	a
b	a	b	a	b
c	a	a	c	c
d	a	b	c	d

Show that $(S, \oplus, \odot)$ is a ring.

3. Let $T = \{q,r,s,t\}$. Define $+$ and $\cdot$ on T, as follows:

$+$	q	r	s	t
q	q	r	s	t
r	r	s	t	q
s	s	t	q	r
t	t	q	r	s

$\cdot$	q	r	s	t
q	q	q	q	q
r	q	r	s	t
s	q	s	q	s
t	q	t	s	r

Show that $(T,+,\cdot)$ is a ring.

4. Are any pairs of the above rings R, S, T isomorphic? Can you find a ring of four elements not isomorphic to any of those above?

5. Find all possible rings (up to isomorphism) with two elements and with three elements. (Use the fact, to be proved later, that $a\cdot 0 = 0\cdot a = 0$ for all $a \in R$, R an arbitrary ring.)

5.3 ELEMENTARY PROPERTIES OF RINGS

In this section we derive some of the properties of rings that follow readily from the ring axioms. Before we proceed, a word about notation and terminology.

For the integer 0 and for all $a \in R$, $0a$ is the additive identity of the group $(R,+)$ which we also denote by 0. Notice that we use the same symbol for the integer zero as for the additive identity of the ring. This is justified since, whether z is the integer 0 or the additive identity 0, we shall show that $za = 0 \in R$ for all $a \in R$ (see Theorem 5.3.1). We must, however, make a careful distinction between na, an integral multiple of the ring element a, with $n \in Z$, and ra, a ring multiple of a, with $r \in R$. There are rings in which every integral multiple na of a ring element a is equal to a ring multiple of a. A ring R has this property if it contains a multiplicative identity. This will be proved in Corollary 5.3.5.

Finally we note that the symbol 0 will usually be used simultaneously to represent the additive identity of several different rings when no ambiguity exists.

Exercise

1. Let $(R,+,\cdot)$ be a ring. Let $a,b \in R$ and $m,n \in Z$. Show that
   i) $(m+n)a = ma + na$,
   ii) $(mn)a = m(na) = n(ma)$. ●

For the remainder of this section, R denotes the ring $(R,+,\cdot)$. The reader should compare Theorems 5.3.1, 5.3.2, and 5.3.3 with Theorems 2.1.2 and 2.1.4 and with Corollary 2.1.5.

Theorem 5.3.1 Let 0 be the zero element of R. Then for any $a \in R$, $a \cdot 0 = 0 \cdot a = 0$.

Proof: $0 = 0 + 0$, since $(R, +)$ is a group. Then $a \cdot 0 = a \cdot (0 + 0) = a \cdot 0 + a \cdot 0$ by the left distributive law. Hence, by Lemma 4.2.1, $a \cdot 0 = 0$, the identity of $(R, +)$. Similarly $0 \cdot a = 0$.

Theorem 5.3.2 For any $a, b \in R$,

$$a(-b) = (-a)b = -(ab).$$

Proof: $a(b + (-b)) = a \cdot 0 = 0$, by Theorem 5.3.1. But by the left distributive law

$$0 = a(b + (-b)) = ab + a(-b).$$

Hence, $a(-b)$ is a right inverse of ab. But $-(ab)$ is an additive inverse of ab and, since $(R, +)$ is a group, ab has a unique inverse $-(ab)$. Hence, $a(-b) = -(ab)$.

Similarly $(-a)b = -(ab)$.

Theorem 5.3.3 For any $a, b \in R$,

$$(-a)(-b) = ab.$$

Proof: $(-a)(-b) = -((-a)b)$ by Theorem 5.3.2, and $-((-a)b) = -(-(ab))$. But, since $(R, +)$ is a group, $-(-(ab)) = ab$ (Corollary 4.2.6, in additive notation).

Theorems 5.3.2 and 5.3.3 are often referred to as the "law of signs."

Theorem 5.3.4 Let $a, b \in R$, and let $m \in Z$. Then $m(ab) = (ma)b = a(mb)$.

Proof: If $m = 0$, then the theorem follows easily, using Theorem 5.3.1 and the fact that $0c = 0$, where c is any element in R. (Here the first 0 is an integer, the second the zero of the ring.)

Assume that $k(ab) = (ka)b$ for $k \geq 0$. Then $(k + 1)(ab) = k(ab) + ab = (ka)b + ab = (ka + a)b$. (Why?) But $ka + a = (k + 1)a$. Hence, $(k + 1)(ab) = [(k + 1)a]b$, and the theorem follows by induction for all $m \geq 0$.

We leave the remainder of the proof as an exercise.

Corollary 5.3.5 Let R contain an element e such that $ae = ea = a$ for all

$a \in R$. Then, for each integer m, there exists an element $r \in R$ such that

$$ma = ra \quad \text{for all} \quad a \in R.$$

That is, every integral multiple is equal to a ring multiple.

Proof: Since $ea = a$ for all $a \in R$, $ma = m(ea) = (me)a$ by Theorem 5.3.4. But $me \in R$. Hence let $r = me$ and $ma = ra$.

Exercises

2. Show that for $a,b,c,d \in R$, a ring,

$$(-a)[d + (-b) + (-c)] = a(b + c) - (ad).$$

3. Complete the proof of Theorem 5.3.4.
4. Prove that for all $m,n \in Z$, and for all elements $a,b \in R$, a ring, that $(mn)(ab) = (ma)(nb) = (na)(mb) = (nma)b = a(nmb)$.
5. Let R be a ring such that i) $a^2 = a$ for all $a \in R$ and ii) whenever $2a = 0$ for some $a \in R$, then $a = 0$. Show that R has exactly one element.
6. Let R be a ring such that $a^2 = a$ for all $a \in R$. Prove that:
   i) $2a = 0$ for all $a \in R$,
   ii) $ab = ba$ for all $a,b \in R$.
   Hint: Consider $(a + b)^2$.

5.4 SOME SPECIAL TYPES OF RINGS

In the definition of a ring, almost no restrictions are placed on the operation of multiplication. It is therefore possible to specialize the definition of a ring in many different ways. We could ask, for example, that $\cdot$ be commutative or that there exist a multiplicative identity or that the product of two nonzero elements be nonzero. In this section we shall examine certain classes of rings defined by various properties of the ring product.

Definition 5.4.1 Let $(R, +, \cdot)$ be a ring. R is called a *commutative* ring if $ab = ba$ for all a,b in R. Otherwise R is called a *noncommutative* ring.

Examples 5.1.2–5.1.8, 5.1.11, and 5.1.12 are commutative rings and Examples 5.1.9 and 5.1.13 are noncommutative. Example 5.1.10 is commutative if and only if the group G is commutative.

Definition 5.4.2 Let $(R, +, \cdot)$ be a ring. R is called a *ring with identity* if there exists an element $e \in R$ such that

$$ae = ea = a \quad \text{for all} \quad a \in R.$$

We shall frequently denote e by 1, and when R is a ring with identity, we shall often write $R \ni 1$. If $R \ni 1$, then $R = \{0\}$ if and only if $1 = 0$. Henceforth, whenever we write $R \ni 1$, we shall assume that $1 \neq 0$.

It should be clear from the examples already given that not all rings have an identity. (Which ones do?) When a ring has an identity, then the identity is unique.

Definition 5.4.3 Let R be a ring. An element $a \neq 0$ in R is called a *left zero divisor* if there exists an element $b \neq 0$ in R such that $ab = 0$. Similarly, an element $b \neq 0$ in R is called a *right zero divisor* if there exists an element $a \neq 0$ in R such that $ab = 0$. A *zero divisor* is an element that is either a right or left zero divisor.

If R is a commutative ring, then the concepts of right and left zero divisor coincide.

The rings $(Z,+,\cdot)$, $(H,+,\cdot)$, $(K,+,\cdot)$, and $(Q,+,\cdot)$ of Section 5.1 have no zero divisors with respect to multiplication. On the other hand, when m is a composite integer, then $(Z_m,+,\cdot)$ has zero divisors. For example, if $m = ab$ in Z, $0 < a < m$, $0 < b < m$, then $ab = 0$ in Z_m. In particular, 2, 3, and 4 are zero dvisors in Z_6.

Exercises

1. Let R be a ring with identity. Prove the identity is unique.
*2. Prove that a ring R has no left zero divisors if and only if R has no right zero divisors.
3. Show that the ring $\mathbb{S}$ of Example 5.1.7 has zero divisors if $S \neq \phi$.
4. Does the ring of Exercise 8, Section 5.1 have zero divisors? ●

Definition 5.4.4 A ring R is said to satisfy the *left* (*right*) *cancellation* law if whenever $ab = ac$ $(ba = ca)$, $a \neq 0$, then $b = c$.

Theorem 5.4.5 R satisfies the left and right cancellation laws if and only if R has no zero divisors.

Proof: Let R satisfy the left cancellation law and suppose $ab = 0$, $a \neq 0$. Then $ab = a \cdot 0$, whence, by cancellation, $b = 0$. Thus a is not a left zero divisor. By Exercise 2, R also has no right zero divisors.

Now let $ab = ac$, $a \neq 0$, and assume a is not a left zero divisor. Then $a(b - c) = 0$, whence $b - c = 0$ and $b = c$.

A similar argument applies when "left" is replaced by "right."

Definition 5.4.6 Let R be a commutative ring, $R \ni 1$, $1 \neq 0$. If R has no zero divisors (equivalently, if R satisfies either cancellation law), we call R an *integral domain.*

The ring of integers is an example of an integral domain. Further examples are the ring of real numbers and the ring $(Z_p,+,\cdot)$, for p a prime.

The next class of rings that we consider has the property that $R^* = R - \{0\}$ is a group with respect to the ring multiplication.

Definition 5.4.7 Let $(R,+,\cdot)$ be a ring and let $R^* = R - \{0\}$. Then R is called a *division ring* if $(R^*,\cdot)$ is a group. If, in addition, R is commutative, that is, $(R^*,\cdot)$ is an abelian group, then R is called a *field*. If R is not commutative, then R is called a *skew field*.

It follows from the definition that a division ring R must contain at least two elements, since $0 \in R$ and $R^* = R - \{0\} \neq \phi$. (Why?) There is, in fact, a division ring with precisely two elements, namely, $(Z_2,+,\cdot)$.

Some authors use the term "field" as we use "division ring," and "commutative field" as we use "field."

Example 5.4.8 The real number system, the rational number system, and the complex number system are examples of fields.

Example 5.4.9 Let p be a prime. Then $(Z_p,+,\cdot)$ is a field.

Example 5.4.10 Let $R = \{a + b\sqrt{2} \mid a,b \text{ rational numbers}\}$. Since R is a subset of the real numbers, we define addition and multiplication in R to be the usual $+$ and $\cdot$ of real numbers. Then it is easy to see that $(R,+,\cdot)$ is a commutative ring. In order to show that R is a field, we must show that $(R^*,\cdot)$ is a group. Since the real number 1 is a multiplicative identity, it remains only to verify that each element in R^* has a multiplicative inverse. Thus, let $x = a + b\sqrt{2}$, not both a and b equal to 0, and let $y = c + d\sqrt{2}$. Then $xy = (a + b\sqrt{2})(c + d\sqrt{2}) = (ac + 2bd) + (ad + bc)\sqrt{2}$. If y is to be the inverse of x, then $xy = 1$, that is,

$$ac + 2bd = 1 \quad \text{and}$$

$$ad + bc = 0.$$

Solving for c and d in terms of a and b, we get $c = \dfrac{a}{a^2 - 2b^2}$ and $d = \dfrac{-b}{a^2 - 2b^2}$, provided that $a^2 - 2b^2 \neq 0$. But as long as not both a and b are zero, $a^2 - 2b^2 \neq 0$, since otherwise $a^2 = 2b^2$, $2 = a^2/b^2$ and $\sqrt{2} = |a/b|$. But, since a and b are rational, $|a/b|$ is rational, contradicting the fact that $\sqrt{2}$ is not rational. (See Exercise 19, Section 2.8.) Hence, we may assume that $a^2 - 2b^2 \neq 0$.

Thus,

$$(a + b\sqrt{2})\left(\frac{a}{a^2 - 2b^2} + \frac{-b}{a^2 - 2b^2}\sqrt{2}\right) = 1,$$

and $(R,+,\cdot)$ is a field.

Example 5.4.11 Let $(H,+,\cdot)$ be the ring of quaternions (Example 5.1.9). We have already seen (Exercise 4, Section 5.1) that H is not commutative. H contains a multiplicative identity, and, by Exercise 5, Section 5.1, for every nonzero element q in H there is a multiplicative inverse q' in H. That is, if $q = a_0 + a_1 i + a_2 j + a_3 k$, then q' can be found by solving four linear equations in four unknowns, similar to our derivation of y in Example 5.4.10. Indeed, $q' = \frac{a_0}{D} - \frac{a_1}{D} i - \frac{a_2}{D} j - \frac{a_3}{D} k$ with $D = a_0^2 + a_1^2 + a_2^2 + a_3^2$. Hence, $(H,+,\cdot)$ is a skew field.

Theorem 5.4.12 If $(R,+,\cdot)$ is a field, then R is an integral domain.

Proof: Let $a,b \in R^*$. Then $ab \in R^*$, since R^* is a group with respect to multiplication. Hence, $ab = ba \neq 0$ for all $b \neq 0$ and, therefore, a is not a zero divisor. Since $1 \in R$, $1 \neq 0$, R is an integral domain.

Exercises

5. Give a definition of a field *directly* in terms of the operations $+$ and $\cdot$ without using the terms "group," "ring," or "division ring."
6. Let (m) denote the set of all integral multiples of a fixed integer m. Let $+$ and $\cdot$ be the usual addition and multiplication of integers restricted to elements of (m). Show that
   i) $((m),+,\cdot)$ is a commutative ring with no zero divisors.
   ii) $((m),+,\cdot)$ has no identity if $|m| \geq 2$.
7. Let F be a field, $a,b \in F$. Prove that if $a \neq 0$, then $ax + b = 0$ always has a solution in F.
8. Let F be a field. Let $a,b,c,d,e,f, \in F$. Prove that if $ad - bc \neq 0$, then the system of equations

$$ax + by = e$$
$$cx + dy = f$$

   has a unique solution in F.

   Under what conditions will this system have a solution even if $ad - bc = 0$? Interpret your result geometrically when F is the field of real numbers.

*9. Prove that $(Z_p,+,\cdot)$, is a field if and only if p is a prime.

10. Let $(R,+,\cdot)$ be an integral domain with n elements, $n \geq 2$. Show that R is a field.
11. Let R be a ring with identity $1 \neq 0$, and with no zero divisors. Prove that $ab = 1$ if and only if $ba = 1$ for $a,b \in R$.
12. Let $(R,+,\cdot)$ be a ring with n elements and no zero divisors, $n \geq 2$. Show that R is a division ring.

13. Let $R = \{a + b\sqrt{p} \mid a,b$ rational numbers, p a prime$\}$. Show that $(R,+,\cdot)$ is a field with $+$ and $\cdot$ the usual addition and multiplication of real numbers. ●

Before leaving this section we state a famous theorem of Wedderburn. The proof will be given in Chapter 7.

Theorem 5.4.13 (Wedderburn) Let D be a division ring with a finite number of elements. Then D is a field.

5.5 HOMOMORPHISMS, KERNELS, AND IDEALS

Definition 5.5.1 Let $(R,+,\cdot)$ be a ring. Let S be a nonempty subset of R. Then S is a *subring* of R if $(S,+,\cdot)$ is also a ring with respect to the operations $+$ and $\cdot$ of R. If $(F,+,\cdot)$ is a field and if the subring $(S,+,\cdot)$ is a field, we call S a *subfield* of F.

Example 5.5.2 Let $(R,+,\cdot)$ be the ring of rational numbers. The set $S = \{a/2 \mid a \in Z\}$ is a subset of R and is a group with respect to addition. The product $\frac{1}{2}\cdot\frac{1}{2} = \frac{1}{4}$ is, however, not in S, and hence S is not a subring of R. The set $T = \{a/2^r \mid r,a \in Z, r \geq 0\}$ is closed with respect to $+$ and $\cdot$ and satisfies all of the properties of a ring. Hence T is a subring of R.

Theorem 5.5.3 Let $(R,+,\cdot)$ be a ring, and let S be a nonempty subset of R. Then S is a subring of R if and only if

i) $a - b \in S$, whenever $a \in S$, $b \in S$.
ii) $ab \in S$, whenever $a \in S$, $b \in S$.

Proof: Condition i) and the fact that $S \neq \phi$ is a necessary and sufficient condition for $(S,+)$ to be a subgroup of $(R,+)$ (Theorem 4.6.3). Condition ii) guarantees that S is closed under multiplication. The rest of the ring axioms follow easily, since R is a ring and $S \subseteq R$.

Henceforth, we shall usually use the same notations for the operations of addition and multiplication in two different rings. This is analogous to our use, in Chapter 4, of the same symbol for the group operations in different groups. Thus, except when stated to the contrary, we shall let $+$ denote addition in all rings and we shall let $\cdot$ (or juxtaposition) denote multiplication.

Definition 5.5.4 Let $(R,+,\cdot)$ and $(T,+,\cdot)$ be rings. Let $f:R \to T$ satisfy

i) $(a + b)f = af + bf$.
ii) $(ab)f = af \cdot bf$.

Then f is called a (ring) *homomorphism* from R to T.

The concept of a ring homomorphism generalizes that of isomorphism defined in Section 5.2. We say that a homomorphism "preserves" the operations of addition and multiplication.

There is, in the theory to follow, a close parallelism between rings and groups. As in the theory of groups, in which subgroups were important, subrings play a vital role in the theory of rings. But as in groups, in which normal subgroups play a very important role, in rings a special type of subring, called an ideal (which occurs as the kernel of a homomorphism), is of greatest interest.

The proofs of many of the subsequent theorems are almost identical to earlier proofs in Chapter 4. An occasional reference to the earlier chapter on groups will bear out these similarities.

Theorem 5.5.5 Let $(R,+,\cdot)$ and $(T,+,\cdot)$ be rings. Let $f:R \to T$ be a homomorphism from R to T. Then $\text{Im } f = \{rf \mid r \in R\}$ forms a subring of T.

Proof: $(\text{Im } f,+)$ is a subgroup of $(T,+)$ by Theorem 4.9.3.
If $r_1 f$ and $r_2 f$ are in $\text{Im } f$, then $r_1 f \cdot r_2 f = (r_1 r_2)f$, since f is a homomorphism. Thus, $r_1 f \cdot r_2 f \in \text{Im } f$. By Theorem 5.5.3, $\text{Im } f$ is a subring of $(T,+,\cdot)$.

Definition 5.5.6 Let $f:R \to T$ be a homomorphism of the ring R to the ring T. We call the set $K = \{x \mid x \in R \text{ and } xf = 0\}$ the *kernel* of f, denoted by $\ker f$.

Theorem 5.5.7 Let $f:R \to T$ be a homomorphism from the ring R to the ring T. Let $K = \ker f$. Then
i) K is a subring of R.
ii) If $k \in K$ and $r \in R$, then kr and rk are both in K.

Proof i) By Theorem 4.9.8, we see that $(K,+)$ is a subgroup of $(R,+)$.
Now let $k \in K$ and $r \in R$. Then $(kr)f = (kf)(rf) = 0 \cdot rf = 0$ and also $(rk)f = 0$. In particular, if $r \in K$, we see that K is closed under multiplication, whence, by Theorem 5.5.3, $(K,+,\cdot)$ is a subring of R.
ii) Since $(rk)f = (kr)f = 0$, kr and $rk \in K$.

Definition 5.5.8 Let $(R,+,\cdot)$ be a ring. A nonempty subset S of R is an *ideal* (*two-sided*) of R if
i) S is a subring of R
ii) Whenever $s \in S$, $r \in R$, then $rs \in S$ and $sr \in S$.

Thus, by Theorem 5.5.7, the kernel of a ring homomorphism is an ideal.

Example 5.5.9 Let Z be the ring of integers. Then the set $(m) = \{nm \mid m \text{ fixed and } n \in Z\}$ forms an ideal in Z.

Example 5.5.10 Let R be a ring. Then the set consisting of 0 alone is an ideal in R. This ideal will usually be denoted by (0), and it is called the *zero ideal*. Also, R is an ideal in R.

Example 5.5.11 Not every subring of a ring is an ideal. For example, let K be the ring of real numbers. Then Z is a subring of K, but Z is not an ideal in K, since $\frac{1}{2} \in K$, $1 \in Z$, but $\frac{1}{2} \cdot 1 \notin Z$.

Exercises

1. Let $(\mathcal{S},+,\cdot)$ be the ring defined in Example 5.1.7. Let $I \subseteq S$. Let $\mathcal{I}$ be the collection of all subsets of I. Show that $(\mathcal{I},+,\cdot)$ is an ideal in $\mathcal{S}$.
2. Show that any ideal I of Z has the form (m) of Example 5.5.9.
3. Let I_1 and I_2 be ideals of the ring R. Show that the following are ideals of R:
   i) $I_1 \cap I_2$
   ii) $I_1 + I_2 = \{a + b \mid a \in I_1, b \in I_2\}$
   iii) $I_1 \cdot I_2 = \{a_1b_1 + a_2b_2 + \cdots + a_nb_n \mid a_i \in I_1, b_i \in I_2\}$, that is, $I_1 \cdot I_2$ is the set of all finite sums of products a_ib_i, $a_i \in I_1$ and $b_i \in I_2$.
4. Let R be a "zero ring," that is, a ring in which $ab = 0$, for all $a,b \in R$. Show that any subgroup of $(R,+)$ is an ideal of R.
5. Show that if I is an ideal of a ring with identity 1 such that $1 \in I$, then $I = R$.
6. Let F be a field. Show that F has only two ideals, namely F and (0).
7. Let R be a commutative ring with identity such that the only ideals of R are R and (0). Show that R is a field.

   Hint: Consider for each $x \in R$ the set $\{rx \mid r \in R\}$.
8. In Exercise 7 show that if we delete either "commutative" or "with identity," then the conclusion does not follow.

   Hint: When "commutative" is deleted, consider matrices.

5.6 QUOTIENT RINGS

We continue to parallel our study of groups, extending the concept of quotient group to that of quotient ring.

Definition 5.6.1 Let R be a ring and let I be an ideal in R. Let $(R/I,+)$ be the quotient group of $(R,+)$ modulo $(I,+)$ ($(R,+)$ is abelian, whence $(I,+)$ is normal in $(R,+)$). On the set R/I, define the sum and product as follows:

$$(a + I) + (b + I) = (a + b) + I$$

$$(a + I)(b + I) = ab + I.$$

Then $(R/I,+,\cdot)$ is called the *quotient ring* of R modulo the ideal I. (We recall that $a + I = \{a + i \mid i \in I\}$ is just a group coset in additive notation, and that the addition defined here is precisely the addition in the quotient group R/I).

We now show that the quotient ring is indeed a ring.

Theorem 5.6.2 Let R be a ring and let I be an ideal in R. Then the quotient ring R/I is a ring.

Proof: Since $(R, +)$ is abelian, so is the quotient group $(R/I, +)$. In order to show that $(R/I, +, \cdot)$ is a ring, we must show that multiplication is well defined, that is, that multiplication does not depend on the choice of coset representative. Thus, suppose

$$a_1 + I = a_2 + I \quad \text{and} \quad b_1 + I = b_2 + I.$$

Then $a_1 = a_2 + i_1$ and $b_1 = b_2 + i_2$, where i_1 and i_2 are in I. Then

$$a_1b_1 = (a_2 + i_1)(b_2 + i_2) = a_2b_2 + a_2i_2 + i_1b_2 + i_1i_2.$$

Since I is an ideal, a_2i_2, i_1b_2, i_1i_2 are all in I, whence $a_1b_1 - a_2b_2 \in I$. Thus, $a_1b_1 + I = a_2b_2 + I$, since $(I, +)$ is a normal subgroup of $(R, +)$. Multiplication in R/I is, therefore, well defined.

We leave the proof of associativity of multiplication and the proof of the distributive law as an exercise.

Theorem 5.6.3 Let R and T be rings. Let $f: R \to T$ be a ring homomorphism. Then $R/\ker f \cong \operatorname{Im} f$.

Proof: As in groups, $(\operatorname{Im} f, +) \cong (R/\ker f, +)$. We must show, however, that there is a group isomorphism between $(\operatorname{Im} f, +)$ and $(R/\ker f, +)$ which also preserves multiplication.

Recall (Theorem 4.10.6) that in showing $(\operatorname{Im} f, +) \cong (R/\ker f, +)$, we let ν: $R/\ker f \to \operatorname{Im} f$ be defined by $(a + \ker f)\nu = af$. We now can easily verify that

$$[(a + \ker f)(b + \ker f)]\nu = (a + \ker f)\nu \cdot (b + \ker f)\nu.$$

Theorem 5.6.4 Let R be a ring, I an ideal in R. Then there exists a homomorphism $f: R \xrightarrow{\text{onto}} R/I$ defined by $rf = r + I$ such that $\ker f = I$. We call f the *natural homomorphism* from R to R/I.

Proof: As for groups, let $af = a + I$. Then f is a homomorphism of the group $(R, +)$ onto $(R/I, +)$ with kernel I. Also,

$$(ab)f = ab + I = (a + I)(b + I) = af \cdot bf.$$

Hence, f is a ring homomorphism.

Theorem 5.6.5 Let R_1 and R_2 be two rings and let f be a homomorphism from R_1 onto R_2. Then f is an isomorphism if and only if $\ker f = (0)$.

Proof: Exercise.

Exercises

1. Complete the proof of Theorem 5.6.2.
*2. Let R be a ring. Show that $R/(0) \simeq R$, as rings.
3. Let F be a field and let R be a ring. Let $f: F \to R$ be a ring homomorphism of F onto R. Show that either $R = (0)$ or $R \simeq F$.
4. Let $f: Z \to F$ be a homomorphism from Z onto the field F. Show that F must be finite with a prime number of elements.
5. Let $f: Z \to Z$ be a homomorphism. Show that either f is the identity map or f is the zero map, that is $af = 0$, for all a.
6. Find all possible quotient rings of Z.
7. Let R and T be rings and let $f: R \to T$ be a ring homomorphism. Let I be an ideal in R. Show that $\{xf \mid x \in I\}$ is an ideal in $\operatorname{Im} f$.
8. Let R be a ring, I an ideal of R, and f the natural mapping from R onto R/I.
   i) Let $\overline{S}$ be a subring of R/I. Prove that the preimage of $\overline{S}$, $S = \{r \in R \mid rf \in \overline{S}\}$, is a subring of R, with $I \subseteq S$, and $\overline{S} = S/I$.
   ii) In **i**), replace "subring" by "ideal."
9. Let R and S be rings, with R containing a subring F which is a field. Let $f: R \to S$ be a homomorphism. Prove that either $F \subseteq \ker f$ or S contains a subring isomorphic to F.

5.7 EMBEDDING THEOREMS AND FIELDS OF QUOTIENTS

We have, on several occasions, discussed the concept of embedding both with sets and with groups. We saw, for example, that the direct product of groups A and B contains a pair of subgroups A_1 and B_1 which are isomorphic to A and B, respectively, and hence, that A and B are embedded in $A \times B$. In this section we shall study some embedding theorems concerning rings. Our principal result will be a method for embedding an integral domain in a field. A special case of our theorem will provide a method for constructing the rational number field from the integers.

Definition 5.7.1 Let R and S be rings and f an isomorphism from R onto a subring of S. Then we say that R is *embeddable* in S or R *can be embedded* in S, and we say f is an *embedding* of R in S.

Definition 5.7.2 Let R be a ring. Then the set of ordered pairs $\{(a,b) \mid a,b \in R,\ b \neq 0\}$ is called the *set of quotients* of R.

Note that the set of quotients of R is nonempty if and only if R has at least two elements.

Theorem 5.7.3 Let R be a commutative ring with at least two elements and with no zero divisors. Then the relation $\sim$ defined by:

$$(a,b) \sim (c,d) \quad \text{if} \quad ad = bc$$

is an equivalence relation on the set of quotients of R.

Proof:

i) $(a,b) \sim (a,b)$ since $ab = ba$.

ii) If $(a,b) \sim (c,d)$, then $(c,d) \sim (a,b)$. For, if $ad = bc$, then $cb = da$.

iii) Suppose $(a,b) \sim (c,d)$ and $(c,d) \sim (e,f)$. Then $ad = bc$ and $cf = de$.

If $a = 0$, then $c = 0$, since $b \neq 0$; and so $e = 0$, since $d \neq 0$. Thus, $0 = af = be = 0$, and $(a,b) \sim (e,f)$.

If $a \neq 0$, then $c \neq 0$, and $e \neq 0$. Now $abcf = abde$, $(bc)(af) = (ad)(be)$, and, since $ad = bc \neq 0$, $af = be$ and $(a,b) \sim (e,f)$.

The reader should note that if we let the ring R be the ring of integers and interpret the definition of quotient in the usual arithmetic sense, then the definition of $\sim$ given above is the definition of equality between fractions, that is, $a/b = c/d$ if $ad = bc$. Note how we use our familiarity with fractions in formulating the next definition.

Definition 5.7.4 Let R be a commutative ring with at least two elements and no zero divisors. Let F be the set of equivalence classes of the set of quotients of R for the equivalence relation given in Theorem 5.7.3. Denote by $[a,b]$ the equivalence class containing (a,b). We define $+$ and $\cdot$ on F as follows:

$$[a,b] + [c,d] = [ad + bc, bd]$$

$$[a,b]\cdot[c,d] = [ac, bd].$$

Then $(F,+,\cdot)$ is called the *field of quotients of* R, or the *quotient field of* R.

Theorem 5.7.5 Let R be a commutative ring with at least two elements and no zero divisors, and let $(F,+,\cdot)$ be the field of quotients of R. Then F is a field and R is embeddable in F.

Proof: We first show that $+$ and $\cdot$ are binary operations on F.

Suppose $[a,b] = [a',b']$ and $[c,d] = [c',d']$. Then

$$[a,b] + [c,d] = [ad + bc, bd] \text{ and}$$

$$[a',b'] + [c',d'] = [a'd' + b'c', b'd'].$$

But since $[a,b] = [a',b']$, $(a,b) \sim (a',b')$ and hence $ab' = ba'$. Similarly, $cd' = dc'$. Hence, $ab'dd' = ba'dd'$ and $cd'bb' = dc'bb'$. Thus $(ad)(b'd') = (a'd')(bd)$ and $(bc)(b'd') = (b'c')(bd)$. Hence, $(ad)(b'd') + (bc)(b'd') = (a'd')(bd) + (b'c')(bd)$, and $(ad + bc)(b'd') = (a'd' + b'c')(bd)$. Therefore, $[ad + bc, bd] = [a'd' + b'c', b'd']$ and addition is a function on $F \times F$. To show that it is a function to F, that is, that F is closed with respect to $+$, we note that $b \neq 0$ and $d \neq 0$, and R has no divisors of zero. Hence, $bd \neq 0$ and $[ad + bc, bd] \in F$.

A similar argument shows that $\cdot$ is a binary operation on F.

To show that $(F,+,\cdot)$ is a field, we observe first that $(F,+)$ is an abelian group. We leave the verification that addition is associative and commutative as an exercise. The zero element of $(F,+)$ is $[0,b]$, $b \neq 0$, $b \in R$. Since $(0,b) \sim (0,d)$, $b \neq 0$, $d \neq 0$, any nonzero element of R can be used to denote $[0,b]$. Thus, $[c,d] + [0,b] = [cb + d0, db] = [bc,bd]$, and, since $bd \neq 0$, we see that $[bc,bd] = [c,d]$. Finally, $[-a,b]$ is the additive inverse of $[a,b]$.

To show that $(F^*,\cdot) = (F - \{O\},\cdot)$ is an abelian group, the reader should first verify that multiplication is both associative and commutative. The multiplicative identity in F is $[b,b]$, where $b \neq 0$, for $[c,d][b,b] = [cb,db] = [c,d]$. If $[c,d] \in F$ and $[c,d] \neq [0,b]$, then $c \neq 0$, whence $[d,c] \in F$. Now $[c,d][d,c] = [cd,dc] = [b,b]$, $b \neq 0$. Thus, $(F^*,\cdot)$ is an abelian group.

The only other property that one must verify to show that $(F,+,\cdot)$ is a field is the distributive law. This is left as an exercise.

To complete the proof of the theorem, it is necessary to show that R can be embedded in F. Define $f: R \to F$ as follows: for any $a \in R$, let $af = [ab,b]$, where b is any nonzero element of R. (Recall that the class $[ab,b]$ depends upon a, but not upon the choice of $b \neq 0$). Then f is an embedding of R in F, since

$$\text{i)}\quad (a_1a_2)f = [a_1a_2b,b] = [a_1a_2b^2,b^2]$$
$$= [a_1b,b][a_2b,b] = a_1f\cdot a_2f,$$
$$\text{ii)}\quad (a_1 + a_2)f = [(a_1 + a_2)b,b] = [a_1b,b] + [a_2b,b]$$
$$= a_1f + a_2f$$

and iii) $a_1f = a_2f$ implies $[a_1b,b] = [a_2b,b]$, whence $a_1b^2 = a_2b^2$ and $a_1 = a_2$, since $b^2 \neq 0$. This completes the proof of Theorem 5.7.5.

We may, in view of the last part of Theorem 5.7.5, consider that R is a subring of F. We do this by replacing an element of the form $[ab,b]$ by a itself. For then $a[c,d] = [ab,b][c,d] = [abc,bd] = [ac,d]$. Thus, although the elements of F are equivalence classes of quotients of R, we may assume that R appears in its "original" form as a subring of F.

In a very strong sense, the field F can be considered the smallest field containing the ring R. Indeed, it is not difficult to prove (Exercise 9) that if R is a subring of a field H, then H must contain a subfield that is isomorphic to F and in which R is "naturally" embedded.

In Theorem 5.7.5, if $R = Z$, the ring of integers, then the field F turns out to be the familiar ring of fractions. In view of our last paragraph, whenever Z is a subring of a field H, then H contains the field of rational numbers, as defined in Definition 5.7.6.

Definition 5.7.6 The field of quotients of the integers is called the field of *rational numbers* Q. The elements of Q are called *rational numbers*.

In place of writing $[a,b]$, we shall henceforth write the more usual a/b.

The role of equivalence relations in constructing rational numbers from integers should be evident. This emphasizes once again the importance of equivalence relations in mathematics.

Corollary 5.7.7 Let R be an integral domain. Then there exists a field F such that R can be embedded in F.

Proof: Exercise.

Exercises

1. Fill in the missing details in the proof of Theorem 5.7.5.
2. Prove Corollary 5.7.7.
3. What well-known field is the quotient field of the ring of even integers?
4. Let I be an ideal of Z, $I \neq (0)$. What is the ring of quotients of I?
5. Let F be a field. Prove that the quotient field of F is isomorphic to F. Thus, show that if F is the field of quotients of an integral domain R, then F is isomorphic to its field of quotients.

*6. Let K be the field of real numbers. Let $C = K \times K$, that is, $C = \{(a,b) \mid a,b \in K\}$. For (a,b) and $(c,d) \in C$, define

$$(a,b) + (c,d) = (a + c, b + d) \quad \text{and}$$
$$(a,b)\cdot(c,d) = (ac - bd, ad + bc).$$

Show that $(C,+,\cdot)$ is a field.

Hint: $(a,b)^{-1} = \left(\dfrac{a}{a^2 + b^2}, \dfrac{-b}{a^2 + b^2}\right)$, if $(a,b) \neq (0,0)$.

*7. In Exercise 6, write (a,b) as $a + bi$. In particular, write $(1,0)$ as $1 + 0i = 1$ and $(0,1)$ as $0 + 1i = i$. Show that $i^2 = -1$.

Exercises 6 and 7 give the usual construction of the complex number system from the real number system.

8. Let A_1 and A_2 be integral domains. Let F_1 and F_2 be their corresponding fields of quotients. If $F_1 \cong F_2$, is $A_1 \cong A_2$?
9. Let A be an integral domain. Let B be a field such that A is a subring of B. Let F be the quotient field of A. Show that F can be embedded in B. (Hence, we may consider F to be the "smallest" field containing A.)
10. Let R be an integral domain with quotient field F. Let f be any isomorphism from R to F. Show that F_f, the quotient field of $(R)f$, is isomorphic to F. ●

Although there exist rings without multiplicative identity, the next theorem shows that any such ring can be considered a subring of a ring with identity.

Theorem 5.7.8 Let R be a ring. Then R can be embedded in a ring R' with identity.

Proof: If R $\ni 1$, let $R' = R$.

Thus, assume that R does not have an identity ($R \not\ni 1$) and let $R' = \{(r,n) \mid r \in R, n \in Z\}$. In R', define

$$(r_1,n_1) + (r_2,n_2) = (r_1 + r_2, n_1 + n_2) \text{ and}$$

$$(r_1,n_1)\cdot(r_2,n_2) = (r_1r_2 + n_2r_1 + n_1r_2, n_1n_2).$$

By direct verification, the reader can easily show that $(R', +, \cdot)$ is a ring. Also, (0,1) is an identity for R', for $(r,n)(0,1) = (r\cdot 0 + n0 + 1r, 1n) = (r,n)$. Thus, R' is a ring with identity.

Next, we let $f: R \to R'$ be defined as follows: $af = (a,0)$, for all $a \in R$. Then f is an embedding of R in R' and the theorem is proved.

Exercises

11. Complete the proof of Theorem 5.7.8
12. Let R be a ring with no zero divisors, and assume that R has no identity. Is the ring R' of Theorem 5.7.8 a ring with no zero divisors?
13. Suppose $R \ni 1$. Is the ring $R' = \{(r,n) \mid r \in R, n \in Z\}$ of Theorem 5.7.8 isomorphic to R?

5.8 *CHARACTERISTICS AND PRIME FIELDS*

In any field it is always possible to find a "smallest" subfield. For example, even though many fields occur as subfields of the field of real numbers (we already know two: Q, the field of rational numbers and $Q(\sqrt{2}) = \{a + b\sqrt{2} \mid a,b \in Q\}$), each of these fields contains the rational number system as a subfield. Indeed, since any subfield of the reals must contain the integer 1 (and hence all integral multiples of 1 and all reciprocals of integers), any subfield must contain the rational numbers. What we shall show is that, in general, the "smallest" field in a given field is obtained simply by taking the identity of the field, and all of its integral multiples and their inverses.

Definition 5.8.1 Let $(R, +, \cdot)$ be a ring. If there exists a least positive integer m such that $ma = 0$ for all $a \in R$, then we say that R has *characteristic m*. If no such positive integer exists, R has *characteristic zero*. We say m or zero is the *characteristic of R*.

To illustrate, the ring $(Z_m, +, \cdot)$ has characteristic m, since if $a \in Z_m$, then m is the least positive integer such that $ma = 0$. On the other hand, the ring Z has characteristic zero.

Theorem 5.8.2 Let $(R, +, \cdot)$ be a ring with identity e. R has characteristic $m > 0$ if and only if m is the least positive integer such that $me = 0$.

Proof: Suppose that R has characteristic m. It follows immediately that $me = 0$.

Conversely, if m is the least positive integer such that $me = 0$ and if $a \in R$, then $ma = m(ea) = (me)a = 0 \cdot a = 0$. Thus, m is the characteristic of R.

Theorem 5.8.3 Let $(R, +, \cdot)$ be an integral domain with characteristic m. Then either $m = 0$ or m is a prime number.

Proof: Suppose $m \neq 0$. Then, if m is not a prime, $m = m_1 m_2$, where $m_i, i = 1,2$, are integers satisfying $1 < m_i < m$.

Then $me = (m_1 m_2)e = (m_1 e)(m_2 e) = 0$. Since R is an integral domain, there are no zero divisors in R. Thus, either $m_1 e = 0$ or $m_2 e = 0$. In either case, by Theorem 5.8.2, the characteristic of R must be less than m, a contradiction. Hence, m must be a prime number.

Corollary 5.8.4 If $(F, +, \cdot)$ is a field, then the characteristic of F is either a prime p or zero.

Proof: By Theorem 5.4.12, F is an integral domain. Now, by Theorem 5.8.3, the characteristic of F is either a prime or zero.

Definition 5.8.5 Let F be a field. Then F is called a *prime field* if the only subfield of F is F itself. If F' is a prime field that is also a subfield of the field F, we call F' a *prime subfield* of F.

Exercises

*1. Prove that the field of rational numbers Q is a prime field.

*2. Prove that $(Z_p, +, \cdot)$, p a prime, is a prime field. •

Lemma 5.8.6 Let F be a field and let F_1 be a subfield of F. Then F and F_1 have the same identity element.

Proof: Clearly, $(F_1^*, \cdot)$ is a subgroup of $(F^*, \cdot)$. By Theorem 4.6.2, a subgroup has the same identity as the full group.

Lemma 5.8.7 If F_1 and F_2 are subfields of a field F, then $F_1 \cap F_2$ is also a subfield of F.

Proof: $(F_1 \cap F_2, +)$ is a subgroup of $(F, +)$ by Theorem 4.7.12. Also, $(F_1 - \{0\}, \cdot)$ and $(F_2 - \{0\}, \cdot)$ are subgroups of $(F - \{0\}, \cdot)$.

Since $(F_1 \cap F_2) - \{0\} = (F_1 - \{0\}) \cap (F_2 - \{0\})$, we have that $(F_1 \cap F_2 - \{0\}, \cdot)$ is a subgroup of $(F - \{0\}, \cdot) = (F^*, \cdot)$. Since the distributive law holds in F, it also holds in $F_1 \cap F_2$. Thus, $F_1 \cap F_2$ is a subfield of F.

Lemma 5.8.8 Let F be a field and let $\{F_\alpha\}$ be a collection of subfields of F. Then $\bigcap F_\alpha$ is a subfield of F.

Proof: Exercise.

Theorem 5.8.9 Every field F contains a unique prime subfield.

Proof: *I. Existence.*

Let $\{F_\alpha\}$ be the collection of all subfields of F. Let $G = \bigcap F_\alpha$. Then G is a subfield of F. If H is a subfield of G, then $H \in \{F_\alpha\}$, and hence G is a subfield of H. Therefore, $G = H$, and G is a prime field.

II. Uniqueness.

Let F_1 and F_2 be prime subfields of F. Then $F_1 \cap F_2$ is a subfield of F by Lemma 5.8.7. But $F_1 \supseteq F_1 \cap F_2$ and F_1 is a prime subfield, so $F_1 = F_1 \cap F_2$. Similarly, $F_2 = F_1 \cap F_2$. Thus, $F_1 = F_2$.

Theorem 5.8.10 If F is a field of characteristic 0, then the prime subfield of F is isomorphic to Q, the field of rational numbers. If F has characteristic p, a prime, then the prime subfield of F is isomorphic to Z_p.

Proof: Let e denote the identity of F. Then $me \in F$, for all integers m.

I. F has characteristic 0. Let F_1' be a subfield of F. Then F_1' contains e, the identity of F. Now since $me = 0$ if and only if $m = 0$, ne and $(ne)^{-1} \in F_1'$ for all $n \neq 0$, $n \in Z$. Thus, $(me)(ne)^{-1} \in F_1'$, for all $m,n \in Z$, $n \neq 0$. Now let $F_1 = \{(me)(ne)^{-1} \mid m,n \in Z,\ n \neq 0\} \subseteq F$. Then clearly F_1 is a field and F_1 is the prime subfield of F, since any subfield contains e and therefore F_1.

We must now show that $F_1 \cong Q$. It is easy to see that, for $m_1, m_2, n_1, n_2 \in Z$, $n_1 \neq 0$, $n_2 \neq 0$, the following is true:

If $(m_1e)(n_1e)^{-1} = (m_2e)(n_2e)^{-1}$, then

$$(m_1e)(n_2e) = (m_2e)(n_1e),$$

$$(m_1n_2)e = (m_2n_1)e,$$

$$(m_1n_2 - m_2n_1)e = 0,$$

$$m_1n_2 - m_2n_1 = 0, \text{ and}$$

$$m_1/n_1 = m_2/n_2.$$

Also, if $m_1/n_1 = m_2/n_2$, then

$$(m_1e)(n_1e)^{-1} = (m_2e)(n_2e)^{-1}.$$

Now, defining a mapping $f: F_1 \rightarrow Q$ as follows:

$$[(me)(ne)^{-1}]f = m/n,$$

and using the fact that $m_1n_1 = m_2/n_2$ if and only if $(m_1e)(n_1e)^{-1} = (m_2e)(n_2e)^{-1}$, we can easily show that f is well defined, 1–1, onto, and an isomorphism. The verification of these properties is left as an exercise.

$$\text{Thus, } F_1 \cong Q.$$

II. F has characteristic p, a prime.

In this case, $pe = 0$ and for $0 < m < p$, $me \neq 0$. In addition, if $m \equiv r \pmod{p}$, where r is a least positive residue mod p, then $me = re$.

Let $F_1 = \{me \mid m = 0,1,2,\ldots, p-1\}$. It is easily shown that F_1 is a subfield of F. (See section 2.12, Example 4.1.6 and Exercise 4, section 4.2). Also, since e is in any subfield, F_1 is the prime subfield of F.

Finally, the mapping $f: F_1 \rightarrow Z_p$ defined by $(me)f = m$, for all $m \in Z_p$, is an isomorphism and $F_1 \cong Z_p$.

Theorem 5.8.11 If F is a field with subfield F_1, then the characteristic of F_1 is equal to the characteristic of F.

Proof: Exercise.

Exercises

3. Complete the proof of Lemma 5.8.8.
4. Complete the proof of Theorem 5.8.10.
5. Prove Theorem 5.8.11.
6. Let $F = \{0,1,x,y\}$. Define operations of $+$ and $\cdot$ on F by the following tables:

$+$	0	1	x	y
0	0	1	x	y
1	1	0	y	x
x	x	y	0	1
y	y	x	1	0

$\cdot$	0	1	x	y
0	0	0	0	0
1	0	1	x	y
x	0	x	y	1
y	0	y	1	x

Show that $(F, +, \cdot)$ is a field with four elements. What is the prime subfield of F?

7. Show that Z_m is a field if and only if m is a prime. Hence, in light of Exercise 10, section 5.4, show that Z_m is an integral domain if and only if m is a prime.
8. Prove that for each integer $m \geq 0$, there exists a ring with characteristic m.
9. Show by example that two nonisomorphic rings may have the same characteristic.
10. Let F be a field with 9 elements. Prove that F has characteristic 3.

*11. Let F be a field with p^n elements, p a prime. Show that F has characteristic p.

*12. Let D be a division ring. Show that D contains a subring F that is isomorphic to Q or to Z_p for some prime p. We call F the *prime subfield* of D.

*13. Let F be a field with characteristic $p > 0$ and let $a, b \in F$.
   i) Prove that $(a + b)^p = a^p + b^p$.
   ii) Prove by induction on n that

$$(a + b)^{p^n} = a^{p^n} + b^{p^n}.$$

14. Let F be a field. Suppose $a \in F$, $a \neq 0$ and m is the least positive integer such that $ma = 0$. Prove that the characteristic of F is m.
15. Let F be a finite field. Prove that F has p^n elements for some prime p.

    Hint: Use Theorem 4.12.17 and the exercise above.

5.9 POLYNOMIAL RINGS

In this section we shall introduce the concept of a polynomial over a ring. Our main purposes are the following: i) the construction of a ring S properly containing a given ring R; and ii) the development of the fundamental properties of polynomials in one variable, with coefficients in a ring. Although the definition given below may appear to bear little resemblance to the concept of a polynomial with which the reader is familiar, we shall later show how the two notions are related.

We shall precisely define the polynomial x in Theorem 5.9.6, but until this is done, it will help the reader if he regards the polynomial $(a_0,a_1,\cdots,a_n,0,0,\cdots,0,\cdots)$ (Definition 5.9.2) as the formal expression $a_0 + a_1x + \cdots + a_nx^n$. With this in mind, the reader should easily be able to follow our more formal development of polynomials.

Definition 5.9.1 Let R be a ring and P_0 the nonnegative integers. An *infinite sequence* of elements of R is a function $f: P_0 \to R$. If $r_j = (j)f$, we denote f by $(r_0,r_1,\cdots,r_n,\cdots)$, and we call r_j the jth term of the sequence.

Definition 5.9.2 Let R be a ring. An infinite sequence $(a_0,a_1,a_2,\cdots,a_n,\cdots)$ of elements of R, with at most a finite number of nonzero terms, is called a *polynomial* over R. The set of all such polynomials is denoted by $R[x]$.

For example, if $R = Z$, then $(1,0,2,1,0,\cdots,0,\cdots)$ and $(0,0,1,0,0,\cdots,0,\cdots) \in R[x]$, but $(0,1,0,1,\cdots,0,1,\cdots) \notin R[x]$.

Exercise

*1. Let $(a_0,a_1,\cdots,a_n,\cdots)$ be a sequence of elements of R. Show that $(a_0,a_1,\cdots,a_n,\cdots) \in R[x]$ if and only if there exists an integer N such that $a_i = 0$, for all $i \geq N$. ●

Since a polynomial is a sequence (that is, a function), if we let $(a_0,a_1,\cdots,a_n,\cdots)$ and $(b_0,b_1,\cdots,b_n,\cdots) \in R[x]$, then $(a_0,a_1,\cdots,a_n,\cdots) = (b_0,b_1,\cdots,b_n,\cdots)$ if and only if $a_i = b_i$, $i = 0,1,2,\cdots$.

Definition 5.9.3 Let $\alpha = (a_0,a_1,\cdots,a_n,\cdots)$, $\beta = (b_0,b_1,\cdots,b_n\cdots)$ be in $R[x]$. Define

$$\alpha + \beta = (a_0 + b_0, a_1 + b_1, \cdots, a_n + b_n, \cdots) \quad \text{and}$$

$$\alpha \cdot \beta = (c_0,c_1,c_2,\cdots,c_n\cdots),$$

where $c_k = \sum_{i=0}^{k} a_ib_{k-i}$. We note that $\sum_{i=0}^{k} a_ib_{k-i} = \sum_{\substack{i+j=k \\ i\geq 0, j\geq 0.}} a_ib_j$, which we shall frequently write as $\sum_{i+j=k} a_ib_j$.

Theorem 5.9.4 $(R[x],+,\cdot)$ is a ring, called the *ring of polynomials over R*.

Proof: We first show that + and · are binary operations on $R[x]$. Thus, let $\alpha = (a_0,a_1,\cdots,a_n,\cdots)$ and $\beta = (b_0,b_1,\cdots,b_n,\cdots)$.

Since there are integers N_1 and N_2 such that $a_k = 0$ for $k \geq N_1$ and $b_\ell = 0$ for $\ell \geq N_2$, it is clear that $a_n + b_n = 0$ for $n \geq \max(N_1,N_2)$, and $c_n = \sum_{i+j=n} a_i b_j = 0$ for $n \geq N_1 + N_2 - 1$. Thus, $\alpha + \beta$ and $\alpha \cdot \beta$ are in $R[x]$.

To show that $(R[x], +)$ is a commutative group, we note that $0 = (0,0,\cdots,0,\cdots)$ is an additive identity and that $-\alpha = (-a_0, -a_1, \cdots, -a_n, \cdots)$ is an additive inverse of α. The associativity of $+$ follows from the associativity of addition in R.

Now we show the associativity of multiplication in $R[x]$.

Thus, let

$$\alpha = (a_0, a_1, \cdots, a_n, \cdots),$$

$$\beta = (b_0, b_1, \cdots, b_n, \cdots), \quad \text{and}$$

$$\gamma = (c_0, c_1, \cdots, c_n, \cdots).$$

Then the ℓth term of $\alpha \cdot \beta$ is $\sum_{i+j=\ell} a_i b_j$ and the sth of $(\alpha \cdot \beta) \cdot \gamma$ is $\sum_{\ell+k=s} \left(\sum_{i+j=\ell} a_i b_j \right) c_k = \sum_{i+j+k=s} (a_i b_j) c_k$. On the other hand, the ℓth term of $\beta \cdot \gamma$ is $\sum_{j+k=\ell} b_j c_k$ and the sth term of $\alpha(\beta\gamma)$ is $\sum_{i+\ell=s} a_i \left(\sum_{j+k=\ell} b_j c_k \right) = \sum_{i+j+k=s} a_i (b_j c_k)$. Since multiplication in R is associative, $(\alpha\beta)\gamma = \alpha(\beta\gamma)$.

Finally, to show that $(R[x], +, \cdot)$ is a ring, we need to verify the distributive laws. This is left as an exercise.

Theorem 5.9.5 Let R be a ring. Then R can be embedded in $R[x]$.

Proof: Let $f: R \to R[x]$ be defined by $rf = (r,0,0,\cdots,0,\cdots)$. Then f is a 1–1 homomorphism (or an embedding) from R to $R[x]$, as the reader may verify.

Since $(r,0,\cdots,0,\cdots)(a_0, a_1, \cdots, a_n \cdots) = (ra_0, ra_1, \cdots, ra_n, \cdots)$, we may replace $(r,0,\cdots,0,\cdots)$ by r and agree to write $r(a_0, a_1, \cdots, a_n, \cdots)$ in place of $(r,0,0,\cdots)(a_0, a_1, \cdots, a_n, \cdots)$. Thus, by Theorem 5.9.5, we may consider R actually to be a subring of $R[x]$.

To facilitate obtaining the usual algebraic representation of polynomials, we shall assume for the next two theorems that R is a ring with identity.

Theorem 5.9.6 Let R be a ring with identity 1. Let x denote the polynomial $(0,1,0,\cdots,0,\cdots)$. Then $x^n = (0,0,\cdots,0,1,0,\cdots)$, where 1 appears as the nth term of $(0,0,\cdots,0,1,0,\cdots)$, and any polynomial $(b_0, b_1, \cdots, b_k, 0, \cdots, 0, \cdots)$ can be expressed in the form $b_0 + b_1 x + b_2 x^2 + \cdots + b_k x^k$.

Proof: $x^1 = x = (0,1,0,\cdots,0,\cdots)$ and the theorem is true for $n = 1$. Assume now that $x^n = (0,0,\cdots,0,1,0,\cdots,0,\cdots)$, where 1 is the nth term of x^n. Then $x^{n+1} = x^n \cdot x = (0,\cdots,0,1,0,\cdots)(0,1,0,\cdots) = (0,\cdots,0,0,1,0,\cdots)$ where 1 is now the $n + 1$st term. The first part of the theorem now holds by induction.

Since $(b_0,b_1,\cdots,b_k,0,\cdots,0,\cdots) = (b_0,0,\cdots,0,\cdots) + (0,b_1,0,\cdots) +\cdots+ (0,0,\cdots,0,b_k,0,\cdots,0,\cdots)$, and since $(0,\cdots,0,b_i,0,\cdots) = b_i(0,\cdots,0,1,0,\cdots) = b_i x^i$, the proof is now complete.

Definition 5.9.7 Let S be a ring and let R be a subring of S. Let $s \in S$ and suppose that $rs = sr$, for all $r \in R$. Then s is called *transcendental over* R if $r_0 + r_1 s +\cdots+ r_{n-1}s^{n-1} + r_n s^n = 0$, $r_i \in R$, implies $r_i = 0$, $i = 0,\cdots,n$. Otherwise, s is called *algebraic over* R.

If $R = Q$, the ring of rational numbers, and $S = K$, the ring of real numbers, then π and e are examples of real numbers transcendental over Q. The number $\sqrt{2}$ is, however, algebraic over Q, since $1(\sqrt{2})^2 + 1(-2) = 0$.

Our method of introducing polynomials over a ring R now enables us to construct a ring S containing an element transcendental over R.

Theorem 5.9.8 Let R be a ring with identity 1. Then there exists a ring S such that R is a subring of S and S has an element transcendental over R.

Proof: By Theorem 5.9.5, $R \subset R[x] = S$. Now consider $x = (0,1,0,\cdots,0,\cdots)$. Then x is transcendental over R, for if there exist $r_0,r_1,\cdots r_n$ in R such that

$$r_0 + r_1 x +\cdots+ r_n x^n = 0, \text{ then}$$

$r_0 + r_1(0,1,0,\cdots) +\cdots+ r_n(0,\cdots,0,1,0,\cdots) = 0$, whence $(r_0,r_1,\cdots,r_n,\cdots) = 0$ and $r_i = 0$, $i = 0,\cdots,n$.

Theorem 5.9.9 Let R be a ring (not necessarily with identity). Then there exists a ring S such that R is a subring of S and such that S has an element transcendental over R.

Proof: By Theorem 5.7.8, R can be embedded in a ring R^* with identity 1. In fact, $R^* = \{(r,n) \mid r \in R, n \in Z\}$. If we identify $(r,0)$ with r, R can be considered a subring of R^*. Then $R \subset R^* \subset R^*[x] = S$, and since x is transcendental over R^*, it is transcendental over R.

The reader should note that if R is a ring without identity, then $R[x]$, as defined in Definitions 5.9.2 and 5.9.3, is embedded in the ring $R^*[x]$. Thus, any element of $R[x]$ has the form

$$a_0 + a_1 x + \cdots + a_n x^n, \quad a_i \in R,$$

even though x need not be an element of $R[x]$. We should note that x is in $R[x]$ if and only if R has an identity. The element x, whether it is in $R[x]$ or not, is called an "indeterminate" over R.

Henceforth, we shall adopt the convention of denoting the polynomial $\alpha = (a_0, a_1, \cdots, a_n, \cdots)$ in $R[x]$ by $\alpha(x) = a_0 + a_1 x + \cdots + a_n x^n = a_n x^n + \cdots + a_1 x + a_0$. Then, given two polynomials

$$r(x) = r_n x^n + r_{n-1} x^{n-1} + \cdots + r_0, \quad \text{and}$$

$$s(x) = s_m x^m + s_{m-1} x^{m-1} + \cdots + s_0,$$

it follows readily from our earlier definitions of addition and multiplication that we add and multiply these polynomials exactly as in high school algebra.

Theorem 5.9.10 Let R be an integral domain. Then $R[x]$ is an integral domain.

Proof: It suffices to verify:

i) $R[x]$ has an identity different from 0.
ii) $R[x]$ is commutative.
iii) $R[x]$ has no zero divisors.

i) Since $R \ni 1$, it can easily be shown that $(1,0,0,0,\cdots,0,\cdots) \neq (0,0,\cdots,0,\cdots)$ is the identity of $R[x]$.

ii) Since R is commutative, observe that if $\alpha(x) = a_0 + a_1 x + \cdots + a_n x^n + \cdots$ and $\beta(x) = b_0 + b_1 x + \cdots + b_m x^m + \cdots$, then the kth term of $\alpha(x) \cdot \beta(x)$ is

$$\sum_{i+j=k} a_i b_j = \sum_{i+j=k} b_j a_i = \sum_{j+i=k} b_j a_i = \sum_{i+j=k} b_i a_j,$$

which is the kth term of $\beta(x) \cdot \alpha(x)$.

iii) Finally, suppose $\alpha(x) \neq 0$ and $\beta(x) \neq 0$ are in $R[x]$. Then, there are integers N_1 and N_2 such that $a_{N_1} \neq 0$, $b_{N_2} \neq 0$ but $a_k = 0$ for $k > N_1$ and $b_k = 0$ for $k > N_2$. Then, in $\alpha(x) \cdot \beta(x)$, the $N_1 + N_2$ term is given by $\sum_{i+j=N_1+N_2} a_i b_j = a_{N_1} b_{N_2} \neq 0$, and so $R[x]$ has no zero divisors.

Definition 5.9.11 If $\alpha(x) \in R[x]$, we define *degree of* $\alpha(x)$ (denoted deg α or deg $\alpha(x)$) as follows:

If $\alpha(x) \neq 0$, then deg $\alpha = N$, provided $a_N \neq 0$, but $a_k = 0$, for $k > N$.

If $\alpha(x) = 0$, then deg $\alpha = -\infty$.

If deg $\alpha = 0$ or $-\infty$, we say that $\alpha(x)$ is a *constant* (polynomial).

We agree to make these conventions concerning $-\infty$: $n + (-\infty) = -\infty$, for all integers n, $(-\infty) + (-\infty) = -\infty$ and $-\infty < n$, for all integers n.

Theorem 5.9.12 If R has no zero divisors, and if $\alpha(x)$ and $\beta(x)$ are in $R[x]$, then $\deg(\alpha(x) \cdot \beta(x)) = \deg \alpha + \deg \beta$.

Proof: Exercise.

Theorem 5.9.13 Let $\alpha(x), \beta(x) \in R[x]$. Then $\deg(\alpha(x) + \beta(x)) \leq \max(\deg \alpha, \deg \beta)$.

Proof: Exercise.

We have had two main reasons for introducing polynomials as infinite sequences. One is to show in a simple way the existence of an element transcendental over R. The second is to emphasize that a polynomial is a sequence formally constructed from a ring and not a function on the ring. Later we shall use a polynomial to define a polynomial function. This is the context in which the reader has utilized polynomials in college algebra and calculus.

Exercises

1. Complete the proof of Theorem 5.9.4.
2. Prove Theorem 5.9.12.
3. Prove Theorem 5.9.13.
4. Let $R = Z_4$ and let $\alpha(x) \in R[x]$, $\beta(x) \in R[x]$. Is it true that $\deg(\alpha(x) \cdot \beta(x)) = \deg \alpha + \deg \beta$?
5. Let S be a set consisting of the following objects: Γ, ⅂, L, ⅃, that is, S = {Γ, ⅂, L, ⅃}. Let R be the ring of all subsets of S, defined according to Example 5.1.7. List all polynomials in $R[x]$ of degree 1 or less. For example, {Γ, ⅃} + {Γ, ⅃}x is such a polynomial.
6. Show that if R and S are isomorphic rings, then $R[x]$ and $S[x]$ are isomorphic.
7. Let R be a commutative ring with identity, let $S = R[x]$ and let $T = S[y]$. We denote T by $R[x, y]$, the ring of polynomials in the two indeterminates x,y over R. Let $R[y] = U$ and let $U[x] = V$. Show that $T = V$.
8. Let S be a ring with subring R, and let a be an element of S transcendental with respect to R. Show that S contains a subring isomorphic to $R[x]$.
9. Let $(Q', \cdot)$ be the multiplicative group of positive rational numbers. Show that $(Q', \cdot) \simeq (Z[x], +)$.

   Hint: Show that every element of Q' can be written in the form $p_1^{\alpha_1} \cdots p_k^{\alpha_k}$ for distinct primes p_i and unique integers α_i.
10. Let p be a prime. Show that the quotient field of $Z_p[x]$ has characteristic p, yet is infinite. (This field, denoted $Z_p(x)$, shows that an infinite field may have characteristic p.)

5.10 DIVISION ALGORITHM FOR POLYNOMIALS

Although arbitrary polynomial rings are of great interest, some of the more important applications arise in the case of a polynomial ring over a field. Hence, for the remainder of this section and also for the next two sections, we shall consider polynomial rings of the form $F[x]$, where F is a field.

Definition 5.10.1 Let $\alpha(x) \in F[x]$, say $\alpha(x) = a_0 + a_1x + a_2x^2 + \cdots + a_nx^n$, with $a_n \neq 0$. We call a_n the *leading coefficient* of $\alpha(x)$ and we call a_0 the *constant term* of $\alpha(x)$. If $a_n = 1$ (the identity of F), $\alpha(x)$ is called a *monic* polynomial.

It turns out that the theory of factorization of integers (See Chapter 2) has a strong analogue in the theory of polynomials in an indeterminate x over a field F. Our point of departure is to prove a division algorithm for polynomials in $F[x]$. This division algorithm, and its proof, is very similar to that for integers. Only now the degree of the polynomial replaces the absolute value of the integer.

Theorem 5.10.2 Division Algorithm for F[x]

Let F be a field. Let $\alpha(x) = a_0 + a_1x + \cdots + a_nx^n$, $a_n \neq 0$, and $\beta(x)$ be elements of $F[x]$. Then there exist unique polynomials $q(x)$ and $r(x)$ in $F[x]$ such that

$$\beta(x) = \alpha(x)q(x) + r(x), \ \deg r(x) < \deg \alpha(x).$$

Proof:

I. *Existence.*

Let $S = \{\beta(x) - \alpha(x)\gamma(x) \mid \gamma(x) \in F[x]\}$. Then $S \neq \phi$, since $\beta(x) \in S$. If the 0 polynomial is in S, then there is a polynomial $\gamma(x)$ such that

$$\beta(x) - \alpha(x)\gamma(x) = 0 \quad \text{and}$$

$$\beta(x) = \alpha(x)\gamma(x).$$

Then $q(x) = \gamma(x)$ and $r(x) = 0$ satisfy the conditions of the theorem.

Thus, assume $0 \notin S$. Then every polynomial in S has nonnegative degree. Choose a polynomial in S of least degree and call it $r(x)$. Thus, there exists a $q(x) \in F(x)$ such that

$$\beta(x) - \alpha(x)q(x) = r(x),$$

$$\beta(x) = \alpha(x)q(x) + r(x).$$

Now $\alpha(x)$ has degree n, since $a_n \neq 0$. Thus, assume that $\deg r(x) = m \geq n$, say $r(x) = r_mx^m + r_{m-1}x^{m-1} + \cdots + r_0$. Since

$$r_ma_n^{-1}x^{m-n}\alpha(x) = r_mx^m + r_ma_n^{-1}a_{n-1}x^{m-1} + \cdots + r_ma_n^{-1}a_0x^{m-n},$$

we see that $r(x) = r_m a_n^{-1} x^{m-n} \alpha(x) + h(x)$, where $h(x) = -r_m a_n^{-1} a_{n-1} x^{m-1} - \cdots - r_m a_n^{-1} a_0 x^{m-n} + r_{m-1} x^{m-1} + \cdots + r_0$, and $\deg h(x) \leq \deg r(x) - 1$. Thus,

$$\beta(x) - \alpha(x)[q(x) + r_m a_n^{-1} x^{m-n}] = h(x) \qquad \text{and} \qquad h(x) \in S.$$

But $\deg h(x) < \deg r(x)$, which contradicts our choice of $r(x)$. Thus, $\deg r(x) < \deg \alpha(x)$, and we have found polynomials $q(x)$ and $r(x)$ such that

$$\beta(x) = \alpha(x)q(x) + r(x), \ \deg r(x) < \deg \alpha(x).$$

II. *Uniqueness.*

Suppose $\beta(x) = q(x)\alpha(x) + r(x)$ and $\beta(x) = q_1(x)\alpha(x) + r_1(x)$, where $\deg r(x) < \deg \alpha(x)$ and $\deg r_1(x) < \deg \alpha(x)$. Then $[q(x) - q_1(x)]\alpha(x) = r_1(x) - r(x)$.

Now, $\deg(r_1(x) - r(x)) < \deg \alpha(x)$. But $\deg\, [(q(x) - q_1(x))\alpha(x)] \geq \deg \alpha(x)$, unless

$$q(x) - q_1(x) = 0.$$

Thus, we must have $q(x) - q_1(x) = 0$ and also $r_1(x) - r(x) = 0$. Hence $q(x) = q_1(x)$ and $r(x) = r_1(x)$.

The reader should review the proof of the division algorithm in Chapter 2 and observe its similarity with the proof just concluded.

Definition 5.10.3 Let $f(x), g(x) \in F[x]$, F a field. $f(x)$ is said to *divide* $g(x)$ if there is a polynomial $h(x) \in F[x]$ such that $g(x) = f(x)h(x)$. We write $f(x) \mid g(x)$. If $f(x)$ does not divide $g(x)$, we write $f(x) \nmid g(x)$.

Definition 5.10.4 Let $f(x) \in F[x]$, F a field, $\deg f(x) \geq 1$. Then $f(x)$ is called *irreducible* if whenever $h(x) \mid f(x)$, either $h(x) = c$ or $h(x) = cf(x)$, where c is a constant.

The development of the polynomial analogue of a prime number and the formulation of a unique factorization theorem for polynomials is left to Exercises 5 and 6. Irreducible polynomials will take the place of prime numbers.

Exercises

1. Where does the proof of the division algorithm fail in the case of

$$\text{i) } Z_4[x]; \qquad \text{ii) } Z[x]?$$

2. Let $\alpha(x) = 4x^3 + x^2 - 2$ and $\beta(x) = 3x + 1$. Find $q(x), r(x) \in Q[x]$, Q the field of rational numbers, such that

$$\alpha(x) = \beta(x)q(x) + r(x).$$

3. Let F be a field. Let $f(x), g(x) \in F[x]$. Define $\gcd(f(x), g(x))$ in analogy with Definition 2.6.2. Show that there exist polynomials $s(x)$ and $t(x) \in F[x]$ such that $\gcd(f(x), g(x)) = f(x)s(x) + g(x)t(x)$.
4. In Exercise 3 let $F = Q$, the rational numbers. Find a gcd of
   i) $x^3 + x - 2$ and $x^4 - x^3 - 2x + 2$
   ii) $x^2 + x + 2$ and $x^5 - x^4 + x^3 - x^2 + x - 1$.
5. Prove Euclid's Lemma: If $f(x) \mid g(x)h(x)$ and if $f(x)$ is irreducible, then either $f(x) \mid g(x)$ or $f(x) \mid h(x)$.
6. Prove the Unique Factorization Theorem for $F[x]$: A monic polynomial $f(x)$, $\deg f(x) \geq 1$, has a unique factorization (up to order of the factors) into irreducible monic polynomials.

5.11 CONSEQUENCES OF THE DIVISION ALGORITHM

Definition 5.11.1 Let F be a field, $f(x) \in F[x]$, with $f(x) = a_0 + a_1x + \cdots + a_nx^n$. We define a function $f: F \to F$ as follows: Let $s \in F$, then $(s)f = a_0 + a_1s + \cdots + a_ns^n$. The function f is called the *polynomial function* corresponding to $f(x)$.

In this section we shall use properties of the polynomial function f to investigate factorization properties of the polynomial $f(x)$.

Definition 5.11.2 Let $f(x), g(x) \in F[x]$, F a field. Denote the polynomial function corresponding to $f(x) + g(x)$ by $f + g$ and the polynomial function corresponding to $f(x) \cdot g(x)$ by $f \cdot g$.

The reader should notice that in general neither $f + g$ nor $f \cdot g$ is the composite function $f \circ g$.

Theorem 5.11.3 Let $f(x), g(x) \in F[x]$, where F is a field and let $s \in F$. Then

i) $(s)[f + g] = (s)f + (s)g$

ii) $(s)[f \cdot g] = (s)f \cdot (s)g$.

Proof:

i) Let $f(x) = a_0 + a_1x + \cdots + a_nx^n$,
$g(x) = b_0 + b_1x + \cdots + b_mx^m$.

Without loss of generality, we may assume $m = n$. (Why?)

Then $f(x) + g(x) = (a_0 + b_0) + (a_1 + b_1)x + \cdots + (a_n + b_n)x^n$.

But $(s)f = a_0 + a_1s + \cdots + a_ns^n$
$(s)g = b_0 + b_1s + \cdots + b_ns^n$, and hence
$(s)f + (s)g = (a_0 + b_0) + \cdots + (a_n + b_n)s^n = (s)(f + g)$,

by definition of the polynomial function $f + g$.
ii) Exercise.

Theorem 5.11.4 The Remainder Theorem Let $f(x) \in F[x]$, F a field. Let $s \in F$, and let $q(x)$ and $r(x)$ be the unique elements of $F[x]$ such that $f(x) = q(x)\cdot(x - s) + r(x)$, $\deg r(x) < \deg(x - s)$. Then $r(x) = d$, d an element of F, and moreover, $d = (s)f$.

Proof: Since $\deg(x - s) = 1$, $\deg r(x)$ is either 0 or $-\infty$. If $\deg r(x) = 0$, then $r(x) = c \neq 0$, for some $c \in F$. If $\deg r(x) = -\infty$, then $r(x) = 0, 0 \in F$. In either case $r(x) = d$ for some $d \in F$.

Since $f(x) = q(x)(x - s) + r(x)$, we have, by Theorem 5.11.3,

$$(s)f = [(s)q](s - s) + (s)r.$$

Thus, $(s)f = (s)r$. But, since $r(x) = d$, an element of F, $(s)r = d$.

Corollary 5.11.5 Let $f(x) \in F[x]$, F a field. Then the polynomial $x - s$ is a factor of $f(x)$ if and only if $(s)f = 0$.

Proof: By the Theorem 5.11.4, if $(s)f = 0$, then writing $f(x) = q(x)(x - s) + r(x)$, we see that $r(x) = 0$, hence $f(x) = q(x)(x - s)$, that is, $(x - s) \mid f(x)$.

On the other hand, if $(x - s) \mid f(x)$, then there exists $q(x)$ such that

$$f(x) = q(x)(x - s),$$

and then

$$(s)f = [(s)q](s - s) = (s)q\cdot 0 = 0.$$

Definition 5.11.6 Let $f(x) \in F[x]$. An element $s \in F$ is called a *root* of the polynomial $f(x)$ or of f, if $(s)f = 0$. We say s *satisfies* the equation $(x)f = 0$.

Theorem 5.11.7 Let $f(x) \in F[x]$, F a field, $\deg f(x) = n \geq 0$. Then f has at most n distinct roots in F.

Proof: We prove the theorem by induction on n. If $\deg f(x) = 0$, then $f(x) = c \neq 0$, so f has no roots in F. Also, trivially, if $\deg f(x) = 1$, then $f(x) = ax + b$, $a \neq 0$, and clearly $-a^{-1}b$ is the only root of f.

Thus, we assume that the theorem is true for $n - 1 \geq 0$. Then for $\deg f(x) = n$, $f(x) = a_0 + a_1x + \cdots + a_nx^n$. Suppose f has a root, say s_1. Then, by Corollary 5.11.5, $x - s_1 \mid f(x)$, and so there exists a polynomial $f_1(x)$ of degree $n - 1$ such that $f(x) = f_1(x)(x - s_1)$. Now, any root of $f(x)$ is either a root of $f_1(x)$ or of $(x - s_1)$. If s_2 is any other root of f such that $s_1 \neq s_2$, then $(s_2)f_1 = 0$. (Why?) Thus, any root of f different from s_1 must satisfy $(x)f_1 = 0$. By induction, f_1 has at most $n - 1$ distinct roots, and so f has at most n distinct roots.

Exercise

1. Define s to be a *root of multiplicity* m of f if $f(x) = f_1(x)\cdot(x - s)^m$ but $(s)f_1 \neq 0$. By modifying the proof of Theorem 5.11.7, prove the following:

If $f(x) \in F[x]$, F a field, $\deg f(x) = n$, and if $s_1, s_2, \cdots, s_k$ are all the distinct roots of $f(x)$, with multiplicities $m_1, m_2, \cdots, m_k$, respectively, then $m_1 + m_2 + \cdots + m_k \leq n$. ●

A fundamental problem in the theory of polynomials is to determine when a given polynomial over a ring can be factored. The fundamental theorem of algebra, which we state here without proof, asserts that every polynomial $f(x) \in C[x]$, C the field of complex numbers, can be *completely* factored, that is, $f(x) = b(x - a_1)\cdots(x - a_n)$ where $b, a_1, \cdots, a_n \in C$ and $n = \deg f(x)$. Equivalently, we have

Theorem 5.11.8 Fundamental Theorem of Algebra Let $f(x) \in C[x]$, where C denotes the field of complex numbers, with $\deg f(x) \geq 1$. Then f has a root in C.

No proof of this theorem exists that does not use techniques of analysis or topology. One can, however, prove by elementary calculus that any odd-degree polynomial over the real numbers has a linear factor with real coefficients. From this point it is possible to prove Theorem 5.11.8 using only algebraic techniques.[15]

Exercises

2. Prove ii) of Theorem 5.11.3.
3. Show that in $Z_p[x]$, p a prime, $(x - a) \mid (x^{p-1} - 1)$, for all $a \in Z_p$, $a \neq 0$. Verify that $(x - 1)(x - 2)\cdots(x - p + 1) = x^{p-1} - 1$.
4. Prove Wilson's Theorem: Let $n \in Z$, $n > 1$. Then $(n - 1)! \equiv -1 \pmod{n}$ if and only if n is a prime number.

   Hint: Consider the roots of $x^{n-1} - 1$.
5. Show that Theorem 5.11.7 does not hold in $Z_m[x]$, if m is not a prime number and $m \neq 4$.

Although a polynomial function over the ring of real numbers is different from the associated polynomial, there does exist a natural 1–1 correspondence between the set of polynomial functions and the set of polynomials. In fact, the polynomial functions over the real numbers form a ring, with respect to the addition and multiplication in Definition 5.11.2, which is isomorphic to $R[x]$, where R denotes the real numbers. However, this relation between a ring of polynomials and the ring of associated polynomial functions does not hold for all rings R. For example, if

[15] See van der Waerden, B. L., [49], Section 70.

$R = Z_p$, p a prime, then the polynomial $\alpha(x) = x^p - x$ is certainly different from the polynomial $\beta(x) = 0$, but the associated polynomial function of each of these is the zero function θ, where $s\theta = 0$, all $s \in Z_p$. It is true, however, that the ring of polynomial functions associated with $R[x]$, R commutative, is always a homomorphic image of $R[x]$ (Exercise 8).

Exercises

6. Let $f(x), g(x) \in Z_5[x]$. Show that if $f(x) = x^2 - 2$ and $g(x) = x^5 + x^2 - x - 2$, then $f = g$, where f and g are the polynomial functions corresponding to $f(x)$ and $g(x)$, respectively.

7. Find all positive integers m such that $x^2 + 2$ is a divisor of $x^5 - 10x + 12$ in $Z_m[x]$.

8. Let R be a commutative ring and let $f(x) = a_0 + a_1x + \cdots + a_nx^n$ be a polynomial in $R[x]$. Let the function $f: R \to R$, defined by $(s)f = a_0 + a_1s + \cdots + a_ns^n$, all $s \in R$, be the *polynomial function associated with the polynomial* $f(x)$. Let T be the set of all polynomial functions associated with $R[x]$. Show that T is a ring and that T is the homomorphic image of $R[x]$. See Definitions 5.11.1 and 5.11.2 and Theorem 5.11.3.

5.12 PRINCIPAL IDEAL RINGS

We shall now consider a class of rings that shares some of the important factorization properties with the ring of integers. The similarity is expressed in terms of the ideals of such rings.

Definition 5.12.1 Let R be a ring. An ideal A in R is called a *principal ideal* in R if there exists an element $a \in A$ such that any element $b \in A$ has the form:

$$b = r_1a + ar_2 + na + \sum_{i=1}^{m} r_ias_i,$$

where $r_1, r_2, r_i, s_i \in R$ and $n, m \in Z$. We denote A by (a). It is not difficult to verify that (a) is simply the intersection of all ideals containing the element a.

If R is a commutative ring with identity 1, then the integral multiple $na = ra$, a ring multiple, where $r = n1 \in R$ and $A = \{ra \mid r \in R\} = (a)$. Note the similarity between this definition and that of a cyclic subgroup.

Definition 5.12.2 A ring R is called a *principal ideal ring* if every ideal A in R is a principal ideal.

Theorem 5.12.3 The ring of integers, Z, is a principal ideal ring.

Proof: Let A be an ideal in Z. If $A = (0)$, then A is principal. Thus, assume $A \neq (0)$.

Then A contains a positive integer, and so, by the law of well ordering, A contains a smallest positive integer, say a. Now let b be any other integer in A. By the division algorithm for integers, there exist unique integers q and r such that

$$b = qa + r, \quad 0 \leq r < a.$$

If $r > 0$, then $r = b - qa \in A$ is a smaller positive integer in A than a, a contradiction. Hence $r = 0$, and so $b = qa$, that is, any element $b \in A$ has the form qa, where $q \in Z$. Thus, $A = (a)$. (See Exercise 6, Section 5.4, and Exercise 2, Section 5.5.)

Theorem 5.12.4 Let F be a field. Then $F[x]$ is a principal ideal ring.

Proof: This proof will essentially parallel that of Theorem 5.12.3, with the concept of degree now replacing that of absolute value.

Thus, let A be an ideal in $F[x]$. If $A = \{0\}$, then $A = (0)$, and we are finished. Hence, assume $A \neq (0)$. Then A contains polynomials of nonnegative degree. By the law of well ordering, there exists a polynomial $f(x) \in A$, $f(x) \neq 0$, such that $\deg f(x) \leq \deg g(x)$, with $g(x)$ any polynomial in A, $g(x) \neq 0$. Let $h(x)$ be any polynomial in A. By the division algorithm, there exist polynomials $q(x)$ and $r(x)$ such that

$$h(x) = f(x) \cdot q(x) + r(x), \quad \deg r(x) < \deg f(x).$$

Since $h(x) \in A$ and $f(x) \in A$, $r(x) = h(x) - f(x)q(x) \in A$.

If $0 \leq \deg r(x)$, A contains a nonzero polynomial of smaller degree than $f(x)$, a contradiction. Hence, $\deg r(x) < 0$, whence

$$\deg r(x) = -\infty, \qquad \text{and} \qquad r(x) = 0.$$

Hence, $h(x) = f(x)q(x)$, and so $A = (f(x))$.

Principal ideal rings that are also integral domains, such as Z and $F[x]$, are called *principal ideal domains*. In such rings we can always define the concept of unique factorization in a way similar to that for the integers. That principal ideal domains satisfy a unique factorization law will be proved in Section 5.16.

Exercises

1. Let R be a principal ideal domain. Show that any quotient ring of R is also a principal ideal ring.

2. Let $f(x), g(x) \in F[x]$, F a field. Show that if $h(x) = \gcd(f(x), g(x))$, then $(h(x)) = (f(x)) + (g(x)) = \{u(x) + v(x) \mid u(x) \in (f(x)), v(x) \in (g(x))\}$.

3. Let R be a principal ideal domain. Then a set of ideals $\{I_i\}$ such that $I_1 \subseteq I_2 \subseteq I_3 \subseteq \cdots \subseteq I_n \subseteq \cdots$ is called a *chain* of ideals in R. Show that such a chain must always be finite.

Hint: Consider the set $\bigcup_{n=1}^{\infty} I_n$. Show that it is an ideal.

4. Let R be a principal ideal domain. Let (a,b) denote the ideal generated by the elements a and b, that is,

$$(a,b) = \{ra + sb \mid r \in R, s \in R\}.$$

Since R is a principal ideal domain, there exists an element d such that $(d) = (a,b)$. Show that there exist elements $s, t \in R$ such that $a = ds$ and $b = dt$. Moreover, show that if e is an element of R for which there are elements x and y such that $a = ex$ and $b = ey$ for some $x, y \in R$, then $d = ew$ for some $w \in R$.

Let $a, b \in Z$ and let $(d) = (a,b)$. Show that d can be chosen so that $d = \gcd(a,b)$.

5.13 PRIME AND MAXIMAL IDEALS

It is easily seen that in Z, the ring of integers, the ideal (p), where p is a prime number, satisfies these two properties: i) if the product $ab \in (p)$, then either $a \in (p)$ or $b \in (p)$; and ii) if $a \notin (p)$, then the set

$$\{ma + np \mid m, n \in Z\} = Z.$$

In this section we shall study commutative rings R that contain ideals satisfying either property i) or ii), and we shall investigate the relationship between i) and ii).

Definition 5.13.1 Let R be a commutative ring. An ideal P in R is called a *prime ideal* if, whenever $ab \in P$, $a \in R$, $b \in R$, then either $a \in P$ or $b \in P$.

An ideal M in R is called a *maximal ideal* in R if i) $M \subset R$ and ii) whenever N is an ideal in R such that $M \subseteq N \subseteq R$, then either $N = M$ or $N = R$.

It is now clear that the ideal (p), where p is a prime, is both a prime ideal and a maximal ideal in the ring Z.

In the ring $F[x]$, F a field, the principal ideal generated by the polynomial $x - s$, $s \in F$, is both a prime ideal and a maximal ideal.

The reader should not conclude from these two examples, however, that there is no distinction between prime and maximal ideals. We consider the ring $Z[x]$. Let A be the set of all polynomials in $Z[x]$ that have constant term zero. Then A is an ideal in $Z[x]$. Moreover, A is a prime ideal, for if $f(x)g(x) \in A$, then either $f(x) \in A$ or $g(x) \in A$. (We leave the proof of this fact for the exercises.) A is not, however, a maximal ideal, for the ideal of all polynomials with even constant term properly contains A yet is not equal to $Z[x]$.

On the other hand, it is also possible for a ring R to have an ideal M that is a maximal ideal but that is not a prime ideal. For example, let p be a prime number, and on the set $Z_p = \{0, 1, \cdots, p - 1\}$ define the usual addition modulo p and define multiplication by setting $ab = 0$, for all $a,b \in Z_p$. Then (0) is a maximal ideal in this ring (why?), but it is clearly not a prime ideal.

Definition 5.13.2 Let R be a commutative ring with 1. Let $A \subseteq R$. Then the *ideal generated by A* is the intersection of all ideals I_α of R such that $A \subseteq I_\alpha$. We denote this ideal by (A). If $I \subseteq R$ and $a \in R$, we shall denote $(I \cup \{a\})$ by (I,a).

Exercises

1. Let R be a ring. Let $\{I_\alpha\}$ be a collection of ideals in R. Show that $\bigcap I_\alpha$ forms an ideal in R.
2. Let R be a commutative ring with 1. Let $A = \{a_\alpha\} \subseteq R$. Show that

$$(A) = \{\Sigma r_i a_{\alpha_i} \mid r_i \in R\},$$

that is, (A) is the set of all finite sums of the form $r_1 a_{\alpha_1} + \cdots + r_k a_{\alpha_k}$.

*3. Let I be an ideal in a commutative ring $R \ni 1$. Let $a \in R$. Prove that if $x \in (I,a)$, then $x = i + ra$, for some $i \in I$, $r \in R$. •

Theorem 5.13.3 Let R be a commutative ring with 1. Let M be a maximal ideal in R. Then M is a prime ideal.

Proof: Let $a,b \in R$, and suppose $ab \in M$. To show that M is a prime ideal, we need to show that either $a \in M$ or $b \in M$. Thus, assume $a \notin M$. Then the ideal $N = (M,a)$ properly contains M. Since M is a maximal ideal in R, $(M,a) = R$, whence $1 \in (M,a)$. Thus, there exists an element $m \in M$ and an element $r \in R$ such that $1 = m + ar$. But then $b = bm + bar$, that is, $b = bm + r(ab)$. Now, $ab \in M$, whence $bm + r(ab) \in M$, that is, $b \in M$ and M is a prime ideal.

The reader should observe how closely this proof resembles the proof of Euclid's Lemma in Chapter 2.

Theorem 5.13.4 Let R be a commutative ring, $R \ni 1$. Let M be a maximal ideal in R. Then the quotient ring R/M is a field.

Proof: Since R is a commutative ring, so is R/M. Thus, the only properties that need verification are i) R/M has an identity, and ii) every nonzero element of R/M has an inverse in R/M.

To show i), we merely observe that $1 + M$ is an identity for R/M.

To show ii), suppose $b + M \neq M$, that is, $b + M$ is a nonzero element in R/M. Since M is a maximal ideal, $(b, M) = R$, that is, there is an $r \in R$ and an $m \in M$ such that $1 = br + m$. Then $r + M$ is the inverse of $b + M$, and R/M is a field.

Theorem 5.13.5 Let R be a commutative ring, $R \ni 1$. Let M be an ideal in R. Then, if R/M is a field, M is a maximal ideal in R.

Proof: Since R/M is a field, it has at least two elements. Hence, there exist elements in R that are not in M. Therefore, let $a \in R$, $a \notin M$. We must show $(M,a) = R$. Now, since $a \notin M$, $a + M$ is a nonzero element in the field R/M. Hence, there exists an element $b + M$ in R/M such that $(a + M)(b + M) = 1 + M$, the identity in the field R/M. That is, there are elements $m_1, m_2, m_3 \in M$ such that

$$(a + m_1)(b + m_2) = 1 + m_3.$$

Thus, $ab + m' = 1$, where $m' = am_2 + bm_1 + m_1m_2 - m_3$ is in M. Finally, for any $r \in R$,

$$r(ab) + rm' = r \cdot 1$$
$$(rb)a + rm' = r, \quad \text{that is,} \quad r \in (a, M).$$

Thus, $(a, M) = R$, and M is a maximal ideal.

Theorems 5.13.4 and 5.13.5 are summarized in the following:

Theorem 5.13.6 Let R be a commutative ring with 1. Let M be an ideal in R. Then R/M is a field if and only if M is a maximal ideal in R.

To illustrate the usefulness of these theorems, we show a method of constructing the field of complex numbers from the real numbers. (See Exercises 6 and 7 in Section 5.7. This method will be discussed more generally in Chapter 7.)

Let K denote the field of real numbers. Then, clearly, the polynomial function corresponding to the polynomial $x^2 + 1$ has no roots in K, since $a^2 \geq 0$, for all $a \in K$. Hence, $x^2 + 1$ has no factorization into first degree polynomials in $K[x]$.

Now let $f(x) \in K[x]$, $f(x) \notin (x^2 + 1)$, the principal ideal generated by $x^2 + 1$. Since the only factors of $x^2 + 1$ have the form either of $c \in F$,

$c \neq 0$, or of $d(x^2 + 1)$, $d \in F$, $d \neq 0$, it follows that $f(x)$ and $x^2 + 1$ are relatively prime in $K[x]$, that is, $\gcd(f(x), x^2 + 1) = 1$ (see Exercise 3, Section 5.10), and so there are polynomials $s(x)$ and $t(x) \in K[x]$ such that $1 = f(x)s(x) + (x^2 + 1)t(x)$, whence $1 \in ((x^2 + 1), f(x))$ and $K[x]$ is equal to the ideal generated by $x^2 + 1$ and $f(x)$. Thus, $(x^2 + 1)$ is a maximal ideal in $K[x]$.

To avoid confusion between the polynomial $x^2 + 1$ and the principal ideal $(x^2 + 1)$, we shall denote the latter by I.

By Theorem 5.13.4, $K[x]/I$ is a field that we now show is isomorphic to the field of complex numbers (see Exercises 6 and 7, Section 5.7). Its elements are of the form $bx + a + I$, where a,b take on all values in K. We denote this element by $\bar{a} + \overline{bx}$. Now let $\bar{a} + \overline{bx}$ and $\bar{c} + \overline{dx} \in K[x]/I$. Then

$$\begin{aligned}&(\bar{a} + \overline{bx}) + (\bar{c} + \overline{dx})\\ &= (a + bx + I) + (c + dx + I)\\ &= (a + c) + (b + d)x + I\\ &= \overline{a + c} + \overline{(b + d)x}\end{aligned}$$

Also,

$$\begin{aligned}&(\bar{a} + \overline{bx})(\bar{c} + \overline{dx})\\ &= (a + bx + I)(c + dx + I)\\ &= ac + bdx^2 + (ad + bc)x + I.\end{aligned}$$

Now,

$$bdx^2 = bd(x^2 + 1) - bd,$$

whence

$$bdx^2 + I = -bd + I,$$

that is,

$$\begin{aligned}&ac + bdx^2 + (ad + bc)x + I\\ &= ac - bd + (ad + bc)x + I.\end{aligned}$$

Thus

$$(\bar{a} + \overline{bx})(\bar{c} + \overline{dx}) = \overline{ac - bd} + \overline{(ad + bc)x}.$$

By considering the case $(a + 0x) + (c + 0x)$ and $(\bar{a} + \overline{0x})(\bar{c} + \overline{0x})$, we see that $\bar{a} + \bar{c} = \overline{a + c}$ and $\bar{a}\bar{c} = \overline{ac}$, for all $a,c \in K$. If we now let $\bar{a} + \overline{bx} \rightarrow a + bi$, $i^2 = -1$, we see that this is an isomorphism. Thus, the field $K[x]/I$ is isomorphic to the field of complex numbers.

Exercises

4. Let F be a field. Let $f(x)$ be irreducible over F. Prove that $(f(x))$ is a maximal ideal in $F[x]$.

5. Let Z_2 be the field with two elements. Show that the polynomial $x^2 + x + 1$ is irreducible over Z_2. Form the field $F = Z_2[x]/(x^2 + x + 1)$, where $(x^2 + x + 1)$ denotes the principal ideal in $Z_2[x]$ generated by $x^2 + x + 1$. Denote the elements of F by
$0 = 0 + (x^2 + x + 1)$, $1 = 1 + (x^2 + x + 1)$,
$\bar{x} = x + (x^2 + x + 1)$, and $\bar{y} = x + 1 + (x^2 + x + 1)$.
Write the multiplication table for F and verify directly that F is a field.

6. Prove that the set of all polynomials with constant term zero is a prime ideal in $Z[x]$.

7. Prove that the set of all polynomials with even coefficients is a prime ideal in $Z[x]$.

Hint: Let $f(x) = a_n x^n + a_{n-1}x^{n-1} + \cdots + a_1 x + a_0$ and $g(x) = b_m x^m + b_{m-1}x^{m-1} + \cdots + b_1 x + b_0$. Let a_i be chosen so that $2 \nmid a_i$, but $2 \mid a_k$, for all $k < i$. Let b_j be chosen or that $2 \nmid b_j$, but $2 \mid b_k$ for all $k < j$. Show that $2 \nmid c_{i+j}$, where c_{i+j} is the coefficient of x^{i+j} in the product $f(x) \cdot g(x)$.

†8. (Eisenstein) Let $f(x) \in Z[x]$, $f(x) = a_n x^n + a_{n-1}x^{n-1} + \cdots + a_0$. Assume there exists a prime p such that $p \mid a_i$, for $0 \le i < n$, $p \nmid a_n$, $p^2 \nmid a_0$. Prove that there do not exist polynomials $g(x)$ and $h(x)$ of degree ≥ 1 in $Z[x]$ such that $f(x) = g(x)h(x)$.

5.14 DIRECT SUMS OF RINGS

At this point we again parallel a useful construction of Chapter 4 (see Section 4.13) to enable us to create "larger" rings from "smaller" ones. That is, given rings R_1 and R_2, we define the direct sum of R_1 and R_2.

Definition 5.14.1 Let R_1, R_2 be rings. Then the set $R_1 \times R_2$ with operations $+$ and $\cdot$ defined by $(a_1,a_2) + (b_1,b_2) = (a_1 + b_1, a_2 + b_2)$ and $(a_1,a_2)\cdot(b_1,b_2) = (a_1 b_1, a_2 b_2)$ is called the direct sum of R_1 and R_2. It is denoted by $R_1 \oplus R_2$.

Theorem 5.14.2 Let R_1 and R_2 be rings. Then the direct sum $R_1 \oplus R_2$ is a ring.

Proof: The zero of $R_1 \oplus R_2$ is simply $(0,0)$. The additive inverse of (a_1,a_2) is $(-a_1,-a_2)$. We leave the remainder of the proof to the reader.

Clearly, the map $f: R_1 \to R_1 \oplus R_2$ defined by $af = (a,0)$, for all $a \in R_1$, is an embedding of R_1 in $R_1 \oplus R_2$. Also, R_2 is embedded in $R_1 \oplus R_2$. Moreover, R_1 and R_2 can be considered ideals in $R_1 \oplus R_2$ in the sense that $\{(a,0) \mid a \in R_1\}$ is an ideal in $R_1 \oplus R_2$ and $\{(0,b) \mid b \in R_2\}$ is an ideal in $R_1 \oplus R_2$.

We also have the following theorem analogous to Theorem 4.13.6.

Theorem 5.14.3 Let R be a ring. Let I_1 and I_2 be ideals of R such that
i) if $r \in R$, there exist elements $a_1 \in I_1$ and $a_2 \in I_2$ such that $r = a_1 + a_2$.
ii) $I_1 \cap I_2 = \{0\}$.
Then $R \cong I_1 \oplus I_2$.

Proof: Suppose $r = a_1 + a_2 = b_1 + b_2$, where $a_i, b_i \in I_i$, $i = 1,2$. Then $a_1 - b_1 = b_2 - a_2 \in I_1 \cap I_2$, whence $a_1 - b_1 = b_2 - a_2 = 0$, that is, $a_1 = b_1$ and $a_2 = b_2$. Thus, any element in R has a unique representation as a sum of elements from I_1 and I_2.

Thus, if we define a map $\varphi: I_1 \oplus I_2 \to R$ by $(a_1, a_2)\varphi = a_1 + a_2$, we see that this map is well defined, onto by i), and 1–1 by the above paragraph. It only remains to show that φ is a homomorphism. Thus,

$$[(a_1,b_1) + (a_2,b_2)]\varphi = [(a_1 + a_2, b_1 + b_2)]\varphi$$
$$= a_1 + a_2 + b_1 + b_2 = a_1 + b_1 + a_2 + b_2 = (a_1,b_1)\varphi + (a_2,b_2)\varphi.$$

Now, on the one hand,

$$[(a_1,b_1)(a_2,b_2)]\varphi = [(a_1a_2, b_1b_2)]\varphi = a_1a_2 + b_1b_2.$$

On the other hand,

$$(a_1,b_1)\varphi \cdot (a_2,b_2)\varphi = (a_1 + b_1)(a_2 + b_2) = a_1a_2 + b_1b_2 + a_1b_2 + b_1a_2.$$

Since a_1b_2 and b_1a_2 are in $I_1 \cap I_2$, they are zero and so

$$[(a_1,b_1)(a_2,b_2)]\varphi = (a_1,b_2)\varphi \cdot (a_2,b_2)\varphi.$$

This concludes the proof that φ is an isomorphism.

Frequently, under the conditions of this theorem we say that R is the *internal direct sum* of the ideals I_1 and I_2 and we write

$$R = I_1 \dotplus I_2.$$[16]

Exercises

1. In Theorem 5.14.3 replace conditions i) and ii) by the single condition: if $r \in R$, then there exist unique elements $a_1 \in I_1$ and $a_2 \in I_2$ such that
$$r = a_1 + a_2.$$

2. Let R_1 have characteristic m and R_2 have characteristic n. Prove that $R_1 \oplus R_2$ has characteristic lcm$[m,n]$. Hence, if $(m,n) = 1$, then $R_1 \oplus R_2$ has characteristic mn.

[16]Our use of $\dotplus$ is not universal. See, for example, Curtis and Reiner, [11].

3. Let R_1 and R_2 be rings with identity. Prove that $R_1 \oplus R_2$ is a ring with identity.

4. Let R be a ring. Let $I = \{a \in R \mid ar = 0, \text{ for all } r \in R\}$. Prove that I is an ideal in R.

5. Let R be a commutative ring with an identity 1. Let R have an element e such that $e^2 = e, e \neq 0, e \neq 1$. Prove that

   i) The set $Re = \{re \mid r \in R\}$ is an ideal of R.
   ii) There exists an ideal R' in R such that $R = R' \dotplus Re$.

6. Let R_1 and R_2 be rings. If R_1 and R_2 are both ______, then $R_1 \oplus R_2$ is ______. In each of the following, replace the above blanks by one of the properties, and either prove or disprove each of the resulting assertions:

   i) commutative
   ii) integral domain(s)
   iii) field(s)
   iv) finite.

7. Let A,B,C,D be rings such that $A \cong B$ and $C \cong D$. Prove that $A \oplus C \cong B \oplus D$.

8. Let m and n be relatively prime positive integers. Prove that the ring Z_{mn} is isomorphic to $Z_m \oplus Z_n$.

   Hint: Show that Z_{mn} contains ideals I_1 and I_2 satisfying Theorem 5.14.3, and then use Exercise 7. Or establish the isomorphism directly.

9. Let m_1 and m_2 be positive integers, $(m_1, m_2) = 1$. Let (m_i) be the principal ideal generated by m_i, $i = 1,2$. Prove that

$$Z/[(m_1) \cap (m_2)] \cong Z/(m_1) \oplus Z/(m_2).$$

10. Let R be a ring and let I_1 and I_2 be distinct maximal two-sided ideals in R. Prove that $R/I_1 \cap I_2 \cong R/I_1 \oplus R/I_2$. (Chinese remainder theorem)

    Hint: See Exercise 9.

5.15 UNIQUE FACTORIZATION DOMAINS: EUCLIDEAN DOMAINS

In section 2.8, we proved that if $n \in Z$, $n > 1$, then there exists a factorization of n into a product of primes, and that this factorization is essentially unique. In addition, in the Exercises of Section 5.10 we indicate that a similar theorem holds in $F[x]$, F a field. Indeed, the division algorithm for polynomials is the tool that we can use to prove that any polynomial $f(x) \in F[x]$, $\deg f(x) \geq 1$, can be factored into irreducible polynomials. Such a proof would mimic the proof of the fundamental theorem of arithmetic. This leads to the following definitions, which are in the same spirit as those in Chapter 2.

Definition 5.15.1 Let R be an integral domain. Let $a,b \in R$. We say that a *divides* b, denoted $a \mid b$, if there exists $c \in R$ such that $b = ac$. We say that $a \in R$ is a *unit* in R if there exists $b \in R$ such that $ab = 1$. The elements a and b are called *associates* if there exists a unit u such that $b = au$.

A nonunit element a is called *prime*,[17] if whenever a is written $a = bc$, then either b is a unit or c is a unit.

In this terminology, we see that the only units in Z are $+1$ and -1, and that both p and $-p$ are now called prime, if p is a prime according to Definition 2.4.2. We see also that the irreducible elements in $F[x]$ are also called primes in the present terminology.

Definition 5.15.2 Let R be an integral domain. R is called a *unique factorization domain* (UFD) if

i) For each nonunit a in R, $a \neq 0$, there exists a factorization $a = b_1 b_2 \cdots b_k$, where the b_i are primes and

ii) If $a = b_1 b_2 \cdots b_k = c_1 c_2 \cdots c_\ell$ are two factorizations of a into primes, then $k = \ell$ and for some permutation π of the subscripts j of the c_j's, we have that b_i and $c_{i\pi}$ are associates, $i = 1, \cdots, k$.

Clearly, both Z and $F[x]$ are UFD's. The similarity in the proofs that Z and $F[x]$ are UFD's encourages us to look for those properties common to Z and $F[x]$ that are used in the proof of the unique factorization theorems.

Definition 5.15.3 Let E be an integral domain and let $d: E \to P_0$, P_0 the set of nonnegative integers. We call E a *Euclidean domain* if

i) $(a)d = 0$ if and only if $a = 0$

ii) $(ab)d = (ad)(bd)$, for all $a,b \in E$

iii) For any $a \in E$, $b \in E$, $b \neq 0$, there exist $q,r \in E$ such that

$$a = bq + r, \qquad (r)d < (b)d.$$

Examples of Euclidean domains are i) Z, with $(m)d = |m|$, for all $m \in Z$; ii) $F[x]$, F a field, where $[f(x)]d = 2^{\deg f(x)}$ (we adopt the convention that $2^{\deg 0} = 2^{-\infty} = 0$); iii) a field F, with $(a)d = 1$, $a \neq 0$ and $(0)d = 0$.

That a Euclidean domain E is a UFD can be proved by imitating the proof that Z is a UFD. The details are left to the exercises. It can also be

[17]Frequently, a nonunit element a is called *prime* if, whenever $a \mid bc$, either $a \mid b$ or $a \mid c$, and a nonunit a is called *irreducible* if, whenever $a = bc$, either b or c is a unit. In the context of principal ideal domains, however, the two concepts coincide (see the proof of Theorem 5.16.7).

shown that a Euclidean domain is a UFD by showing that it is a principal ideal domain, which in turn is shown to be a UFD. This is our scheme in the next section.

Exercises

1. Let E be a Euclidean domain. Prove each of the following:
   i) a is a unit in E if and only if $(a)d = 1$
      Hint: Consider $(aa^{-1})d$.
   ii) If a and b are associates, then $(a)d = (b)d$.
2. Let E be a Euclidean domain. Prove that E is a principal ideal domain.
   Hint: Let A be an ideal in E, $A \neq (0)$. A contains an element a such that $(a)d \geq 1$. Let $a \in A$, $a \neq 0$ be chosen so that $(a)d \leq (b)d$, all $b \in A$, $b \neq 0$. Using iii) of Definition 5.13.3, show that $A = (a)$ (see the proof of Theorem 5.12.3).
3. Let E be a Euclidean domain. Let $a,b \in E$. Let (a,b) be the ideal generated by a and b. Since (a,b) is principal, $(a,b) = (c)$, for some $c \in E$. Show that c is a common divisor of a and b. Show that if $e \mid a$ and $e \mid b$, then $e \mid c$, and hence, show that c is a *greatest common divisor of a and b*. Also show that there exist s and $t \in E$ such that $c = as + bt$. Moreover, prove that if c_1 and c_2 are both gcd's of a and b, then c_1 and c_2 are associates.
4. Let E be a Euclidean domain. Let p be a prime element of E. Prove that if $p \mid ab$, then either $p \mid a$ or $p \mid b$ (see proof of Euclid's Lemma 2.7.2).
5. Let $a \in E$, a Euclidean domain. Suppose that $a \neq 0$, $(a)d > 1$ (a is a nonunit). Show that a has at least one factorization into prime elements of E.
6. Let E be a Euclidean domain. Prove that E is a UFD.
7. Let E be a Euclidean domain. Let $F = \{a \in E \mid (a)d \leq 1\}$. Suppose that for $a,b \in F$, $a + b \in F$. Prove that F is a field.
8. Let E be a Euclidean domain. Let p be a nonzero, nonunit element such that when $p \mid ab$, then also $p \mid a$ or $p \mid b$. Prove that p is a prime.
9. Let p be a prime in an integral domain. Let q be an associate of p. Show that q is a prime.

5.16 UNIQUE FACTORIZATION DOMAINS: PRINCIPAL IDEAL DOMAINS

In the last section we outlined in the exercises a proof that every Euclidean domain is a UFD. One step of the proof showed that every Euclidean domain is also a principal ideal domain (PID). Nevertheless, every principal ideal domain is also a UFD. The first major step is to prove that any element $a \neq 0$ in a PID has a factorization into primes.

Lemma 5.16.1 Let R be a principal ideal domain and let $a,b \in R$. Then $a \mid b$ if and only if $(b) \subseteq (a)$.

Proof: Let $a \mid b$. Then there exists c such that $b = ac$. Clearly, $b \in (a)$, so $(b) \subseteq (a)$. Conversely, if $(b) \subseteq (a)$, then there exists c in R such that $b = ac$, and so $a \mid b$.

Lemma 5.16.2 Let R be a principal ideal domain. Let p be a prime and suppose that $p \nmid a$. Then there exist elements s and t in R such that $1 = ps + at$.

Proof: Let A be the ideal generated by p and a, that is, $A = \{px + ay \mid x \in R, y \in R\}$. Since A is a principal ideal, there exists $c \in A$ such that $A = (c)$, and so we can find s and t such that $ps + at = c$. Since $(p) \subseteq A = (c)$, by Lemma 5.16.1, $c \mid p$. Similarly, $c \mid a$. Since p is a prime, c is either a unit or an associate of p. In the latter case, $c = pu$, u a unit, whence $c \mid a$ implies $p \mid a$. This is impossible, so c is a unit. Thus, there exists e such that $ce = 1$. Hence, $p(se) + a(te) = ce = 1$, and the proof is complete.

Lemma 5.16.3 Let R be a PID. Let $\{I_n \mid n = 1,2,\cdots\}$ be a chain of ideals in R, that is, $I_1 \subseteq I_2 \subseteq I_3 \subseteq \cdots$. Then there exists an integer N such that $I_k = I_N$, all $k \geq N$.

Proof: Let $I_n = (a_n)$, and let $I = \bigcup_{n=1}^{\infty} I_n$. Since $I_k \subseteq I_\ell$, $k \leq \ell$, we can prove easily that I is an ideal. For, let $a,b \in I$. Then clearly there exists k such that $a \in I_k$ and $b \in I_k$. Since I_k is an ideal, $a - b \in I_k$, whence $a - b \in I$. It is also easy to prove that if $a \in I$, $r \in R$, then $ar \in I$. Since I is an ideal, there exists an element $c \in R$ such that $I = (c)$. But since I is a union of sets, $c \in I_N$ for some N. Thus, $I \subseteq I_N$, whence $I_k \subseteq I_N$, all $k \geq N$. Since also $I_N \subseteq I_k$, all $k \geq N$, necessarily $I_k = I_N$, all $k \geq N$.

Lemma 5.16.4 Let R be a PID. Let A be an ideal in R, $A \neq R$. Then there exists a maximal ideal M in R such that $A \subseteq M$. Moreover, $M = (p)$, where p is a prime.

Proof: Let $I_1 = A$. If A is not a maximal ideal, there exists an ideal I_2 such that $I_1 \subseteq I_2 \subseteq R$. If I_2 is not maximal, there exists an ideal I_3 such that $I_1 \subseteq I_2 \subseteq I_3 \subseteq R$. By Lemma 5.16.3, this process must stop after a finite number of steps. Thus, there does exist a maximal ideal M in R such that $A \subseteq M$.

By Theorem 5.13.3, M is a prime ideal. Now let $M = (p)$. If p is not a prime, then $p = ab$, for some nonzero nonunits a and b. Also, $a \notin (p)$, for if $a \in (p)$, then $a = pc$, for some c, whence $p = ab = pbc$, $bc = 1$ and b is a unit, a contradiction. Thus, $a \notin (p)$ and similarly $b \notin (p)$. But this contradicts that (p) is a prime ideal. Thus, p is a prime.

Lemma 5.16.5 Let R be a PID. Let $a \in R$, $a \neq 0$, a not a unit. Then there exists a prime $p \in R$ such that $p \mid a$.

Proof: Since a is not a unit, $(a) \subset R$, whence by Lemma 5.16.4, $(a) \subseteq (p)$, for some ideal (p), where p is a prime. Then $p \mid a$, by Lemma 5.16.1.

Theorem 5.16.6 Let R be a PID. Let $a \in R$, $a \neq 0$, a not a unit. Then a has a factorization into primes in R.

Proof: By Lemma 5.16.5, there exists a prime p_1 such that $p_1 \mid a$, that is, $a = p_1 a_1$. If a_1 is a unit, then a is a prime by Exercise 9, Section 5.15, and the proof is completed.

If a_1 is not a prime, by Lemma 5.16.5, there exists a prime p_2 such that $a_1 = p_2 a_2$. Again, if a_2 is a unit, then $p_2 a_2$ is a prime, whence $a = p_1(p_2 a_2)$ is a product of primes.

If a_2 is not a prime, we find that $a_2 = p_3 a_3$, p_3 a prime. Continuing, we find primes $p_1, p_2, \cdots, p_n, \cdots$ and elements $a_1, a_2, \cdots, a_n \cdots$ such that $a_i \mid a_{i-1}$, $i = 2, 3, \cdots$. Thus, by Lemma 5.16.1, $(a_1) \subseteq (a_2) \subseteq (a_3) \subseteq \cdots$. By Lemma 5.16.3, there exists an integer N such that $(a_N) = (a_{N+1}) = \cdots$. Thus, $a_{N+1} = a_N u = a_{N+1} p_{N+1} u$, whence $p_{N+1} u = 1$. Thus p_{N+1} is a unit, which contradicts that p_{N+1} is a prime. Thus, a_N must be a prime, whence $a = p_1 p_2 \cdots p_N a_N$ is a factorization of a into primes.

Theorem 5.16.7 Let R be a PID. Then R is a UFD.

Proof: Theorem 5.16.5 established the existence of one prime factorization for an element $a \in R$, $a \neq 0$, a not a unit.

Suppose now that p is a prime and $p \mid ab$. If $p \nmid a$, then by Lemma 5.16.2, $1 = ps + at$, for some $s, t \in R$. Then $p(bs) + at = b$ and clearly, $p \mid b$. (Thus, we have a generalization of Euclid's lemma.)

Now let $a = p_1 \cdots p_N = q_1 \cdots q_M$ be two prime factorizations for a. Then $p_1 \mid (q_1 \cdots q_M)$, and so $p_1 \mid q_i$, some i. We may assume that $i = 1$. Since q_1 is a prime, p_1 and q_1 must be associates. The theorem now follows by induction (see Theorem 2.8.2, II).

We now have that a Euclidean domain is a PID and a PID is a UFD. Neither of the converses is true. As examples, let K be the real numbers and let $K[x, y]$ be the ring of all polynomials in indeterminates x and y over K. Then $K[x, y]$ is a UFD, but the ideal (x, y) is not principal (see Section 5.17).

The ring A of all complex numbers of the form $a + b\left(\frac{1 + \sqrt{-19}}{2}\right)$, $a, b \in Z$ is a PID, but this ring is not Euclidian.[18]

We mention here that the motivation for studying ideals can be traced to the classical theory of algebraic integers (see, for example, Pollard [43] or MacDuffee [35]). There exist rings of algebraic integers that are integral domains and in which unique factorization fails. But in these rings, an arbitrary nonzero ideal can be expressed uniquely as the product of prime ideals. Hence, by a shift in point of view from elements to ideals, a form of unique factorization does hold for these rings.

Exercises

1. Show that (x, y) is not a principal ideal in $K[x, y]$.
2. A ring R is said to satisfy the *maximum condition* on ideals if any nonempty collection $\mathfrak{F}$ of ideals contains an element I such that no J in $\mathfrak{F}$ satisfies $I \subset J$. We call I a maximum element of $\mathfrak{F}$.

   A ring R is said to satisfy the *ascending chain condition* (ACC) on ideals if whenever $I_1 \subseteq I_2 \subseteq \cdots$, I_j an ideal, there exists an integer N such that $I_j = I_N$ for all $j \geq N$ (see Lemma 5.16.3).

   Prove that a ring R satisfies the ascending chain condition on ideals if and only if it satisfies the maximum condition on ideals.
3. Let A be an ideal in a principal ideal domain. Prove that $A = P_1 P_2 \cdots P_n$, where P_i is a prime ideal in R, and that this factorization is unique up to order.

   (The product of two ideals A and B is defined as the set of all finite sums of products ab, $a \in A$, $b \in B$ [see Exercise 3, Section 5.5]. The product of n ideals is defined analogously).
4. An ideal I in a commutative ring $R \ni 1$ is said to be *finitely generated* if there exists a finite set $\{x_1, \cdots, x_n\} \subseteq I$ such that every element of I has the form $r_1 x_1 + \cdots + r_n x_n$, $r_i \in R$. Prove that every ideal in such a ring R is finitely generated if and only if R satisfies the ACC on ideals.

5.17 UNIQUE FACTORIZATION DOMAINS: THE POLYNOMIAL RING R[x] OVER THE UFD R

In the last two sections we have obtained sufficient conditions for a ring to be a UFD. We shall now prove that whenever R is a UFD, then so is $R[x]$. To prove this result, we shall use the fact that $F[x]$ is a UFD, where F is the quotient field of R.

[18] The interested reader should consult, for example, Zariski and Samuel [52] or Jacobson [23], vol. I, concerning $K[x,y]$. For details concerning A, he should see the paper by T. S. Motzkin, *Bulletin of the American Mathematical Society*, vol. 55 (1949), pp. 1142–1146.

To begin, we observe that the concept of greatest common divisor can be defined in a UFD (see Exercise 6, Section 2.8). Thus, if $a = p_1^{e_1} \cdots p_r^{e_r}$ and $b = q_1^{f_1} \cdots q_r^{f_r}$, $e_i \geq 0$, $f_i \geq 0$, and p_i and q_i are prime and associates, $i = 1, \cdots, r$, then a gcd of a and b is $(a,b) = p_1^{\min(e_1, f_1)} \cdots p_r^{\min(e_r, f_r)}$. In addition, we see that d satisfies (i) $d \mid a$ and $d \mid b$ and (ii) if $e \mid a$ and $e \mid b$, then $e \mid d$. Moreover, any element satisfying (i) and (ii) is a gcd of a and b. We leave the verifications for the reader. We also point out that we can define the gcd of a set of n elements of R, $n > 0$, and this is also left for the reader.

Definition 5.17.1 Let $f(x) = a_0 + a_1x + \cdots + a_nx^n \in R[x]$. If

$$a = \gcd(a_0, a_1, \cdots, a_n),$$

then $f(x) = a(a_0' + a_1' + \cdots + a_n'x^n)$, where

$$\gcd(a_0', \cdots, a_n') = 1.$$

The element a in R (determined up to a unit) is called the *content* of $f(x)$ and is denoted $C(f(x))$. If $g(x) = b_0 + b_1x + \cdots + b_nx^n \in R[x]$, with $\gcd(b_0, b_1, \cdots, b_n) = 1$, then $g(x)$ is called a *primitive* polynomial.

Now the prime elements in $R[x]$ can easily be determined. First, if p is a prime in R, then clearly p is also a prime in $R[x]$. Second, if $f(x)$ is an irreducible polynomial over R, then $f(x)$ is a prime in $R[x]$, provided that $C(f(x)) = 1$, for otherwise $f(x) = af^*(x)$, where a is itself a product of primes in R and hence in $R[x]$. Thus, the prime elements of $R[x]$ are the primes in R and the irreducible primitive polynomials in $R[x]$.

We now proceed to our main result via a sequence of lemmas (and corollaries to the lemmas).

Lemma 5.17.2 Let R be a UFD with quotient field F. Let $f_1(x)$ and $f_2(x)$ be primitive polynomials in $R[x]$. Then $f_1(x)$ and $f_2(x)$ are associates in $R[x]$ if and only if they are associates in $F[x]$.

Proof: Since R is a subring of F, clearly if $f_1(x)$ and $f_2(x)$ are associates in $R[x]$, then they are associates in $F[x]$. It is the converse that will be of greater importance.

Thus, if $f_1(x)$ and $f_2(x)$ are associates in $F[x]$, there is a unit a in $F[x]$ such that $f_1(x) = af_2(x)$. But a must also be a unit in F, whence $a = b/c$, b, $c \in R$. Then $cf_1(x) = bf_2(x) \in R[x]$. Since $C(f_1(x)) = C(f_2(x)) = 1$, if a prime p in R divides c, it also divides b. Thus, it is easy to see that b and c must be associates in R. But this implies that $f_1(x)$ and $f_2(x)$ are associates in $R[x]$.

Lemma 5.17.3 Gauss Let R be a UFD and let $f(x)$ and $g(x)$ be primitive polynomials in $R[x]$. Then $f(x)g(x)$ is also primitive in $R[x]$.

Proof: Let $f(x) = a_0 + a_1x + \cdots + a_nx^n$, $g(x) = b_0 + b_1x + \cdots + b_mx^m$, and $f(x)g(x) = c_0 + c_1x + \cdots + c_{n+m}x^{n+m}$, where

$c_k = \sum_{i+j=k} a_i b_j$, $k = 0, \cdots, n + m$. If $f(x)g(x)$ is not primitive, there exists a prime $p \in R$ such that $p \mid c_i$ in R, for all i. However, there is a smallest integer s such that $p \nmid a_s$ but $p \mid a_i$, for $i < s$, and there is a smallest integer t such that $p \nmid b_t$ but $p \mid b_i$, for $i < t$. Now $c_{s+t} = a_0 b_{s+t} + a_1 b_{s+t-1} + \cdots + a_s b_t + \cdots + a_{s+t} b_0$. Since $p \mid a_i$, for $i < s$,

$$p \mid (a_0 b_{s+t} + \cdots + a_{s-1} b_{t+1})$$

and since $p \mid b_i$, for $i < t$,

$$p \mid (a_{s+1} b_{t-1} + \cdots + a_{s+t} b_0).$$

Thus, since $p \mid c_{s+t}$, we have that $p \mid a_s b_t$. Since R is a UFD, either $p \mid a_s$ or $p \mid b_t$, a contradiction. Thus, $f(x)g(x)$ is primitive.

Corollary 5.17.4 Let R be a UFD and let $f(x)$ and $g(x) \in R[x]$. Then $C(f(x)g(x)) = C(f(x))C(g(x))$.

Proof: Exercise.

Corollary 5.17.5 Let R be a UFD, with quotient field F. Let $f(x) \in R[x]$, $\deg f(x) > 0$, and $f(x)$ an irreducible primitive polynomial in $R[x]$. Then $f(x)$ is irreducible over F.

Proof: If $f(x)$ is not irreducible over F, then $f(x) = g(x)h(x)$, where $\deg g(x) \geq 1$, $\deg h(x) \geq 1$, and $g(x), h(x) \in F[x]$. Since F is the quotient field of R, $g(x) = (a_0/b_0) + (a_1/b_1)x + \cdots + (a_n/b_n)x^n$ and $h(x) = (c_0/d_0) + (c_1/d_1)x + \cdots + (c_m/d_m)x^m$, $a_i, b_i, c_j, d_j \in R$. Now $g(x) = (a_0 b_1 b_2 \cdots b_n/b) + (a_1 b_0 b_2 \cdots b_n/b)x + \cdots + (a_n b_0 b_1 \cdots b_{n-1}/b)x^n$, where $b = b_0 b_1 \cdots b_n$. Thus, $g(x) = (1/b)g_1(x) = (a/b)g_2(x)$, where $g_2(x) \in R[x]$, $g_2(x)$ is primitive, and $a = C(g_1(x))$. Similarly,

$$h(x) = (c/d)h_2(x),$$

where $h_2(x)$ is primitive.

Thus, $f(x) = g(x)h(x) = (a/b)(c/d)g_2(x)h_2(x)$, whence $bd\, f(x) = acg_2(x)h_2(x)$ with $g_2(x)$ and $h_2(x)$ primitive in $R[x]$. Since $f(x)$ and $g_2(x)h_2(x)$ are clearly associates in $F[x]$, and since $f(x)$ and $g_2(x)h_2(x)$ are primitive in $R[x]$, they are associates in $R[x]$ by Lemma 5.17.2. But this implies that $f(x)$ is not irreducible over R, a contradiction.

We can now prove the main result.

Theorem 5.17.6 If R is a UFD, then so is $R[x]$ a UFD.

Proof: Let $f(x) \in R[x]$. Then $f(x) = C(f(x))\, f_1(x)$, where $C(f(x))$ is in R and $f_1(x)$ is primitive. Since R is a UFD, $C(f(x)) = p_1 \cdots p_k$, where each p_i is prime in R (and hence in $R[x]$). Also, by arguing on the degree of $f_1(x)$ and using the fact that in $R[x]$, $g(x)$ primitive and $g(x) = g_1(x)g_2(x)$ implies $g_1(x)$ and $g_2(x)$ are primitive (Corollary 5.17.4), we have that $f_1(x) = p_1(x)\cdots p_s(x)$, where each $p_i(x)$ is irreducible and primitive (and hence prime) in $R[x]$. Thus, $f(x) = p_1 \cdots p_k p_1(x) \cdots p_s(x)$ is a prime factorization for $f(x)$ in $R[x]$.

Finally, if also $f(x) = q_1 \cdots q_\ell q_1(x) \cdots q_t(x)$ is a second prime factorization for $f(x)$ in $R[x]$, then $q_1 \cdots q_\ell$ and $p_1 \cdots p_k$ are associates (arguing on the content of polynomials), whence $f_1(x) \cdots f_s(x)$ and

$$q_1(x) \cdots q_t(x)$$

are associates in $R[x]$. But since these polynomials are also associates in $F[x]$, which is a UFD (Theorems 5.12.4 and 5.16.7), we see that $s = t$, and we may assume that $f_i(x)$ and $q_i(x)$, $i = 1, \cdots, s$, are associates in $F[x]$. But then, by Lemma 5.17.2, $f_i(x)$ and $q_i(x)$ are associates in $R[x]$, $i = 1, \cdots, s$. Finally, since $p_1 \cdots p_k$ and $q_1 \cdots q_\ell$ are associates in the UFD R, $k = \ell$ and we may assume that p_i and q_i are associates, $i = 1, \cdots, k$. This completes the proof.

Before leaving the subject of unique factorization, we mention that a factorization theory can be developed for noncommutative rings.[19]

Exercises

1. a) Prove that in a UFD, the two characterizations of gcd (a,b) given in the text are equivalent.
   b) Define $\gcd(a_1, \cdots, a_n)$ in two different ways, where $a_1, \cdots, a_n \in R$, a UFD. Show that the two definitions are equivalent.
   c) Define the notion of lcm of a and b, $a, b \in R$, a UFD, in two different ways and show they are equivalent.
2. Let R be a UFD. Prove that if p is a prime in R, then p is a prime in $R[x]$.
3. Prove Corollary 5.17.4.
4. Show there exist infinitely many nonisomorphic UFD's of the form $F[x]$, where F is a field.
5. Show that if R is a UFD, then so is $R[x_1, \cdots, x_n]$, the ring of polynomials in n indeterminates with coefficients in R. ($R[x_1, \cdots, x_n]$ is defined inductively by $R[x_1, \cdots, x_n] = (R[x_1, \cdots, x_{n-1}])[x_n]$).
6. Let F be a field. Show that $F[x, y]$, the ring of polynomials in two indeterminates with coefficients in F, is not a PID, but is a UFD.
   Hint: Consider the ideal (x, y).
7. Let $f(x)$ be a monic polynomial in $Z[x]$. Suppose $f(x)$ has a root in Q, the field of rational numbers. Prove that this root is an integer.

5.18 CHARACTERIZATION OF THE INTEGERS

We shall conclude this chapter by giving an axiomatic characterization of the integers. To set the stage the reader should recall the properties

[19] The reader may consult the recent papers of P. M. Cohn (*Transactions American Mathematical Society*, Vol. 109, pp. 313–331).

$A_0 - A_4$, $M_0 - M_4$, D, O_1 and O_2 of Section 2.1 and property O_3 of Section 2.2. We now see that $A_0 - A_4$, $M_0 - M_4$, and D are simply the defining properties of an integral domain, and we shall show that there is precisely one integral domain (up to isomorphism) that satisfies properties O_1, O_2, and O_3.

Definition 5.18.1 Let I be an integral domain. Then I is called an *ordered* integral domain if there exists a subset I^+ of I such that the following two conditions are true:
i) For each $a \in I$, one and only one of the following holds: $a \in I^+$, $a = 0$, or $-a \in I^+$
ii) If a and b are in I^+, then $a + b \in I^+$ and $ab \in I^+$.

Definition 5.18.2 Let I be an ordered integral domain. Let $a,b \in I$. Then we say *a is less than b* (equivalently, *b is greater than a*) and write $a < b (b > a)$ if $b - a \in I^+$.

We shall use the symbols $\leq$ and $\geq$ in the obvious ways.

Along the lines of the discussion in Chapter 2, it is easy to see that for a and b in I, either $a < b$, $a = b$, or $a > b$. Also, $a \in I^+$ if and only if $0 < a$, and similarly, $-a \in I^+$ if and only if $a < 0$.

Definition 5.18.3 Let I be an ordered integral domain. Let $S \subseteq I$, $S \neq \phi$. Then S is called *well ordered* if for any $T \subseteq S$, $T \neq \phi$, there exists $t \in T$ such that $t \leq t'$, for all $t' \in T$.

If I is replaced by the ring of integers and S by the set of positive integers, then this definition becomes the law of well ordering.

Before we give a characterization of the integers, we require the following lemmas.

Throughout the remainder of this section, I will denote an ordered integral domain such that I^+ is well ordered.

Lemma 5.18.4 Let $a \in I, a \neq 0$. Then $a^2 \in I^+$.

Proof: Either $a \in I^+$ or $-a \in I^+$. If $a \in I^+$, then $a^2 = a \cdot a \in I^+$, by Definition 5.18.1. If $-a \in I^+$, then $a^2 = (-a)(-a) \in I^+$, again by Definition 5.18.1.

Corollary 5.18.5 Let e be the multiplicative identity of I. Then $e \in I^+$.

Proof: $e \neq 0$ and $e = e^2$.

Lemma 5.18.6 Let $a \in I^+$. Then $e \leq a$.

Proof: Let $a \in I^+$ and assume $a < e$. Then the set

$$S = \{a \in I^+ \mid a < e\}$$

is not empty. Since $S \subseteq I^+$, $S \neq \phi$, we see from the fact that I^+ is well ordered that S has an element m such that $m \leq s$, for all $s \in S$. Of course, $0 < m$. Thus, $0 < m < e$. But then $0 < m^2 < e \cdot m = m < e$. But $0 < m^2 < m$ contradicts our choice of m. Hence $S = \phi$ and $e \leq a$, for all $a \in I^+$.

Lemma 5.18.7 Let $a \in I^+$. Then there exists an integer $m > 0$ such that $a = me$.

Proof: Suppose I^+ has an element a that is not of the form me, $m \in Z, m > 0$. Then $S = \{a \in I^+ \mid a \neq me \text{ for any } m \in Z, m > 0\} \neq \phi$. Since I^+ is well ordered, there exists an element $b \in S$ such that $b \leq a$, all $a \in S$. Now $b \neq 1 \cdot e = e$ (for otherwise, $b \notin S$), and so, by Lemma 5.18.6, $e < b$. But then $0 < b - e < b$. Thus, $b - e \notin S$ and $b - e$ has the form $(m-1)e$, $m - 1 \in Z$, $m - 1 > 0$. Thus, $b = (m-1)e + e = me$, contradicting that $b \in S$. Thus, $S = \phi$ and the lemma is proved.

Lemma 5.18.8 $I^+ = \{me \mid m \in Z, m > 0\}$.

Proof: By Corollary 5.18.5, $1e = e \in I^+$, and, if $ke \in I^+$, then $ke + e = (k+1)e \in I^+$. Hence, by mathematical induction, any element of the form me, $m \in Z$, $m > 0$, is in I^+. By Lemma 5.18.7, every element of I^+ is of this form.

Lemma 5.18.9 Let $a \in I$. Then $a = me$, $m \in Z$.

Proof: If $a = 0$, then $a = 0e$, the second 0 denoting the integer 0.

If $a \neq 0$, then either $a \in I^+$, whence a has the form me, $m \in Z$, $m > 0$, by Lemma 5.18.8, or $-a \in I^+$, whence $-a = me$, $m > 0$, and so $a = (-m)e$.

Lemma 5.18.10 Let $m \in Z$. Then $me = 0$ if and only if $m = 0$.

Proof: If $m = 0$, then $me = 0$ trivially. Now suppose $me = 0$. If $m \neq 0$, then either m or $-m$ is positive. If m is positive, then by Lemma 5.18.8, $me \in I^+$ and so $me \neq 0$. If m is negative, then $(-m)e \in I^+$, whence again $me \neq 0$. Thus, $me = 0$ implies $m = 0$.

We can now prove our main result for this section.

Theorem 5.18.11 Let I be an ordered integral domain and let I^+ be well ordered. Then I and Z are isomorphic as rings.

Proof: Let $f: Z \to I$ be defined as follows:

$$mf = me, \text{ for all } m \in Z.$$

Clearly, f is a function and it is onto by Lemma 5.1.8.9. It is also easy to see that f is 1–1. Thus, it remains to show f preserves addition and multiplication. Thus

$$(m + n)f = (m + n)e = me + ne = mf + nf$$

$$\text{and} \quad (mn)f = (mn)e = (me)(ne) = mf \cdot nf.$$

This completes the proof.

CHAPTER 6

Topics in the Theory of Groups

6.1 A BASIS THEOREM FOR FINITELY GENERATED ABELIAN GROUPS

The direct product operation on a pair of groups A and B can be considered a procedure for "constructing" a "big" group $A \times B$ from the "smaller" parts A and B. By repeating this procedure on the set of groups $\{A, B, A \times B\}$, we can obtain the groups $A \times A$, $A \times A \times B$, $B \times B$, $B \times A \times A$, and so on. The set of groups so constructed is then referred to as the set of groups generated by A and B by the process of forming direct products. It has the property that for any pair of groups G and H in this set, the group $G \times H$ is also in the set.

Conversely, if a set of groups $\mathfrak{S}$ is given and we know that this set is "closed" under the formation of direct products (that is, if for each pair $G, H \in \mathfrak{S}$, $G \times H \in \mathfrak{S}$), then we may ask whether there exists a proper subset of $\mathfrak{S}$ that "generates" $\mathfrak{S}$. If, in fact, such a subset, say $\mathfrak{J}$, exists and is "small," then much can be learned about an arbitrary group G in $\mathfrak{S}$ from the fact that G is a direct product of groups (with possible repetitions) in the set $\mathfrak{J}$. We have already examined precisely such a situation in Section 4.13. There we considered the set $\mathfrak{S}$ of all finite abelian groups each of whose nonidentity elements has order p, with p a fixed prime. Clearly, the direct product of any two such groups is in the set $\mathfrak{S}$. We ask: Is there a small subset of $\mathfrak{S}$ that generates $\mathfrak{S}$ by the process of forming direct products, and if so, what is the smallest possible such subset? The answer is provided by Theorem 4.13.9, which states that any such group can be written as a direct product of a finite number of copies of the group C_p, the cyclic group of order p. That is, $\mathfrak{S}$ is generated by the set consisting of the single group C_p, and clearly C_p is not the direct product of smaller groups.

Theorem 4.13.9 is an example of a *basis theorem* for the set of groups $\mathfrak{S}$. In this section we shall derive a basis theorem for a very large class of abelian groups.

Definition 6.1.1 Let G be a group and A be a finite set of generators of G, that is, $G = (A)$. Then G is said to be *finitely generated.*

Every finite group is, of course, an example of a finitely generated group since the group is generated by the set of all of its elements. The additive group of integers, on the other hand, is an example of a finitely generated group that is infinite. Finally, if Q is the additive group of rational numbers, then Q is not finitely generated. For, if $\{a_1/b_1, \cdots, a_n/b_n\}$ is a finite set of rational numbers in lowest terms, then there exists a prime p that does not divide $b_1, b_2, \cdots, b_n$. Since

$$a_i/b_i + a_j/b_j = (a_ib_j + a_jb_i)/b_ib_j,$$

it follows that p will not divide the denominator of any rational number in the subgroup generated by $\{a_1/b_1, \cdots, a_n/b_n\}$, and hence that $1/p$ is not contained in the subgroup. Therefore, no finite set of rationals generates the additive group Q.

Before we state the main theorem we shall consider a special case.

Theorem 6.1.2 Let G be a finite cyclic group of order $n = p_1^{\alpha_1} \cdots p_k^{\alpha_k}$ for different primes $p_1, \cdots, p_k$. Then $G = A_1 \dot{\times} A_2 \dot{\times} \cdots \dot{\times} A_k$, with A_i a cyclic group of order $p_i^{\alpha_i}$. That is, any finite group can be written as a direct product of cyclic groups of prime power order.

Proof: Since G is a finite cyclic group, it has a single generator, say a, of order $n = p_1^{\alpha_1} \cdots p_k^{\alpha_k}$. It is easy to see that the element $a_i = a^{n/p_i^{\alpha_i}}$ has order $p_i^{\alpha_i}$. We shall show that G is the direct product of the groups $A_i = (a_i)$, $i = 1, \cdots, k$. Clearly, $G = A_1A_2 \cdots A_k$, and we need show only that $A_i \cap \hat{A}_i = E$ where $\hat{A}_i = A_1 \cdots A_{i-1}A_{i+1} \cdots A_k$. Now every element of $\hat{A}_i$ is a product of elements of orders $p_1^{\beta_1}$, $p_2^{\beta_2}$, $\cdots, p_{i-1}^{\beta_{i-1}}, p_{i+1}^{\beta_{i+1}}, \cdots, p_k^{\beta_k}, \beta_j \leq \alpha_j, j = 1, \cdots, k$, and since G is abelian, the order of every such element is just the product of these orders (see Exercise 8, Section 4.7). But every element of A_i has order a power of p_i and hence $A_i \cap \hat{A}_i = E$. Thus $G = A_1 \dot{\times} A_2 \dot{\times} \cdots \dot{\times} A_k$.

We have therefore shown that every finite cyclic group is contained in the class of groups "generated" by the cyclic groups of prime power order.

We now give a lemma that will be used in the proof of the main theorem of this section. The proofs we give of the lemma and the theorem are due to R. Rado (*J. London Math. Soc.*, (26), 1951, pp. 74–75).

Lemma 6.1.3 Let $A = \{a_1, \cdots, a_k\}$ be a finite nonempty subset of elements of an abelian group G and let $n_1, \cdots, n_k$ be a set of integers with $\gcd(n_1, \cdots, n_k) = 1$ and $n_1 \neq 0$. If $b_1 = a_1^{n_1} a_2^{n_2} \cdots a_k^{n_k}$, there exists a set of elements $\{b_2, \cdots, b_k\}$ such that if $B = \{b_1, b_2, \cdots, b_k\}$, then $(A) = (B)$. That is to say, the sets A and B generate the same subgroup of G.

Proof: Let $n = |n_1| + |n_2| + \cdots + |n_k|$. The proof is by course-of-values induction on n.

If $n = 1$, then $|n_1| = 1$ and $n_i = 0$ for $2 \leq i \leq k$. Thus, $b_1 = a_1^{\pm 1}$, and we may choose $b_i = a_i$ for $2 \leq i \leq k$. Then, clearly, $(A) = (B)$.

Now assume that $n > 1$. Since $(n_1, \cdots, n_k) = 1$, it follows that at least two of the n_i are different from zero, that is, $n_1 \neq 0$ and $n_i \neq 0$ for some $i > 1$. Hence, either $|n_1 \pm n_i| < |n_1|$ or $|n_1 \pm n_i| < |n_i|$. Interchanging n_1 and n_i, if necessary, we may assume that $|n_1 \pm n_i| < |n_1|$. Hence, $n' = |n_1 \pm n_i| + |n_2| + \cdots + |n_k| < n$ and $(n_1 \pm n_i, n_2, \cdots, n_k) = 1$. Clearly, $(A) = (A')$ where $A' = \{a_1, a_2, \cdots, a_{i-1}, a_1^{\mp 1} a_i, \cdots, a_k\}$. If $b' = a_1^{n_1 \pm n_i} a_2^{n_2} \cdots a_{i-1}^{n_{i-1}} (a_1^{\mp 1} a_i)^{n_i} \cdots a_k^{n_k}$, then, by induction, since $n' < n$, there exist $b_2, \cdots, b_k$ so that $(A') = (b', b_2, \cdots, b_k)$. But, since G is abelian, $b' = b_1$. Hence,

$$(A) = (A') = (b_1, b_2, \cdots, b_k).$$

Theorem 6.1.4 Basis Theorem for Finitely Generated Abelian Groups Let G be a finitely generated abelian group. Then

$$G = A_1 \dot{\times} A_2 \dot{\times} \cdots \dot{\times} A_n$$

where A_i is either an infinite cyclic group or a cyclic group of prime power order.

Proof: Since G is finitely generated, there is an integer m such that G has a set of generators containing m elements. Among such sets of generators, choose one $\{a_1, \cdots, a_m\}$ satisfying the following properties:

i) $|a_i| \leq |a_j|$ for $i \leq j$.

ii) If $\{b_1, \cdots, b_m\}$ is another set of generators ordered as in i), and $|a_i| = |b_i|, i = 1, \cdots, j$, then $|a_{j+1}| \leq |b_{j+1}|$. (If u is an element of infinite order and v one of finite order, then we write $|u| > |v|$ or $|u| \geq |v|$).

It follows from the LWO that such a set exists. For among all generating systems of m elements ordered to satisfy i), we begin by selecting those whose first elements have the minimal order; then, among these, we select those sets whose second elements have the minimal order; and so on for m steps. Among those generating sets obtained at the end of this process, we simply choose any one and let it be $\{a_1, \cdots, a_m\}$. Clearly this set satisfies conditions i) and ii).

Since $\{a_1,\cdots,a_m\}$ generates G, $G = (a_1)\cdots(a_m)$. To show that G is a direct product of these cyclic groups, it suffices to show that whenever $a_1^{\alpha_1}\cdots a_m^{\alpha_m} = e$, then $a_i^{\alpha_i} = e$ for $i = 1,\cdots,m$ (see Exercise 1, Section 4.13). Hence, assume that there is a set of integers $\alpha_1,\cdots,\alpha_m$ such that $a_1^{\alpha_1}a_2^{\alpha_2}\cdots a_m^{\alpha_m} = e$ and that $a_i^{\alpha_i} \neq e$ for some i. Let j be the first subscript for which $a_j^{\alpha_j} \neq e$, and let $(\alpha_j,\alpha_{j+1},\cdots,\alpha_m) = \alpha$. We may assume that α_j is a least positive residue modulo the order of a_j. If $\alpha_k = \alpha'_k\alpha$, for $k = j,\cdots,m$, then

$$a_j^{\alpha_j}\cdots a_m^{\alpha_m} = (a_j^{\alpha'_j}\cdots a_m^{\alpha'_m})^{\alpha} = e$$

and $(\alpha'_j,\cdots,\alpha'_m) = 1$. Hence, by Lemma 6.1.3, if $A = \{a_j,\cdots,a_m\}$ and $b = a_j^{\alpha'_j}a_{j+1}^{\alpha'_{j+1}}\cdots a_m^{\alpha'_m}$, then there exist elements $b_j,b_{j+1},\cdots,b_m$, b equal to one of the b_i's, such that if $B = \{b_j,\cdots,b_m\}$, then $(A) = (B)$. Now we may assume that $|\,b_i\,| \leq |\,b_{i+1}\,|$, $i = j,\cdots,m-1$. Then if $|\,a_{k-1}\,| \leq |\,b_j\,| \leq |\,a_k\,|$, for some $k < j$, using the properties of $\{a_1,\cdots,a_m\}$, we see that $|\,a_k\,| \leq |\,b_j\,|$, whence $|\,a_k\,| = |\,b_j\,|$. Also, it is easy to see that our choice of $\{a_1,\cdots,a_m\}$ now implies that $|\,b_j\,| = |\,a_k\,| = \cdots = |\,a_{j-1}\,|$, so $\{a_1,\cdots,a_{j-1},b_j,\cdots,b_m\}$ satisfies i). But $|\,b_j\,| \leq |\,b\,| \leq \alpha \leq \alpha\alpha'_j = \alpha_j < |\,a_j\,|$, contradicting ii). Thus $a_i^{\alpha_i} = e$, $i = 1,\cdots,m$, and hence, G is a direct product of the cyclic subgroups (a_i). We may now eliminate those a_i equal to e, and G is a direct product of nontrivial cyclic groups. If (a_i) is finite, not of prime power order, then, by Theorem 6.1.2, (a_i) is the direct product of cyclic groups of prime power order. Hence, G is the direct product of cyclic groups, either infinite or of prime power order.

Corollary 6.1.5 Every finite abelian group is the direct product of cyclic groups of prime power order.

Proof: Exercise.

Although Theorem 6.1.4 asserts that a finitely generated abelian group can be decomposed into a direct product of infinite cyclic groups and cyclic groups of prime power order, it still remains to be shown that this decomposition is essentially unique. We shall prove part of this fact here, with the remainder proved in Theorem 7.2.17.

For the remainder of this section, if G is a group, then G^k will denote the set $\{g^k \mid g \in G\}$, where k is a fixed nonnegative integer.

Lemma 6.1.6 Let G be an abelian group, and let A and B be finite subgroups. Then

i) if $n = \operatorname{lcm}[\,|\,A\,|, |\,B\,|\,]$,
$(A \times B)^n = E$ and $(AB)^n = E$

ii) $(A \times B)^r = A^r \times B^r$.

iii) If $G = A \dot{\times} B$ and if $A^m = E$, then $G^m = B^m$.

Proof: The proof of this theorem is left to the exercises.

Lemma 6.1.7 Let

$$(a_1) \dot{\times} \cdots \dot{\times} (a_m) \dot{\times} (b_1) \dot{\times} \cdots \dot{\times} (b_n)$$

and

$$(c_1) \dot{\times} \cdots \dot{\times} (c_r) \dot{\times} (d_1) \dot{\times} \cdots \dot{\times} (d_s)$$

be two decompositions of a finitely generated abelian group G, in which each (a_i) and (c_i) is a cyclic group of prime power order and each (b_i) and (d_i) is infinite cyclic. If $H = \{g \in G \mid g^k = e \text{ for some integer } k \neq 0\}$, then H is a subgroup of G and

$$H = (a_1) \dot{\times} \cdots \dot{\times} (a_m) = (c_1) \dot{\times} \cdots \dot{\times} (c_r).$$

Proof: Exercise.

By Cauchy's theorem, if $p \mid |H|$, p a prime, then H has an element of order p. Clearly, then, a power of p must appear among the orders of the (a_i)'s (and the (c_i)'s) if and only if $p \mid |H|$.

Definition 6.1.8 Let G be a finitely generated abelian group. A *canonical decomposition* of G into cyclic subgroups is a decomposition of the form

$$G = (a_{11}) \dot{\times} \cdots \dot{\times} (a_{1n_1}) \dot{\times} (a_{21}) \dot{\times} \cdots \dot{\times} (a_{mn_m}) \\ \dot{\times} (b_1) \dot{\times} \cdots \dot{\times} (b_s), \qquad (*)$$

where $|(a_{ij})| = p_i^{\alpha ij}$, p_i a prime, $p_i \neq p_j$, for $i \neq j$,

$$p_i^{\alpha ij} \geq p_i^{\alpha ik}, \text{ for } k \geq j,$$

and $|(b_j)| = \infty$.

The indexed set $\{p_i^{\alpha ij}\}$ is called the *set of invariants* of the group H (defined in Lemma 6.1.7). We shall prove that this set of invariants and s (another invariant) completely describe the decomposition of G (and hence, we justify the use of the terms canonical and invariant).

Now any two decompositions of G can be put into the form (*) (with possibly different sets of invariants). If, however, $G_{p_i} = \{g \in G \mid g^{p_i^\alpha} = e$, for some $\alpha \neq 0\}$, where $p_i \mid |H|$, then $G_{p_i} = (a_{i1}) \dot{\times} (a_{i2}) \dot{\times} \cdots \dot{\times} (a_{in_i})$. Thus, by proving that whenever $G_{p_i} = (a_{i1}) \dot{\times} \cdots \dot{\times} (a_{in_i}) = (c_{i1}) \dot{\times} \cdots \dot{\times} (c_{im_i})$, then $n_i = m_i$ and $|a_{ij}| = |c_{ij}|$, we shall have proved that the decomposition of H is unique (up to isomorphism of factors). We note that $|G_{p_i}| = p_i^{\alpha_i}$, for some $\alpha_i > 0$.

Theorem 6.1.9 Let G be a finite abelian group of order p^α that contains cyclic subgroups $P_1, \cdots, P_s$ with $|P_i| \geq |P_j| > 1$, for $i \leq j$, and such that $G = P_1 \dot{\times} \cdots \dot{\times} P_s$. If $G \cong R_1 \times \cdots \times R_t$, with R_k a cyclic group of order p^{α_k} and $|R_\ell| \geq |R_m| > 1$ for $\ell \leq m$, then $s = t$ and $P_i \cong R_i$ for $i = 1, \cdots, s$.

Proof: If $p^\alpha = |P_1| > |R_1|$, then, on the one hand, since $|R_1| \geq |R_i|, i \geq 1$, $G^{p^{\alpha-1}} = \{g^{p^{\alpha-1}} \mid g \in G\} \cong (R_1 \times \cdots \times R_t)^{p^{\alpha-1}} = E$ by Lemma 6.1.6, and on the other hand, $G^{p^{\alpha-1}} \supseteq P_1{}^{p^{\alpha-1}} \supset E$, a contradiction. Similarly, $|P_1| < |R_1|$ yields a contradiction. Thus, $|P_1| = |R_1|$. If $|P_i| = |R_i|$ for $i = 1, \cdots, s$, then, since $|G| = |P_1| \cdots |P_s| = |R_1| \cdots |R_t|$, it follows that $s = t$ and thus $P_i \cong R_i$, $i = 1, \cdots, s$. Hence, assume that n is the first subscript for which $|P_n| \neq |R_n|$ and we may assume that $|P_n| > |R_n| = p^\beta$. Now consider $G^{p^\beta} = \{g^{p^\beta} \mid g \in G\}$. Since $|R_n| \geq |R_m|$ for $n \leq m$,

$$G^{p^\beta} \cong (R_1 \times \cdots \times R_t)^{p^\beta} \cong R_1{}^{p^\beta} \times \cdots \times R_{n-1}{}^{p^\beta},$$

while

$$G^{p^\beta} = (P_1 \dot{\times} \cdots \dot{\times} P_s)^{p^\beta} = P_1{}^{p^\beta} \dot{\times} \cdots \dot{\times} P_{n-1}{}^{p^\beta} \dot{\times} P_n{}^{p^\beta} \dot{\times} \cdots \dot{\times} P_s{}^{p^\beta}.$$

But, since $|P_i| = |R_i|, i = 1, \cdots, n-1$, it follows that

$$\begin{aligned} |G^{p^\beta}| &= |R_1{}^{p^\beta} \times \cdots \times R_{n-1}{}^{p^\beta}| \\ &= |P_1{}^{p^\beta} \dot{\times} \cdots \dot{\times} P_{n-1}{}^{p^\beta}| \, |P_n{}^{p^\beta} \dot{\times} \cdots \dot{\times} P_s{}^{p^\beta}|. \end{aligned}$$

Finally, since $|P_n{}^{p^\beta}| > 1$ and

$$|R_1{}^{p^\beta} \times \cdots \times R_{n-1}{}^{p^\beta}| = |P_1{}^{p^\beta} \dot{\times} \cdots \dot{\times} P_{n-1}{}^{p^\beta}|,$$

we have a contradiction.

Theorem 6.1.10 Let G be a finitely generated abelian group such that
i) $G = (a_{11}) \dot{\times} \cdots \dot{\times} (a_{mn_m}) \dot{\times} (b_1) \dot{\times} \cdots \dot{\times} (b_s)$
ii) $G = (c_{11}) \dot{\times} \cdots \dot{\times} (c_{un_u}) \dot{\times} (d_1) \dot{\times} \cdots \dot{\times} (d_t)$
are canonical decompositions of G (the (b_i)'s and the (d_i)'s are the factors of infinite order). Then there is a 1–1 correspondence between the finite factors of the decompositions that pairs isomorphic groups. Moreover, $s = t$.

Proof: Using the group H and the G_{p_i}'s defined above, and using Theorem 6.1.9, the first conclusion follows easily. We shall defer the proof that $s = t$ until Section 7.2, in which we can use some elementary facts from linear algebra.

Corollary 6.1.11 Let H be a finite abelian group. Then any decomposition of H into a direct product of cyclic groups of prime power order is unique (up to the number of factors and their orders).

Proof: Exercise.

As a result of these theorems we can now exhibit all finite abelian groups up to isomorphism. For example, if $n = 180$, then the only possible sets of invariants for an abelian group G of order 180 are

$$\{2, 2, 3, 3, 5\}$$
$$\{2, 2, 9, 5\}$$
$$\{4, 3, 3, 5\}$$

and
$$\{4, 9, 5\}.$$

The corresponding groups are

$$C_2 \times C_2 \times C_3 \times C_3 \times C_5$$
$$C_2 \times C_2 \times C_9 \times C_5$$
$$C_4 \times C_3 \times C_3 \times C_5$$

and
$$C_4 \times C_9 \times C_5$$

where C_i is the cyclic group of order i.

Exercises

1. Prove Corollary 6.1.5.
2. Prove the following directly, without using Theorem 6.1.4 or Corollary 6.1.5:

   Let G be a finite abelian group of order $u = p_1^{\alpha_1} \cdots p_k^{\alpha_k}$ for distinct primes p_i, and let A_i be the set of all elements of G of order a power of the prime p_i. Show that each A_i is a subgroup of G and $G = A_1 \dot{\times} A_2 \dot{\times} \cdots \dot{\times} A_k$.

   Prove the same result using Corollary 6.1.5.
3. How many abelian groups (up to isomorphism) are there of order $n = p_1 p_2^2 p_3^3 p_4^4$, for distinct primes p_1, p_2, p_3, p_4?

†4. Let G be a finite abelian group, and let a be an element of G of maximal order. Show that either G is cyclic or there exists a subgroup H such that $G = (a) \dot{\times} H$.

5. Let G be a finite abelian group of order n and let d be a positive divisor of n. Show that G has a subgroup of order d.
6. Do Exercise 11, Section 4.7, using the basis theorem.
7. Prove Lemma 6.1.6.
8. Complete the details of the proof of the first part of Theorem 6.1.10.
9. Prove Corollary 6.1.11.

6.2 SYLOW THEOREMS

The theorem of Lagrange, which states that the order of a subgroup H of a finite group G divides the order of G, has played a fundamental role in our investigations of finite groups. This theorem shows a connection between the kinds of subgroups that a finite group can have and the arithmetic properties of the integer n, its order. In this section and the next we shall consider this connection further.

A question that arises immediately is whether the converse of Lagrange's theorem is true, that is, given a positive divisor d of the order of a finite group G, is there a subgroup of G of order d? That this is not always true can be seen by examining A_4, the group of all even permutations on $X_4 = \{1,2,3,4\}$. The order of A_4 is 12, 6 is a divisor of 12, but A_4 contains no subgroup of order 6. This can be shown as follows:

If A_4 had a subgroup of order 6, it would have to be isomorphic either to the cyclic group of order 6, or to the group S_3. Now, every element of A_4 different from (1) has the form (abc) or $(ab)(cd)$—a,b,c,d are distinct (why?)—and these elements have orders 3 and 2, respectively. A_4 therefore contains no element of order 6, and hence does not contain a cyclic subgroup of order 6. We now recall that the group S_3 contains (1 2) and (1 2 3), a pair of elements of orders 2 and 3, respectively, whose product (1 3) has order 2. But any element of order 2 in A_4 has the form $(ab)(cd)$, any element of order 3 in A_4 has the form (abc) (a,b,c,d distinct), and $(ab)(cd)(abc) = (acd)$, which has order 3. Hence, A_4 contains no subgroup isomorphic to S_3. We see that therefore even though 6 divides the order of A_4, A_4 contains no subgroup of order 6.

We now find ourselves in a very common mathematical situation. We have an extremely useful theorem whose converse happens to be false. We may still ask, however, if there is some modified converse that is true? Let us state the false converse precisely and ask what modifications might prove fruitful.

False converse of Lagrange's theorem Let G be a finite group of order n, and let d be a positive divisor of n. Then G contains a subgroup of order d.

In this statement we make no restrictions on G, except that it be finite, and none on d, except that it be a positive divisor of n. Hence, we may ask: Is the statement true if we somehow restrict the class of finite groups? We have already shown, in fact, that if G is a finite abelian group, then G does contain a subgroup of every "possible" order, that is, for each positive integer d dividing the order of G, G contains a subgroup of order d (see Exercise 5, Section 6.1). It is not hard to find examples of nonabelian groups that also satisfy the property, for example, S_3. We shall soon display a large class of such groups.

We may also restrict the converse to Lagrange's theorem by putting some conditions on the integer d. Again we have already proved such a theorem in Chapter 4, for Theorem 4.12.8 states that if d is a prime divisor of the order of a finite group G, then G contains a subgroup of order d. One of the most important restricted converses of Lagrange's theorem is a generalization of Theorem 4.12.18 to the case $d = p^\alpha$, where p is a prime. This theorem is known as the first Sylow theorem, and is of fundamental importance in the study of finite groups.

Theorem 6.2.1 ***First Sylow Theorem*** Let G be a finite group of order n, and let $p^\alpha \mid n$, p a prime. Then G contains a subgroup of order p^α.

Proof: We may assume that $\alpha \geq 1$, for otherwise the theorem is trivial. Now, let G be a minimal counterexample, that is, $|G| = n$, $p^\alpha \mid n$, G has no subgroup of order p^α, and $|G|$ is minimal with respect to these properties. Thus, if H is a group, $|H| < |G|$, and if $p^\beta \mid |H|$, then H has a subgroup of order p^β.

If the prime p divides the order of the center of G, $C(G)$, then $C(G)$ contains a subgroup of order p, say A (Theorem 4.12.17). Since A is a subgroup of the center, A is normal in G. Hence, G/A is a group of order less than n, and $p^{\alpha-1} \mid |G/A|$, since $p^\alpha \mid n$. Hence, since G is a minimal counterexample, G/A contains a subgroup H/A of order $p^{\alpha-1}$. Hence the subgroup H of G has order p^α, a contradiction.

If p does not divide the order of $C(G)$, then we consider the class equation: $n = |G| = |C(G)| + \mu_1 + \mu_2 + \cdots + \mu_r$, with $\mu_i > 1$, $1 \leq i \leq r$. Since $p \mid n$ and $p \nmid |C(G)|$, then p does not divide μ_j for some j, $1 \leq j \leq r$. But μ_j is the index of a subgroup M of G, and since $n = [G:M] \cdot |M| = u_j |M|$, $|M|$ is divisible by p^α. Since $\mu_j > 1$, M is a proper subgroup of G, and hence, M contains a subgroup of order p^α that is also a subgroup of G. This again contradicts the choice of G as a counterexample, and the theorem is proved.

Definition 6.2.2 Let G be a finite group of order n, and let p^α be the highest power of the prime p that divides n. Then a subgroup of G of order p^α is called a *p-Sylow subgroup*.

In general, a p-Sylow subgroup is of interest only when $p^\alpha \mid n$ for $\alpha > 0$. The reader should also note that a p-Sylow subgroup of a group need not be unique. For example, S_3 contains three subgroups of order 2.

Corollary 6.2.3 For each prime p, the finite group G contains a p-Sylow subgroup.

Proof: This follows directly from Theorem 6.2.1 and Definition 6.2.2.

We can now enlarge the class of groups for which the converse of Lagrange's theorem is true. To the class of all finite abelian groups we may add those groups whose order is a power of a prime.

Definition 6.2.4 Let G be a group each of whose elements has order a power of the prime p. Then G is called a *p-group*. We recall that if G is a finite p-group, then $|G| = p^\alpha$ (see Corollary 4.12.19).

Corollary 6.2.5 Let G be a finite p-group. Then, for each positive divisor d of $|G|$, G contains a subgroup of order d.

Proof: Apply Theorem 6.2.1 and Definition 6.2.4.

Exercises

1. Let G be a group of order 72. a) Show that G contains subgroups of orders 2, 4, 8, 3, 9. b) Show that if a subgroup of order 8 is normal in G, then G contains a subgroup of order 24.

2. Let $G \cong A_1 \times A_2 \times \cdots \times A_n$, where A_i is a p_i-group for primes $p_1, p_2, \cdots, p_n$. Show that for each positive divisor d of $|G|$, G has a subgroup of order d.

†3. Let G be a group of order p^α for some prime p. Show every subgroup of order $p^{\alpha-1}$ is normal in G.

Hint: Let H be a subgroup of order $p^{\alpha-1}$. Show that H has an element g such that $g \in C(G)$, the center of G. Consider $G/(g)$ and proceed by induction.

4. Let G be a group of order 20. Show that a 5-Sylow subgroup is normal in G.

Hint: Use Exercise 19, Section 4.8.

5. Let S be a p-Sylow subgroup of G. Show that $g^{-1}Sg$ is also a p-Sylow subgroup of G for any $g \in G$. ●

The remaining Sylow theorems give some detailed information about the Sylow subgroups of a finite group G. We first state the main theorem and then give some elementary lemmas required in the proof.

Theorem 6.2.6 Sylow Let S be a p-Sylow subgroup of a finite group G. Then

i) Any p-Sylow subgroup of G is a conjugate of S and hence, any two p-Sylow subgroups of G (for the same prime p) are conjugate.

ii) Any subgroup P of G of order a power of p is a subgroup of some p-Sylow subgroup.

iii) The number of p-Sylow subgroups of G is congruent to 1 modulo p and divides the order of G.

Lemma 6.2.7 Let A and B be subgroups of a group G. The number of conjugates of A induced by B, that is, of the form $b^{-1}Ab, b \in B$, is equal to $[B:B \cap N_G(A)]$, where $N_G(A)$ is the normalizer of A in G.

Proof: If $b_1, b_2 \in B$, then $b_1^{-1}Ab_1 = b_2^{-1}Ab_2$ if and only if

$$b_2 b_1^{-1} A b_1 b_2^{-1} = A,$$

that is, if and only if $b_1 b_2^{-1} \in N_G(A) \cap B$. This is in turn equivalent to the condition that b_1 and b_2 are in the same right coset of $N_G(A) \cap B$

in B. Hence, the number of distinct conjugates of A induced by B is the number of distinct right cosets of $N_G(A) \cap B$ in B, which is $[B:N_G(A) \cap B]$.

Lemma 6.2.8 Let S be a p-Sylow subgroup of G. Then every subgroup of $N_G(S)$ of order a power of p is a subgroup of S.

Proof: Since $S \lhd N_G(S)$, if P is a p-group and $P \subseteq N_G(S)$, then PS is a subgroup of $N_G(S)$ and $|PS| = \dfrac{|P|\,|S|}{|P \cap S|}$, by Exercise 19, Section 4.8. Hence, PS is a p-group and, since S is a p-Sylow subgroup of G, $|PS| \leq |S|$. But S is clearly a subgroup of PS. Consequently, $S = PS$ and $P \subseteq S$.

Proof of Theorem 6.2.6: We begin by showing that if S is a p-Sylow subgroup of G, then the number of conjugates of S in G is congruent to 1 modulo p.

iii′) If S is a normal subgroup of G, then the result is trivial. Hence, assume that T is a conjugate of S, $T \neq S$, and let $\{T_i\}$ be the set of conjugates of T induced by S. By Lemma 6.2.7, the number of elements in $\{T_i\}$ is $|\{T_i\}| = [S:S \cap N_G(T)] = p^\beta$, for some β. Moreover, $\beta > 0$, for, if $\beta = 0$, then $S = S \cap N_G(T)$ and $S \subseteq N_G(T)$. But then, $T = S$ by Lemma 6.2.8, a contradiction. Hence $|\{T_i\}|$ is a positive power of p.

Now, if T_j is a conjugate of S different from S and not in $\{T_i\}$, then the number of conjugates of T_j induced by S is again a positive power of p. Moreover, no conjugate of T_j by S is also a conjugate of T by S, for, if $s_1^{-1}T_js_1 = s_2^{-1}Ts_2$, then $s_1s_2^{-1}Ts_2s_1 = T_j$ and $T_j \in \{T_i\}$, a contradiction. Finally, the set of conjugates of S induced by S is simply $\{S\}$. Hence, the set of all conjugates of S can be decomposed into a pairwise disjoint union of sets, the first, $\{S\}$, consisting of a single element and each of the remaining containing a positive prime power number of elements. Hence, the total number of conjugates of S is congruent to 1 modulo p.

ii) Now let $P \subseteq G$ be a p-group. We can now repeat the above argument, allowing P to induce conjugates of S. Thus, P induces $[P:P \cap N_G(S_i)]$ conjugates of the group S_i, a conjugate of S in G. Now if each of the classes $\{S_i\}$ contains a positive power of p number of elements, then the total number of conjugates of S is a multiple of p, a contradiction. Thus for some conjugate S_i of S, $[P:P \cap N_G(S_i)] = 1$ and $P \subseteq N_G(S_i)$. Hence, by Lemma 6.2.8, $P \subseteq S_i$.

i) In the above argument let P be any p-Sylow subgroup of G. Then $P \subseteq S_i$ for some conjugate S_i of S. But $|P| = |S_i|$ and therefore $P = S_i$. Hence, any two p-Sylow subgroups are conjugate. It therefore follows that the total number of p-Sylow subgroups of G is congruent to 1 modulo p and equals $[G:N_G(P)]$, which divides $|G|$.

As an application of the Sylow theorems, we determine all groups of order pq, with p and q distinct primes. In particular, since we know that r every positive integer n there is a cyclic group of order n, we shall termine necessary and sufficient conditions on the primes p and q such hat the only group (up to isomorphism) of order pq is cyclic.

Lemma 6.2.9 Let $|G| = pq$, p and q primes with $p > q$. Then, if S is a p-Sylow subgroup of G, S is normal in G.

Proof: Let S be a p-Sylow subgroup of G. If S is not normal in G, then $S = N_G(S)$ and the number of subgroups of order p is $[G:N_G(S)] = q$. But, on the other hand, there are at least $1 + p$ subgroups of order p in G and $p > q$, a contradiction. Hence $S \lhd G$.

Theorem 6.2.10 Let $|G| = pq$, p and q primes with $p > q$. If $p \not\equiv 1 \pmod q$, then G is cyclic. If $p \equiv 1 \pmod q$, then either G is cyclic or G is a nonabelian group generated by two elements a and b which satisfy the following relations: $a^q = e$, $b^p = e$, $a^{-1}ba = b^s$, $s \not\equiv 1 \pmod p$ and $s^q \equiv 1 \pmod p$.

Proof: Since $p > q$, it follows from Lemma 6.2.9 that $S \lhd G$. Hence the factor group G/S is cyclic of order q and there exists $a \in G$ of order q such that aS is a generator of G/S. (Why?) Since S is cyclic, it has a generator b of order p and clearly a and b generate the group G. Since $a^{-1}Sa = S$, $a^{-1}ba = b^s$ for some positive integer s. It follows from Exercise 5, Section 4.5, that $a^{-(p-1)}ba^{p-1} = b^{s^{p-1}}$. But $s^{p-1} \equiv 1 \pmod p$ and hence, $b^{s^{p-1}} = b$. But, if $q \nmid p - 1$, then $a^{-(p-1)}ba^{p-1} = b$ implies that $ab = ba$ by Exercise 24, Section 4.7, and G is abelian. Thus, from Exercise 9, Section 4.7, G is cyclic. Therefore, if $p \not\equiv 1 \pmod q$, G is cyclic.

If G is not abelian, then, since $a^{-1}ba = b^s$, $b^s \neq b$, and so, $s \not\equiv 1 \pmod p$. Furthermore, $a^{-q}ba^q = b^{s^q}$. But $a^q = e$, and so, $b = b^{s^q}$, whence $s^q \equiv 1 \pmod p$.

Exercises

6. Classify all groups of order 10.
7. Show that for each prime p, there are exactly two nonisomorphic groups of order $2p$.
8. Let H be a normal subgroup of the finite group G and suppose that $|H| = p^\alpha$. Show that H is contained in every p-Sylow subgroup of G.
9. Let N be the normalizer in G of a p-Sylow subgroup of G. Show that N is its own normalizer.

*10. (Frattini Lemma) Let H be a normal subgroup of a finite group G, and let T be a p-Sylow subgroup of H.
    i) Show that for each $g \in G$, there is an $h \in H$ such that $g^{-1}Tg = h^{-1}Th$.
    ii) Show that if $N = N_G(T)$, then $G = HN$.

11. Let S be a p-Sylow subgroup of G. Show that if $S \lhd G$ and α is an automorphism of G, then $(S)\alpha = S$.
12. Show that if G is a group of order $p^\alpha q$, with p, q primes and $p > q$, then G contains a unique normal subgroup of index q.
13. Show that if G is a group of order $p^2 q$, with p,q primes and $2 < p < q$, then G contains a unique normal subgroup of order q. For what primes p,q is this false?

†14. Show that a group of order 561 is abelian.

6.3 NORMAL SERIES AND SOLVABLE GROUPS

The first Sylow theorem asserts, in particular, that if G is a group of order $p^\alpha m$, p a prime, with $(p,m) = 1$, then G has a subgroup of order p^α. If we seek to conclude that G has a subgroup of order p^α *and* also a subgroup of order m, then it is not difficult to show that this does not hold for all finite groups. For the order of the group A_5 is $60 = 2^2 \cdot 3 \cdot 5$ and, by the first Sylow theorem, A_5 contains a subgroup of order 4. A_5 does not, however, contain a subgroup of order 15. This may be shown as follows: 1) Any group B of order 15 is of the type discussed in Theorem 6.2.10 with $p = 5$ and $q = 3$. Since $5 \not\equiv 1 \pmod 3$, it follows that B is cyclic and hence contains an element of order 15. 2) If A_5 contains a subgroup of order 15, then it must contain a permutation of order 15. Now every permutation is A_5 has the form (1), $(ab)\,(cd)$, (abc) or $(abcde)$, and none of these has order 15. Hence, A_5 contains no subgroup of order 15.

As in the previous section, we are led to consider the class of finite groups for which this modification of the first Sylow theorem is true. It certainly includes the class of all abelian groups, all p-groups, and direct products of pairs of such groups. Our aim is to formulate a concise description of this set of groups in terms of the "normal series" structure of a group.

Exercise

1. Let the group G have the following property: If $|G| = p^\alpha m$ with $(p^\alpha, m) = 1$ and p a prime, then G has a subgroup of order m. Show that if $|G| = uv$, $(u,v) = 1$, then G has a subgroup of order u (and one of order v).

Hint: Let $|G| = p_1^{e_1} p_2^{e_2} \cdots p_r^{e_r}$. Let H_i be a subgroup of order $p_1^{e_1} \cdots p_{i-1}^{e_{i-1}} p_{i+1}^{e_{i+1}} \cdots p_r^{e_r} = |G|/p_i^{e_i}$, $i = 1, \cdots, r$. Use the "product theorem" (Exercise 19, Section 4.8) to show that $|H_i \cap H_j| = |G|/p_i^{e_i} p_j^{e_j}$, $i \neq j$. Repeat the argument to show that $|H_i \cap H_j \cap H_k| = |G|/p_i^{e_i} p_j^{e_j} p_k^{e_k}$, i, j, and k distinct. Now complete the proof of the exercise. ●

Definition 6.3.1 Let G be a group and let $N_0, N_1, \cdots, N_r$ be a sequence of subgroups of G satisfying:

$$G = N_0 \triangleright N_1 \triangleright \cdots \triangleright N_{r-1} \triangleright N_r = E,$$

where $N_i \triangleright N_{i+1}$ denotes $N_{i+1} \triangleleft N_i$. Such a sequence of groups is called a *normal series* of G. The factor groups N_i/N_{i+1} are called *normal factors* of G.

First, it should be remarked that every group G has a "trivial" normal series N_0, N_1, with $G = N_0$ and $E = N_1$. In this case, there is precisely one normal factor, namely G itself. Second, if N_2 is normal in N_1 and N_1 is normal in N_0, it need not follow that N_2 is normal in N_0. This can be seen by considering the group D_4 of all symmetries of a square, Example 4.1.8. Let $N_2 = \{e, v\}$, $N_1 = \{e, v, h, r_2\}$ and $N_0 = G$. Since N_1 is abelian and N_2 is a subgroup of N_1, N_2 is normal in N_1 and, since N_1 has index 2 in $N_0 = G$, N_1 is normal in N_0. But N_2 is not normal in N_0 since $r_1^{-1} v r_1 = h \notin N_2$. That is, the relation "A is normal in B" is not transitive, and hence, the normality of N_{i+1} in N_i does not necessarily imply that N_{i+1} is normal in G.

It is possible to strengthen the notion of normality so that a form of transitivity does hold. For, if $G \triangleright N \triangleright M$, then M will be normal in G if M is invariant under the inner automorphisms of G. But since $G \triangleright N$, any inner automorphism of G, restricted to N, will be an automorphism, possibly outer, of N. Hence, if M is invariant under *all* automorphisms of N, then M will be invariant under the inner automorphisms of G.

Definition 6.3.2 Let A be a subgroup of G. If $(A)\alpha = A$ for all automorphisms α of G, then A is called a *characteristic subgroup* of G.

The argument above thus proves the following:

Theorem 6.3.3 Let N be a normal subgroup of a group G, and let M be a characteristic subgroup of N. Then M is normal in G.

Exercises

2. Let S be a p-Sylow subgroup of the group G. Show that if $S \triangleleft G$, then S is characteristic in G.

3. Find a normal series of S_3 consisting of three distinct subgroups. Do the same for C_6, the cyclic group of order 6. What are the normal factors of these series?

4. Find a normal series of D_4 consisting of four subgroups each one of which is normal in G.

5. Let G be a finite group and $N_0, \cdots, N_r$ a normal series of G. Show that $|G|$ is equal to the product of the orders of the normal factors $N_0/N_1, \cdots, N_{r-1}/N_r$. ●

Now suppose that R is a normal subgroup of the group G. We construct the normal series

$$G \triangleright R \triangleright E,$$

and we examine the normal factors G/R and $R/E \simeq R$. If R contains a normal subgroup S, then we may expand the original series by inserting S:

$$G \triangleright R \triangleright S \triangleright E.$$

If G/R contains a normal subgroup $\overline{Q}$, then, by Theorem 4.10.11, G contains a normal subgroup Q containing R, and the series can be further expanded by inserting Q:

$$G \triangleright Q \triangleright R \triangleright S \triangleright E.$$

This procedure that we have illustrated of expanding a given normal series is called "refinement."

If $N_0, N_1, \cdots, N_r$ is a normal series of a group G, then it is possible that $N_i = N_{i+1}$ for some i. Hence, the set $\{N_0, N_1, \cdots, N_r\}$ may contain fewer than $r + 1$ elements. It will nevertheless often be convenient to refer to the set $\{N_0, N_1, \cdots, N_r\}$ as a normal series when the ambiguity is not misleading.

Definition 6.3.4 Let $\mathfrak{N} = \{N_0, \cdots, N_r\}$ be a normal series of a group G. Then the normal series $\mathfrak{M} = \{M_0, \cdots, M_s\}$ is said to be a *refinement* of $\mathfrak{N}$ if $\mathfrak{N} \subseteq \mathfrak{M}$. $\mathfrak{M}$ is said to be a *proper refinement* of $\mathfrak{N}$ if $\mathfrak{N} \subset \mathfrak{M}$, that is, if there is an $M_j \in \mathfrak{M}$ such that $M_j \neq N_i$, for all $N_i \in \mathfrak{N}$, and $\mathfrak{N} \subseteq \mathfrak{M}$.

Exercises

*6. Let $\mathfrak{N}$ be a normal series of a finite group G with $\mathfrak{M}$ a proper refinement of $\mathfrak{N}$. Show that there exists a sequence of refinements $\mathfrak{M}_1 = \mathfrak{N}$, $\mathfrak{M}_2; \cdots, \mathfrak{M}_k = \mathfrak{M}$ such that $\mathfrak{M}_{i+1}$ is obtained by adding a single subgroup to $\mathfrak{M}_i$, $i = 1, \cdots, k - 1$.

7. Let $\mathfrak{N} = \{N_0, \cdots, N_k\}$ be a normal series of a group G and let $\overline{\mathfrak{M}}_i = \{\overline{N}_{i0}, \overline{N}_{i1}, \cdots, \overline{N}_{ij_i}\}$ be a normal series of N_i/N_{i+1}. If $\mathfrak{M}_i = \{N_{i0}, N_{i1}, \cdots, N_{ij_i}\}$ with $\overline{N}_{ie} = N_{ie}/N_{i+1}$, then show that $\bigcup_{i=0}^{k-1} \mathfrak{M}_i$ is a normal series of G. •

It follows from Exercise 5 that, if G is a finite group, any normal series may be refined to a point at which no further proper refinements are possible. If G is infinite, this need not be the case, as can be seen by examining the additive group of integers $(Z, +)$. For if L_2 is the subgroup of even integers, then

$$G \triangleright L_2 \triangleright E$$

is a normal series that can be refined to

$$G \rhd L_2 \rhd L_4 \rhd E$$

where L_4 is the subgroup of multiples of 4 and so on, with $L_8, L_{16}, \cdots$.

Definition 6.3.5 Let $\mathfrak{N} = \{N_0, \cdots, N_r\}$ be a normal series of the group G such that every refinement of $\mathfrak{N}$ is itself and $N_i \neq N_j$, $i \neq j$ $i,j = 0, \cdots, r$. Then $\mathfrak{N}$ is called a *composition series* of G and the factor groups N_i/N_{i+1} are called *composition factors*. We call r the *length* of $\mathfrak{N}$.

Example 6.3.6 If $G = S_3$, then $A_3 \lhd G$ and S_3, A_3, E is a normal series of S_3. But $|A_3| = 3$ and $|S_3/A_3| = 2$. Hence, since neither of these groups contains any proper nontrivial subgroups, no refinement of this series is possible, and so it is a composition series.

In general then (see Exercise 11), a normal series of a group G is a composition series if and only if each factor contains only itself and the trivial group as normal subgroups.

Definition 6.3.7 A group G is called *simple* if G contains no nontrivial proper normal subgroup.

Theorem 6.3.8 Let $\mathfrak{N} = \{N_0, \cdots, N_r\}$, $N_i \neq N_j$, for $i \neq j$, be a normal series of a group G. Then $\mathfrak{N}$ is a composition series if and only if each of the groups N_i/N_{i+1} is simple.

Proof: Exercise.

We have already shown (see Corollary 4.8.7) that the group of prime order p is simple in a rather trivial way, since this group contains no nontrivial proper subgroup and hence no normal one. The first example of a nonabelian simple group is the group A_5 that contains several nontrivial proper subgroups but no normal ones.[20]

Exercises

8. Which of the normal series obtained in Exercises 2 and 3 are composition series?
9. Find composition series for S_4; for S_5.
10. Prove that every finite group G has a composition series.
11. Let N be a normal subgroup of a group G, and let $\overline{\mathfrak{N}} = \{\overline{N}_0, \cdots, \overline{N}_k\}$ be a normal series of $\overline{G} = G/N$. Show that if N_i is the inverse image in G of $\overline{N}_i$ in $\overline{G}$, ($\overline{N}_i = N_i/N$), then $\mathfrak{N} = \{N_0, \cdots, N_k, E\}$ is a normal series of G and $\overline{N}_i/\overline{N_{i+1}} \cong N_i/N_{i+1}$. Conclude that if $\overline{\mathfrak{N}}$ is a com-

[20] For a proof that A_5 is simple, the reader should see, for example, Kurosh [31], vol. I, or Rotman [45].

position series of G/N and N is simple, then $\mathfrak{N}$ is a composition series of G. •

Just as the orders of a set of composition factors of G give a factorization of $|G|$, so we may think of these factor groups as providing a "decomposition" of the group G itself. That is to say, the group G is "built up" by first taking the subgroup N_{r-1}, "adjoining" the factor group N_{r-2}/N_{r-1}, thus obtaining the group N_{r-2}, and so on, until we obtain $N_0 = G$. Our next question is, to what extent is this decomposition unique? Since a composition series of a group G may be obtained by refining any given normal series until no further refinements are possible, what happens if we start with two different normal series of a group G? Do we always end up with same composition series, or at least with the same composition factors? Let us consider an example.

Example 6.3.9 Let G contain normal subgroups $N \cong S_3$ and $M \cong C_2$, the cyclic group of order 2, such that $G = NM$ and $N \cap M = E$. That is, $G \cong S_3 \times C_2$. Consider the two normal series:

I. $G \triangleright N \triangleright E$

II. $G \triangleright M \triangleright E$.

The factors of I are $G/N \cong C_2$ and $N \cong S_3$. C_2 is simple, but S_3 contains A_3 as a normal subgroup. Hence, I. can be refined to

I′. $G \triangleright N \triangleright R \triangleright E$, with $R \cong A_3$.

The factors of I′ are:

$$G/N \cong C_2$$
$$N/R \cong C_2$$
$$R/E \cong A_3.$$

Each of these is simple, with orders 2, 2, and 3, respectively, hence I′ is a composition series of G.

The factors of II are $G/M \cong S_3$ and $M \cong C_2$. S_3 contains the normal subgroup A_3 and so II can be refined to

II′. $G \triangleright RM \triangleright M \triangleright E$, with $R \cong A_3$.

The factors of *II′* are:

$$G/RM \cong C_2$$
$$RM/M \cong A_3$$
$$M/E \cong C_2.$$

Again these are all simple and so II′ is a composition series.

Now while I′ and II′ are not the same series, the *composition factors* of I′ and II′ are the same, both in type and in the number of times each one occurs. The fact that this is true for all groups G that have a composition series is known as the Jordan-Hölder theorem (Theorem 6.3.15). This remarkable property justifies the use of the word decomposition in describing the factors of a composition series. For just as the prime powers in the factorization of a positive integer n are invariants of n, so the simple factors of a composition series and the multiplicity with which each one occurs are invariants of G. We remark that this analogy is not exact. For while the prime powers in the factorization of a positive integer n completely determine n, there exist nonisomorphic groups with identical composition factors. For example, the group S_3 and the group C_6 both have C_2 and C_3 as composition factors.

For certain classes of groups, the composition factors of a given group G are very easy to determine.

Theorem 6.3.10 Let G be a finite abelian group of order n, with prime power factorization $n = \prod_{i=1}^{r} p_i^{\alpha_i}$. Then each composition factor of G is a cyclic group of order p_i for some i satisfying $1 \leq i \leq r$, and there are precisely α_i composition factors of order p_i.

Proof: Since G is abelian, every subgroup and every factor group of G is abelian. Hence the composition factors of G are simple abelian groups. But the only simple abelian groups are those of prime order. Since $|G|$ is the product of the orders of the composition factors of G, it follows that there must be α_i composition factors of order p_i for $i = 1, \cdots, r$.

Theorem 6.3.11 Let G be a finite p-group. Then each composition factor of G is a group of order p.

Proof: Exercise.

Exercises

12. Prove Theorem 6.3.11.
13. Let $\mathcal{G}$ and $\mathcal{H}$ be the sets of composition factors of groups G and H respectively. Show that the set of composition factors of $G \times H$ is $\mathcal{G} \cup \mathcal{H}$. •

Before we proceed to the proof of the Jordan-Hölder theorem, we first need a lemma derived by Hans Zassenhaus which can be thought of as a generalization of the second isomorphism theorem.

Lemma 6.3.12 Zassenhaus Let A, A', B and B' be subgroups of a group G with $A' \lhd A$ and $B' \lhd B$. Then

$$A'(A \cap B') \lhd A'(A \cap B),$$

$$B'(B \cap A') \lhd B'(B \cap A)$$

and $$[A'(A \cap B)]/[A'(A \cap B')] \simeq [B'(B \cap A)]/[B'(B \cap A')].$$

Proof: We will prove the lemma by constructing a group H that is a homomorphic image of the groups $A'(A \cap B)$ and $B'(B \cap A)$, having as kernels the subgroups $A'(A \cap B')$ and $B'(B \cap A')$, respectively. This will establish the normality of these subgroups as well as the isomorphism of the factor groups.

Since $B' \lhd B$, it is easy to verify that $A \cap B' \lhd A \cap B$ and similarly since $A' \lhd A$, $A' \cap B \lhd A \cap B$. Thus, since the products of two normal subgroups is a normal subgroup, $C = (A' \cap B)(A \cap B') \lhd A \cap B$.

We define H as follows:

$$H = (A \cap B)/[(A' \cap B)(A \cap B')] = (A \cap B)/C.$$

Clearly since $A' \lhd A$ and $A \cap B$ is a subgroup of A, $A'(A \cap B)$ is a subgroup of A. We now define the mapping $f: A'(A \cap B) \to H$ as follows:

$$(a'a)f = aC \quad \text{where} \quad a' \in A',\ a \in A \cap B.$$

i) f is well defined. Suppose that $a_1'a_1 = a_2'a_2$, with $a_i' \in A'$ and $a_i \in A \cap B$. Then $(a_1'a_1)f = a_1C$ and $(a_2'a_2)f = a_2C$. But $a_1a_2^{-1} = (a_1')^{-1}a_2'$, and hence $a_1a_2^{-1} \in A' \cap B$ since $(a_1')^{-1}a_2' \in A'$ and $a_1a_2^{-1} \in B$. Therefore, $a_1(A' \cap B) = a_2(A' \cap B)$ and $a_1(A' \cap B)(A \cap B') = a_2(A' \cap B)(A \cap B')$ that is, $a_1C = a_2C$.

ii) f is a homomorphism. Let $a_1'a_1, a_2'a_2 \in A'(A \cap B)$. Then $a_1'a_1a_2'a_2 = a_1'a_2''a_1a_2$ for some $a_2'' \in A'$ since $A' \lhd A'(A \cap B)$. Hence $((a_1'a_1)(a_2'a_2))f = (a_1'a_2''a_1a_2)f = a_1a_2C = (a_1C)(a_2C) = (a_1'a_1)f(a_2'a_2)f$.

iii) $\operatorname{Ker} f = A'(A \cap B')$. Let $a'a \in A'(A \cap B')$. Then $(a'a)f = aC = C$ since $a \in (A' \cap B) \subseteq C$, and $A'(A \cap B') \subseteq \ker f$. If $(a'a)f = aC = C$, then $a \in C$ and $a \in (A' \cap B)(A \cap B')$. Hence $a = uv$, $u \in A' \cap B$ and $v \in A \cap B'$. But then $a'a = a'uv = a''v$ with $a'' \in A'$ and $v \in A \cap B'$. Hence, $a'a \in A'(A \cap B')$ and $\ker f = A'(A \cap B') \lhd A'(A \cap B)$.

iv) f is onto H. This is clear since for each $a \in A \cap B$, $a \in A'(A \cap B)$. Thus

$$A'(A \cap B)/A'(A \cap B') \simeq \operatorname{Im} f = H.$$

A perfectly symmetrical argument for $B'(B \cap A)$ yields $B'(B \cap A') \lhd B'(B \cap A)$ and

$$B'(B \cap A)/B'(B \cap A') \simeq H.$$

This completes the proof of the lemma.

If we consider the special case $B \subseteq A$ and $B' = E$, then the lemma becomes

$$A'B/A' \simeq B/(B \cap A'),$$

the second isomorphism theorem.

Definition 6.3.13 Let $\mathfrak{N} = \{N_0, \cdots, N_r\}$ and $\mathfrak{M} = \{M_0, \cdots, M_s\}$ be normal series of groups G and H respectively. $\mathfrak{N}$ and $\mathfrak{M}$ are said to be *equivalent* if the factors of $\mathfrak{N}$ and $\mathfrak{M}$ are isomorphic in pairs, that is, there is a 1–1 correspondence between the factors of $\mathfrak{N}$ and $\mathfrak{M}$ such that corresponding factors are isomorphic. Note that this implies that $r = s$.

Theorem 6.3.14 Schreier Let $\mathfrak{N} = \{N_0, \cdots, N_r\}$ and $\mathfrak{M} = \{M_0, \cdots, M_s\}$ be two normal series of a group G. Then there exist refinements $\mathfrak{N}'$ of $\mathfrak{N}$ and $\mathfrak{M}'$ of $\mathfrak{M}$ which are equivalent.

Proof: Let $N(i, j) = N_{i+1}(N_i \cap M_j)$
and $M(i, j) = M_{j+1}(M_j \cap N_i)$.

Then if we let $i = 0, \cdots, r$ and $j = 0, \cdots, s$ and define $N(r, j) = M(i, s) = E$, we obtain two sets of $(r + 1)(s + 1)$ (not necessarily distinct) subgroups of G. We first show that the set $\mathfrak{N}' = \{N(i, j) \mid i = 0, \cdots, r,\ j = 0, \cdots, s\}$ is a refinement of $\mathfrak{N}$.

Consider the set of groups $\mathfrak{N}_i = \{N(i, j) \mid j = 0, \cdots, s$ and some fixed $i, 1 \leq i \leq r\}$. Then $N(i, 0) = N_{i+1}(N_i \cap M_0) = N_{i+1}N_i = N_i$ and $N(i, s) = N_{i+1}(N_i \cap M_s) = N_{i+1}E = N_{i+1}$. If $j \geq j'$, $N(i, j) \subseteq N(i, j')$ since $M_j \subseteq M_{j'}$. Hence, the set of groups $\mathfrak{N}_i$ forms a chain of subgroups between N_i and N_{i+1}, and it follows from the Zassenhaus lemma that $N(i, j) \rhd N(i, j + 1)$. Therefore $\mathfrak{N}'$ is a refinement of $\mathfrak{N}$.

A similar argument shows that $\mathfrak{M}' = \{M(i, j) \mid i = 0, \cdots, r,\ j = 0, \cdots, s\}$ is a refinement of $\mathfrak{M}$.

But by the Zassenhaus lemma, $N(i, j)/N(i, j + 1) \simeq M(i, j)/M(i + 1, j)$ for all $i = 0, \cdots, r - 1$ $j = 0, \cdots, s - 1$ and $N(i, s)/N(i + 1, 0) \simeq M(i, s)/M(i + 1, s) \simeq N(r, j)/N(r, j + 1) \simeq M(r, j)/M(0, j + 1) \simeq E$. Hence $\mathfrak{N}'$ and $\mathfrak{M}'$ are equivalent.

Theorem 6.3.15 Jordan-Hölder Let G be a group with composition series $\mathfrak{N}$ and $\mathfrak{M}$. Then $\mathfrak{N}$ and $\mathfrak{M}$ are equivalent.

Proof: Since $\mathfrak{N}$ and $\mathfrak{M}$ are composition series, only trivial refinements are possible and hence $\mathfrak{N}$ and $\mathfrak{M}$ are equivalent.

The reader should note that the Jordan-Hölder theorem does not restrict G to a finite group, but rather requires only that G be a group with a composition series (see Section 7.9).

We are now ready to formulate a description of those finite groups satisfying the modified form of the first Sylow theorem, which we discussed at the beginning of this section. More generally, we wish to consider those finite groups G satisfying the following condition: $|G| = mn$, with $(m,n) = 1$, and G contains subgroups A and B of orders m and n, respectively.

Definition 6.3.16 Let G be a finite group. Then G is called *solvable*[21] if G has a normal series with abelian factors.

Before we state and prove the main theorem we collect some elementary facts about this class of groups.

Theorem 6.3.17 A finite group G is solvable if and only if every composition factor is cyclic of prime order.

Proof: If every composition factor of a group G is cyclic, then any composition series is a normal series with abelian factors, and hence G is solvable.

Now suppose that G is solvable, and hence that G contains a normal series with abelian factors. By Theorem 6.3.10, each of these factors has a composition series whose factors are cyclic of prime order, and hence, by Exercise 6, G has a composition series whose factors are cyclic of prime order.

Exercises

14. Prove that all groups of order pq, p and q distinct primes, are solvable.
15. Prove that every p-group is solvable for any prime p.
16. Let A and B be solvable groups. Prove that $A \times B$ is solvable.
17. Let G and H be two solvable groups of the same order, and let $\mathfrak{N}$ be a composition series of G and $\mathfrak{M}$ a composition series of H. Show that $\mathfrak{N}$ and $\mathfrak{M}$ are equivalent. •

We may now put Theorem 6.3.10 and Theorem 6.3.17 together as follows:

Corollary 6.3.18 A finite group G of order n is solvable if and only if it has a composition series equivalent to a composition series of some abelian group of order n.

[21] It is important to note that the concept of solvability did not appear historically in this context. As we stated in Section 4.1, motivation for studying the notion of a group came originally from the problem of determining which polynomials had roots that could be expressed in a standard way in terms of the coefficients of the polynomial. The Galois theory provides the answers to this problem (see Artin, [2]) by devising a technique for associating to each polynomial a finite group G. The problem of whether or not the polynomial in question, say $f(x)$, has a root, that is, whether or not the polynomial equation $(x)f = 0$ is *solvable*, is reduced to determining whether the group G is solvable in the sense defined above. It was only much later (1928, 1933) that the connection between solvability and the existence of certain subgroups of G was discovered. This discovery was of major importance in the theory of finite groups.

This corollary provides the motivation for suspecting that a solvable group has "many" subgroups, for a finite abelian group of order n contains at least one subgroup of order d for each positive divisor d of n.

Next we show that solvability is a property "inherited" by subgroups and factor groups.

Theorem 6.3.19 Let G be solvable, and let A be a subgroup of G. Then A is solvable.

Proof: Let $\mathfrak{N} = \{N_0, \cdots, N_r\}$ be a normal series of G with abelian factors. Consider the set $\{N_0 \cap A, N_1 \cap A, \cdots, N_r \cap A\}$. Since $N_0 = G$, $N_0 \cap A = A$; since $N_r = E$, $N_r \cap A = E$; and it is easy to see that $N_{i+1} \cap A \lhd N_i \cap A$. Hence, $\{N_0 \cap A, N_1 \cap A, \cdots, N_r \cap A\}$ is a normal series that we shall show has abelian factors. By the second isomorphism theorem, $(N_i \cap A)/(N_{i+1} \cap A) \simeq (N_i \cap A)N_{i+1}/N_{i+1}$. But $(N_i \cap A)N_{i+1}/N_{i+1}$ is a subgroup of N_i/N_{i+1}, which is abelian, and hence $(N_i \cap A)/(N_{i+1} \cap A)$ is abelian for all $i = 0, \cdots, r - 1$. Therefore, A is solvable.

Theorem 6.3.20 Let G be solvable and N a normal subgroup of G. Then G/N is solvable.

Proof: Consider the series $G \rhd N \rhd E$ and refine it to a composition series. We leave the remainder of this proof as an exercise.

Exercises

18. Complete the proof of Theorem 6.3.20.

*19. Let G be a finite group and N a normal subgroup of G. Show that if N is solvable and G/N is solvable then G is solvable.

More generally show that if $\{N_0, \cdots, N_r\}$ is a normal series of G with solvable factors, then G is solvable.

20. Let G be a group of order pqr, p, q and r primes. Show that if G contains a nontrivial proper normal subgroup, then G is solvable. ●

There is another characterization of solvability that is often very useful in practice and again shows the connection between solvable groups and abelian groups.

If a and b are elements of a group G, then $ab = bac$ for some $c \in G$. If a and b commute, then, of course, $c = e$. In general $c = a^{-1}b^{-1}ab$. An element of this form is called a *commutator* and is usually designated by (a,b).

Definition 6.3.21 Let G be a group. Denote by G' the subgroup generated by the set of all commutators $(a,b) = a^{-1}b^{-1}ab$ of G, for all $a,b \in G$. G' is called the *commutator subgroup* of G.

Exercises

21. Compute the commutator subgroups of S_3, A_4, D_4, and S_4.

*22. Let G' be the commutator subgroup of a group G.
   a) Show that G' is a characteristic subgroup of G.
   b) Show that G/G' is abelian.
   c) Show that if $N \triangleright G$ and G/N is abelian, then $N \supseteq G'$.
   d) Show that G' may be defined as the intersection of all normal subgroups of G whose factor groups are abelian.

23. Show that if G is solvable, $G \neq E$, then $G' \subset G$.

24. Show that if G is simple, then either $G' = G$ or $G' = E$. •

In a sense, G' provides a measure of how much G differs from an abelian group. We may now form the commutator subgroup of G' which we denote by $G^{(2)}$ and so on, obtaining a string of subgroups $G \triangleright G^{(1)} \triangleright G^{(2)} \triangleright G^{(3)} \triangleright \cdots$, where $G^{(1)} = G'$.

If this string terminates, that is, if $G^{(n)} = E$ for some n, then we have a normal series each of whose factors is abelian (Exercise 21b). Hence such a group must be solvable. In fact, the converse is also true.

Theorem 6.3.22 Let G be a finite group. G is solvable if and only if $G^{(n)} = E$ for some integer n.

Proof: We have already shown that if $G^{(n)} = E$ for some n, then G is solvable. Hence assume that G is solvable, and let $\mathfrak{N} = \{N_0, N_1, \cdots, N_r\}$, $N_i \neq N_j$ for $i \neq j$, be a normal series of G with abelian factors. Thus G/N_1 is abelian and hence $N_1 \supseteq G^{(1)}$. Since $G^{(1)}$ is a subgroup of a solvable group, $G^{(1)}$ is solvable and $G^{(1)}$ is a proper subgroup of G (unless $G = E$). Similarly, $G^{(2)}$ is a proper subgroup of $G^{(1)}$, unless $G^{(1)}$ is the identity, and so on. Since G is finite, this properly decreasing chain of subgroups must terminate, that is, $G^{(n)} = E$ for some integer n.

We are now ready to state and partially prove the main result of this section, which is partly an extension of the Sylow theorems to solvable groups.

Theorem 6.3.23 ***P. Hall*** Let G be a finite group of order n. Then G is solvable if and only if whenever $n = uv$, with $(u, v) = 1$, G contains a subgroup of order u (and one of order v).

Furthermore, if G is solvable, and $|G| = uv$, $(u,v) = 1$, then

i) all subgroups of order u are conjugate

ii) if A is a subgroup of order u_1, where $u_1 \mid u$, then A is contained in some subgroup of order u.

We will only prove that if G is solvable, then G contains a subgroup of order u, where $|G| = uv$, $(u,v) = 1$. The converse requires that we use some results from the theory of group representations.[22]

[22] We refer the interested reader to Hall, Marshall [14], (Theorem 9.3.3, Theorem 16.8.7).

Before we proceed with the proof, we need

Lemma 6.3.24 Let G be a solvable group and let N be a minimal normal subgroup ($G \triangleright N \supset E$ and if $N \supset M \supset E$, then M is not normal in G). Then $|N| = p^\alpha$ for some prime p.

Proof: Let N be a minimal normal subgroup of the solvable group G. Since N is solvable, $N' \subset N$ and since N' is characteristic in $N, N' \triangleleft G$. Hence, $N' = E$ and therefore N is abelian. By Theorem 6.1.5, N is the direct product of its Sylow subgroups and hence if N_p is a p-Sylow subgroup of N, N_p is normal in G by Exercise 11, Section 6.2 and Theorem 6.3.3. But since N is a minimal normal subgroup of G, $N_p = N$ and $|N| = p^\alpha$.

Proof (Theorem 6.3.23): Let G be a minimal counterexample.

I. Suppose that G contains a normal subgroup N of order $u_1 v_1$ with $u_1 u_2 = u$, $v_1 v_2 = v$, and $v_1 < v$. Then $|G/N| = u_2 v_2 < uv = |G|$, and so the theorem holds for G/N. Thus, G/N contains a subgroup of order u_2, say H/N, since $(u_2, v_2) = 1$. Then $|H| = u_2 u_1 v_1 = uv_1 < uv$. Hence, H contains a subgroup of order u which is of course a subgroup of G, a contradiction.

II. Now assume that for every normal subgroup K of G, $|K| = u_1 v$ with $u_1 u_2 = u$. If N is a minimal normal subgroup, then, by Lemma 6.3.24, $|N| = p^\alpha$, p a prime, and $p^\alpha = v > 1$ since $(u, v) = 1$, that is, N is the unique p-Sylow subgroup of G. (If $p^\alpha \neq v$, then N is a normal subgroup of G falling under Case I, which we have ruled out. Thus $p^\alpha = v$). Then G/N is solvable and hence has a minimal normal subgroup H/N of order q^β with q a prime different from p. Clearly, $H \triangleleft G$ and $|H| = p^\alpha q^\beta$. Let Q be a q-Sylow subgroup of H. Then $H = NQ$. If $Q \triangleleft H$, then Q is characteristic in H by Exercise 2, and hence Q is normal in G by Theorem 6.3.3. But then G contains a normal subgroup Q of order $u_1 = u_1 v_1$ with $v_1 = 1 < v$, a contradiction. Hence Q is not normal in H and $N_G(Q)$ does not contain H. Thus, since $H = NQ$, we have $N \not\subseteq N_G(Q)$. Therefore, $|N_G(Q)| = u_1 p^{\alpha'}$, where $u_1 \mid u$ and $\alpha' < \alpha$, that is, $|N_G(Q)| = u_1 p^{\alpha'} < uv$.

Now it follows from Exercise 10, Section 6.2 that

$$G = HN_G(Q) \quad \text{and} \quad |G| = uv = up^\alpha = \frac{|H|\,|N_G(Q)|}{|H \cap N_G(Q)|}$$

$$= \frac{p^\alpha q^\beta \,|N_G(Q)|}{|H \cap N_G(Q)|}$$

(see Exercise 19, Section 4.8). Now, $|H \cap N_G(Q)| = p^{\alpha''} q^\beta$ since Q is contained in its own normalizer and $H \cap N_G(Q) \subseteq H$. Hence,

$$uv = \frac{p^\alpha q^\beta \,|N_G(Q)|}{p^{\alpha''} q^\beta} = p^{\alpha - \alpha''} |N_G(Q)| = p^{\alpha - \alpha'' + \alpha'} u_1$$

and since $(u,p) = 1$, $|N_G(Q)| = u$. Thus, G has a subgroup of order u, contradicting that G is a minimal counterexample. This completes the proof of the theorem.

In this brief introduction to solvable groups, we have only lightly touched on elementary facts. Current research in this area, however, is both extensive and vigorous. Indeed, some remarkable successes have only recently been achieved in settling many outstanding problems in this area. Most notable of these is the theorem of Feit and Thompson which asserts that every finite group of odd order is solvable. This theorem, which settles a long standing conjecture of W. Burnside, implies that every nonabelian simple group must be of even order.

The proof of the Feit-Thompson theorem is deep and nonelementary.[23] For their outstanding result, Feit and Thompson were awarded the Cole Memorial Prize by the American Mathematical Society in 1965.

6.4 GENERATORS AND RELATIONS; FREE GROUPS

So far in our study of groups we have had many occasions to show that a given group G is isomorphic to a group that is a familiar and concrete mathematical system. For example, Theorem 4.7.8 states that a finite cyclic group of order n is isomorphic to the additive group of residue classes of integers modulo n, and Cayley's Theorem (4.11.5) states that every group is isomorphic to a group of permutations. There are, in fact, many other very important results along these lines that we have not been able to present due to the somewhat limited scope of our investigation. The great variety of ways of "representing" a given group G affords some of the most valuable techniques in the theory of groups. For it is thereby possible to utilize the special properties of the specific representation—for example, permutations or residue classes—to study the group in question. On the other hand, it is extremely useful to have a procedure for representing a group G that in some sense directly reflects the properties of *G as a group* and does not depend on the special properties of its elements as members of some preassigned mathematical system. In this section we shall develop such a procedure, known as representation by "generators and relations," which is based on the point of view that the elements of a group can be thought of as "letters" and the group operation as the formation of "words" in these letters.

[23] Feit, W. and Thompson, J. G., "Solvability of Groups of Odd Order," *Pacific Journal of Mathematics*, vol. 13 (1963), pp. 775–1029.

Definition 6.4.1 Let $\mathcal{A} = \{a_\alpha \mid \alpha \in \Delta\}$ be a collection of symbols a_α, called *letters*, where Δ is some index set. A *word* on $\mathcal{A}$ is either i) a symbol of the form $a_{\alpha_1}^{\epsilon_1} a_{\alpha_2}^{\epsilon_2} \cdots a_{\alpha_r}^{\epsilon_r}$, with $a_{\alpha_i} \in \mathcal{A}$, $\epsilon_i = \pm 1$, $1 \le i \le r$, or ii) the symbol 1 called the *empty word.*

From this point, we shall drop the exponent 1 from a_α^1 whenever convenient and identify a_α^1 with a_α.

It should be emphasized that the set $\mathcal{A}$ is simply a collection of symbols and nothing more. A word is formed merely by stringing out a sequence of elements of $\mathcal{A}$ in some order, with possible repetitions, and assigning an exponent of either 1 or -1 to each letter. Notice that a_1^{-1} suggests the role of the inverse of a_1, and when we introduce a group containing sets of these symbols as elements, this will indeed be the case. But at this point there is no group in sight and the words should simply be regarded as formal objects. We now define a binary operation on the set of all words on the set $\mathcal{A}$.

Definition 6.4.2 Let W be the set of all words on $\mathcal{A} = \{a_\alpha \mid \alpha \in \Delta\}$. We define the operation $\circ$ on W by juxtaposition, that is if $w_1 = a_{\alpha_1}^{\epsilon_1} \cdots a_{\alpha_r}^{\epsilon_r}$ and $w_2 = a_{\beta_1}^{\delta_1} \cdots a_{\beta_s}^{\delta_s}$, $\alpha_i, \beta_j \in \Delta$, $\epsilon_i = \pm 1$, $\delta_j = \pm 1$, $1 \le i \le r$, $1 \le j \le s$, then $w_1 \circ w_2 = a_{\alpha_1}^{\epsilon_1} \cdots a_{\alpha_r}^{\epsilon_r} a_{\beta_1}^{\delta_1} \cdots a_{\beta_s}^{\delta_s}$. If $w_1 = 1$, then $w_1 \circ w_2 = w_2$. If $w_2 = 1$, then $w_1 \circ w_2 = w_1$.

We leave it for the reader to verify that this operation is a binary operation on W. We remark that two words are equal if and only if they are identical as formal strings of symbols, disregarding occurrences of the empty word 1.

Exercises

*1. Prove that the operation of juxtaposition is a binary operation on the set W of all words on $\mathcal{A} = \{a_\alpha \mid \alpha \in \Delta\}$ (Definition 6.4.2).

*2. Show that juxtaposition of words is associative. •

According to our definition of words as formal strings of letters with exponents, it follows that two words are equal if they are identical as formal strings. But in our attempt to create a group from W in which a^{-1} will play the role of the inverse of a^1 and 1 the role of the identity, it will be necessary to identify certain pairs of words: 1 and $a^{-1}a^1$, for example. We therefore introduce an equivalence relation on W that identifies those formally distinct words that will represent the same group element.

Definition 6.4.3 Let u and v be words on $\mathcal{A} = \{a_\alpha \mid \alpha \in \Delta\}$. We say that u is equivalent to v, denoted by $u \sim v$, if there exists a sequence of words

$$u = u_1, u_2, \cdots, u_n = v, \quad n \ge 1,$$

such that $u_{i+1} = w_1 a_i^{\theta_i} a_i^{-\theta_i} w_2$ and $u_i = w_1 w_2$, or $u_{i+1} = w_1 w_2$ and $u_i = w_1 a_j^{\theta_j} a_j^{-\theta_j} w_2$, with $a_i, a_j \in \mathcal{A}$, $\theta_i, \theta_j = \pm 1$, and w_1, w_2 words on $\mathcal{A}$. The set of all words equivalent to the word w will be denoted by $\overline{w}$.

Thus, two words are equivalent if one can be obtained from the other by a finite sequence of insertions and deletions of words of the form $a_i a_i^{-1}$ or $a_i^{-1} a_i$. Hence, the words $u = a_1 a_2^{-1} a_1 a_1^{-1} a_3$ and $v = a_1 a_2 a_2^{-1} a_2^{-1} a_3$ are equivalent since

$$u = u_1,\ u_2 = a_1 a_2^{-1} a_3,\ u_3 = a_1 a_2 a_2^{-1} a_2^{-1} a_3 = v.$$

Theorem 6.4.4 The relation $\sim$ on the set of words W on $\mathcal{A} = \{a_\alpha \mid \alpha \in \Delta\}$ is an equivalence relation

Proof: Exercise.

If a word w contains a string of the form $a_i^{\theta_i} a_i^{-\theta_i}$, then this can be deleted and a shorter word is obtained to which w is equivalent. A word that contains no such "substrings" is called *reduced*. For example, $a_1 a_2^{-1} a_3$, $a_2 a_2 a_1 a_2 a_1^{-1}$ and 1 are reduced words while $a_1 a_2^{-1} a_2 a_3$ is not reduced.

The importance of reduced words as representatives of the equivalence classes of W is now shown.

Theorem 6.4.5 Let W be the set of all words on the set $\mathcal{A} = \{a_\alpha \mid \alpha \in \Delta\}$, and let $\sim$ be the relation given in Definition 6.4.3. Then each equivalence class $\overline{w}$ contains precisely one reduced word. That is, if w_1 and w_2 are reduced words, then $w_1 \sim w_2$ if and only if $w_1 = w_2$.

Proof: To show that $\overline{w}$ contains at least one reduced word, we simply choose an arbitrary word in w, say w_1. If w_1 is reduced, then we are finished. Otherwise w_1 contains some $a^\epsilon a^{-\epsilon}$ with $a \in \mathcal{A}$ and $\epsilon = \pm 1$. By successively eliminating such "subwords," we obtain a chain of words, each containing two fewer symbols than the previous. Hence, if w_1 contains t symbols, then in at most $t/2$ steps we obtain a reduced word equivalent to w_1.

Now let $w \sim v$. We will show that if $w = u_1, u_2, \cdots, u_n = v$ is a chain of minimal length establishing that $w \sim v$ and if v is reduced, then $u_i = U_i a^\epsilon a^{-\epsilon} V_i$ and $u_{i+1} = U_i V_i$ for $i = 1, \cdots, n-1$ where U_i and V_i are words on $\mathcal{A}$. That is, the minimal chain is obtained by a sequence of deletions only.

Thus, assume that some insertions do occur in the chain $w = u_1, u_2, \cdots, u_n = v$. Let the last such insertion occur as we go from u_j to u_{j+1}, that is, $u_j = X_j Y_j$, $u_{j+1} = X_j \mathbf{a}^\epsilon \mathbf{a}^{-\epsilon} Y_j$, and at each $k > j$, we proceed in the manner $u_k = X_k b^\delta b^{-\delta} Y_k \to u_{k+1} = X_k Y_k$. (We write $u_m \to u_{m+1}$ to indicate we pass from u_m to u_{m+1} in the chain. Also, the particular $\mathbf{a}^\epsilon$ and $\mathbf{a}^{-\epsilon}$ inserted in the step $u_j \to u_{j+1}$, will be in **boldface**). Since v is a reduced word, $\mathbf{a}^\epsilon\mathbf{a}^{-\epsilon}$ does not occur in v. Hence, at least one of $\mathbf{a}^\epsilon$ and $\mathbf{a}^{-\epsilon}$ must be removed in some deletion.

Thus, let $u_r \to u_{r+1}$, $r > j$ be the step in which the first of either $\mathbf{a}^\epsilon$ or $\mathbf{a}^{-\epsilon}$ is deleted. There are several possibilities.

I. $\mathbf{a}^\epsilon$ and $\mathbf{a}^{-\epsilon}$ are deleted in the same step. But then the step $u_j \to u_{j+1}$ is superfluous, and a shorter chain from w to v could be obtained by omitting the steps $u_j \to u_{j+1}$ and $u_r \to u_{r+1}$, a contradiction.

II. $\mathbf{a}^\epsilon$ is removed while $\mathbf{a}^{-\epsilon}$ remains. Then $u_r = X_r'a^{-\epsilon}\mathbf{a}^\epsilon\mathbf{a}^{-\epsilon}Y_r'$, where $X_r'a^{-\epsilon}$ and Y_r' are obtained from X_j and Y_j, respectively, by deletions (possibly zero) only. But then we see that when we delete $a^{-\epsilon}\mathbf{a}^\epsilon$, we are left with $X_r'\mathbf{a}^{-\epsilon}Y_r' = X_r'a^{-\epsilon}Y_r'$. Thus, again we have gained nothing by inserting the $\mathbf{a}^\epsilon\mathbf{a}^{-\epsilon}$ at step $u_j \to u_{j+1}$, and a shorter chain could be obtained by omitting that step. This is again a contradiction.

III. $\mathbf{a}^{-\epsilon}$ is removed, while $\mathbf{a}^\epsilon$ remains. This situation is similar to that of II.

Thus, we observe that the last insertion $\mathbf{a}^\epsilon\mathbf{a}^{-\epsilon}$ is unnecessary in any minimal chain from w to v. Thus, if v is reduced, only deletions are needed in going from w to v in a minimal chain. So, if w is also reduced, the only possible chain is $w = u_1 = v$. Hence, $\overline{w}$ contains only one reduced word.

Exercises

3. Prove Theorem 6.4.4.
4. Let w_1 and w_2 be reduced words. Then show that $w_1w_2 \sim 1$ if and only if whenever $w_1 = a_1^{\epsilon_1}a_2^{\epsilon_2}\cdots a_r^{\epsilon_r}$, then $w_2 = a_r^{-\epsilon_r}\cdots a_2^{-\epsilon_2}a_1^{-\epsilon_1}$. ●

We are now ready to define the group formed from equivalence classes of words.

Definition 6.4.6 Let W be the set of all words on the set

$$\mathfrak{A} = \{a_\alpha \mid \alpha \in \Delta\}$$

and let F denote the set of equivalence classes of words,

$$F = \{\overline{w} \mid w \in W\}.$$

We define the binary operation $\cdot$ on F as follows:

$$\overline{w_1}\cdot\overline{w_2} = \overline{w_1w_2}$$

where w_1w_2 is the product of Definition 6.4.2 (juxtaposition). We call the pair $(F, \cdot)$, or simply F, the *free group on* $\mathfrak{A}$. If the set $\mathfrak{A}$ is finite containing n elements we say that F is *a free group on n generators*, or *a free group of rank n*.

Theorem 6.4.7 The free group $(F, \cdot)$ on the set $\mathfrak{A} = \{a_\alpha \mid \alpha \in \Delta\}$ is a group.

Proof: We must first show that $\cdot$ is a binary operation on F. Thus let w_1, w_2, w_1', w_2' be words in F such that $w_1 \sim w_1'$ and $w_2 \sim w_2'$, that is, $\overline{w_1} = \overline{w_1}'$ and $\overline{w_2} = \overline{w_2}'$. Then there is a sequence of words $w_1 = u_1, u_2, \cdots, u_r = w_1'$ and a sequence $w_2 = v_1, \cdots, v_s = w_2'$, and hence, the sequence $w_1 w_2 = u_1 w_2, u_2 w_2, \cdots, u_r w_2 = w_1' w_2 = w_1' v_1, w_1' v_2, \cdots, w_1' v_s = w_1' w_2'$ establishes that $w_1 w_2 \sim w_1' w_2'$. Hence, $\overline{w_1 w_2} = \overline{w_1' w_2'}$.

To show associativity we note that since juxtaposition is an associative operation,

$$\overline{w_1} \cdot (\overline{w_2} \cdot \overline{w_3}) = \overline{w_1} \cdot \overline{(w_2 w_3)} = \overline{w_1 (w_2 w_3)}$$

$$= \overline{(w_1 w_2) w_3} = \overline{(w_1 w_2)} \cdot \overline{w_3} = (\overline{w_1} \cdot \overline{w_2}) \cdot \overline{w_3}.$$

Clearly the class $\overline{1}$ is an identity element, and if

$$w_1 = a_{\alpha_1}^{\epsilon_1} a_{\alpha_2}^{\epsilon_2} \cdots a_{\alpha_r}^{\epsilon_r}$$

and $$w_2 = a_{\alpha_r}^{-\epsilon_r} \cdots a_{\alpha_1}^{-\epsilon_1}, \quad \text{then} \quad \overline{w_1}\,\overline{w_2} = \overline{1}.$$

Hence $(F, \cdot)$ is a group.

Usually in discussing the elements of a free group we do not refer to classes of equivalent words but rather treat the individual words themselves as elements of the group calling words *equal* when they are equivalent. So, for example, in the case of the free group on the single letter a, F is the infinite cyclic group, and we say that $aa^{-1}a$ and a represent the same element of the group, or that $aa^{-1}a = a$. We could also have defined the free group as the set of all *reduced* words. Then the products of a pair of words w_1, w_2 would be the reduced word equivalent to the product $w_1 w_2$.

As is customary, we will denote the word $\underbrace{aa \cdots a}_{n \text{ times}}$ by a^n.

Exercises

5. Prove that if G is a free group, then G is abelian if and only if G is a free group on one generator.

6. Let G be a free group and let $A = \{x^n \mid x \in G, n \text{ a fixed integer}\}$. Show that (A) is a normal subgroup of G.

7. Let G be a free group on generators $\{a, b, c\}$. Show that the subgroup of G generated by $\{a, b\}$ is a free group on two generators. What about the subgroup generated by $\{a^2 b, ab\}$? ●

The next theorem shows the fundamental role played by the concept of a free group.

Theorem 6.4.8 Every group is a homomorphic image of a free group.

Proof: Let G be a group and let $S = \{g_\alpha \mid \alpha \in \Delta\}$ be a set of generators for G. We shall show that if we regard the set S as a formal set of letters, then G is a factor group of the free group on S. To avoid using the elements of S ambiguously, let $T = \{h_\alpha \mid \alpha \in \Delta\}$ and note that the index set of T is the same as that of S (and hence the mapping $\varphi: S \to T$, $g_\alpha \varphi = h_\alpha$ is a 1–1 correspondence between S and T). Let F be the free group on T and let $f: F \to G$ be defined as follows: if $w = h_{\alpha_1}{}^{\epsilon_1} \cdots h_{\alpha_r}{}^{\epsilon_r}$ is a word on T, then $\overline{w}f = g_{\alpha_1}{}^{\epsilon_1} \cdots g_{\alpha_r}{}^{\epsilon_r}$.

To show that the mapping is well defined, suppose that

$$w \sim w' = h_{\beta_1}{}^{\delta_1} \cdots h_{\beta_s}{}^{\delta_s}.$$

Hence $\overline{w'}f = g_{\beta_1}{}^{\delta_1} \cdots g_{\beta_s}{}^{\delta_s}$. But since $w \sim w'$, there is a sequence

$$w = u_1, u_2, \cdots, u_t = w'$$

satisfying the conditions of Definition 6.4.3, and thus there is a sequence of elements of G:

$$\overline{w}f = \overline{u}_1 f, \overline{u}_2 f, \cdots, \overline{u}_t f = \overline{w'}f.$$

Now, either $u_{i+1} = v_1 h_\alpha{}^{\theta_\alpha} h_\alpha{}^{-\theta_\alpha} v_2$ with $u_i = v_1 v_2$, or $u_{i+1} = v_1 v_2$ with $u_i = v_1 h_\beta{}^{\theta_\beta} h_\beta{}^{-\theta_\beta} v_2$. In the first case

$$\overline{u_{i+1}} f = (\overline{v}_1 f) g_\alpha{}^{\theta_\alpha} g_\alpha{}^{-\theta_\alpha} (\overline{v}_2 f) = (\overline{v}_1 f) \cdot (\overline{v}_2 f) = \overline{v_1 v_2} f = \overline{u}_i f,$$

and the same holds true in the second case. Hence, $\overline{w}f = \overline{w'}f$ and f is well defined.

Since S is a set of generators of G, f is clearly onto.

To show that f is a homomorphism, let $\overline{w}_1, \overline{w}_2 \in F$. Then $(\overline{w}_1 \cdot \overline{w}_2)f = \overline{(w_1 w_2)}f$. But since the mapping simply amounts to replacing the h's in w_1 and w_2 by the corresponding g_α's, it follows readily that $\overline{(w_1 w_2)}f = (\overline{w}_1 f)(\overline{w}_2 f)$. Hence, G is a homomorphic image of F.

If G is a group with generating set $S = \{g_\alpha \mid \alpha \in \Delta\}$, then it follows from the theorem above that G can be completely described by specifying a homomorphism f from the free group F on S (or a set in 1–1 correspondence with S) onto G, or equivalently by specifying its kernel. If the kernel N has a relatively small number of generators, then G can be easily specified by the set of generators of N. For example, if G is the cyclic group of order d, then $G \cong F/N$ where F is the free group on the single generator a and N is the subgroup generated by the element a^d (see Example 4.10.7).

We express this by saying that the group G has generator a and *relation* $a^d = e$, that is, $(aN)^d = N$.

We are now ready to define the "representation of a group by generators and relations."

Definition 6.4.9 Let G be a group, and let $\mathfrak{A} = \{a_\alpha \mid \alpha \in \Delta\}$ be a set of generators of G. Let F be the free group on $\mathfrak{A}$ considered as formal symbols and let $W = \{\overline{w}_\beta \mid \beta \in \Gamma\}$ be a subset of F. We say that G is given by *generators* $\{a_\alpha \mid \alpha \in \Delta\}$ *and relations* $\{w_\beta = 1 \mid \beta \in \Gamma\}$, where $w_\beta \in \overline{w}_\beta$, if $G \simeq F/N$, where N is the smallest normal subgroup of F containing $\{\overline{w}_\beta \mid \beta \in \Gamma\}$, and where the isomorphism is induced by the mapping $a_\alpha f = \bar{a}_\alpha N$. When $\mathfrak{A}$ and the set $\{\overline{w}_\beta \mid \beta \in \Gamma\}$ are finite, this is written as $G = (a_1,\cdots,a_n \mid w_1 = \cdots = w_m = 1)$, where w_i is usually taken to be the reduced word of $\overline{w}_i$.

As usual, the "smallest" normal subgroup is simply the intersection of all normal subgroups containing the set $\{\overline{w}_\beta \mid \beta \in \Gamma\}$. Put another way, N is generated by the set $\{\overline{w}_\beta \mid \beta \in \Gamma\}$, together with all its conjugates.

This presentation of the group G is sometimes described without reference to free groups at all. We simply say that G is generated by the elements $\{a_\alpha \mid \alpha \in \Delta\}$, that the relations $w_\beta = 1$, $\beta \in \Gamma$, hold in G, and that any relation on the generators "follows" from these relations.

We note that if G is a free group, then every relation on G is of the form $1 = 1$, and we say that a free group has no relations, that is, a free group is relation free. This follows immediately from Theorem 6.4.5.

Example 6.4.10 If G is the cyclic group of order d, then

$$G = (a \mid a^d = 1).$$

We have in fact previously verified that if F is the free group on one generator and $N = \{g^{-1}a^{dk}g \mid d \text{ fixed in } Z,\ k \in Z,\ g \in F\}$, then $N \lhd F$ and $G \simeq F/N$.

Example 6.4.11 Let G be the symmetric group S_3. Then $G = (a,b \mid a^2 = b^3 = (ab)^2 = 1)$. This can be shown as follows: Let F be the free group on $\{a,b\}$, and let f be the mapping $f: F \to S_3$ defined by:

$$af = (1\ 2) \quad \text{and} \quad bf = (1\ 2\ 3)$$

Then, since $a^2f = b^3f = (ab)^2f = 1$, the words a^2, b^3, and $(ab)^2$ are contained in the kernel N. Thus, we must show that any word of F in the kernel of f is in N, or equivalently, that for any $\overline{w} \in F/N$, $\overline{w} = \overline{1}$ is a consequence of $\overline{a^2} = \overline{b^3} = \overline{(ab)^2} = 1$. We leave this as an exercise.

Example 6.4.12 Let G be the group D_4 of symmetries of the square. Then it is easy to see that G is generated by r_1, the rotation of 90° and h, the reflection through the horizontal axis. Further, these elements satisfy the relations $r_1^4 = e$, $h^2 = e$ and $(r_1h)^2 = e$. To show that $G = (a,b \mid a^4 = b^2 = (ab)^2 = 1)$, it is only necessary to show that the order of F/N is eight, where F is the free group of rank 2 and N is the normal subgroup generated by the words a^4, b^2 and $(ab)^2$.

An easy consequence of our main theorem shows that "adding a relation" to a given group produces a factor group.

Theorem 6.4.13 Let G be the group given by generators $\{a_\alpha \mid \alpha \in \Delta\}$ and relations $\{w_\beta = 1 \mid \beta \in \Gamma\}$. Then the group given by the same generators and an additional relation is a factor group of G.

Proof: Exercise.

We conclude by remarking that any subgroup of a free group is also a free group.[24]

Exercises

8. Complete the arguments in Examples 6.4.11 and 6.4.12.
9. Show that the free group of rank 2 is nonabelian.
10. Show that $G = (a,b \mid a^2 = b^3 = 1)$ is nonabelian.
11. Prove Theorem 6.4.13.
12. Represent all groups of order 8 by generators and relations (see Section 4.14).
13. Show that any group G generated by elements a,b and satisfying relations $a^8 = b^2a^4 = ab^{-1}ab = 1$ has order at most 16.
14. Let $G = (a_1,\cdots,a_n \mid w_1 = \cdots = w_r = 1)$ and $H = (b_1,\cdots,b_m \mid u_1 = \cdots = u_s = 1)$. Represent $G \times H$ by generators and relations.
15. Show that the relations given at the end of Theorem 6.2.10 is a set of defining relations for a nonabelian group of order pq.
16. Let G be generated by two elements $\{a,b\}$ and relations

$$\{(w_\beta)^2 = 1 \mid \beta \in \Gamma\}$$

where $\{w_\beta\}$ is the set of all words on $\{a,b\}$. Show that G is finite. What is its order?
17. In 16, replace the relations $\{w_\beta^2 = 1 \mid \beta \in \Gamma\}$ by $\{w_\beta^3 = 1 \mid \beta \in \Gamma]$.

Hint: Show that every word is equivalent to a reduced word in a,b,a^{-1},b^{-1} consisting of at most five symbols.

†18. Let $G = (a_1,\cdots,a_n \mid a_i^{-1}a_j^{-1}a_ia_j = 1 \text{ all } i,j)$. Show that G is abelian. G is called the *free abelian group on n generators.*

[24] For a proof of this nontrivial theorem, we refer the reader to Kurosh [30], vol. I.

CHAPTER 7

Topics in the Theory of Rings

It would be highly inconvenient to continue our study of rings without a knowledge of at least some of the fundamentals of linear algebra. Although our primary purpose is to learn more about the structure of rings, we shall nevertheless develop enough linear algebra to be of general use, as well as to facilitate obtaining important structure theorems for two types of rings: 1) finite fields and 2) semisimple rings with descending chain condition.

In addition to proving the existence of finite fields with p^n elements, for each prime p and integer $n > 0$, we shall prove Wedderburn's theorem on finite division rings (Theorem 5.4.13). Our method of proof will also allow us to prove a renowned theorem of Jacobson. Finally, by introducing the axiom of choice, we shall obtain several characterizations of semisimple rings, including those in terms of injective and projective modules.

7.1 VECTOR SPACES

Definition 7.1.1 Let $(V,+)$ be an abelian group, let Δ be a division ring with identity 1, and let $f:\Delta \times V \to V$, where we denote $(\delta,v)f$ by δv. Then V is called a *vector space over* Δ if for all $\delta_1,\delta_2 \in \Delta$, $v_1,v_2 \in V$, the following hold:

i) $\delta_1(v_1 + v_2) = \delta_1 v_1 + \delta_1 v_2$

ii) $(\delta_1 + \delta_2)v_1 = \delta_1 v_1 + \delta_2 v_1$

iii) $(\delta_1 \delta_2)v_1 = \delta_1(\delta_2 v_1)$

iv) $1\, v_1 = v_1$.

We call the elements v of V *vectors* and the elements δ of Δ *scalars*. We also call δv the scalar multiple of v by δ.

We should note that we use the symbol $+$ in two different ways: one is to denote the addition in V, the other the addition in Δ, but no confusion will result from this.

Note that in Definition 7.1.1, the scalars δ are written to the left of the vectors v. Hence, V is often called a left vector space. If we were to write the scalars to the right of the vectors, we would have a right vector space.

Definition 7.1.2 Let $(V,+)$ be an abelian group, let Δ be a division ring with identity 1, and let $g: V \times \Delta \to V$, where we denote $(v,\delta)g$ by $v\delta$. Then V is called a *right vector space over* Δ if for all $\delta_1,\delta_2 \in \Delta$, $v_1,v_2 \in V$, the following hold:

i′) $(v_1 + v_2)\delta_1 = v_1\delta_1 + v_2\delta_1$
ii′) $v_1(\delta_1 + \delta_2) = v_1\delta_1 + v_1\delta_2$
iii′) $v_1(\delta_1\delta_2) = (v_1\delta_1)\delta_2$
iv′) $v_1 1 = v_1$.

The essential difference between a vector space and a right vector space is the difference between iii) and iii′). Indeed, in case Δ is commutative, then we can consider a vector space over Δ to also be a right vector space over Δ, simply by defining $v\delta$ to be δv. For then

$$\begin{aligned} v(\delta_1\delta_2) &= (\delta_1\delta_2)v = (\delta_2\delta_1)v = \delta_2(\delta_1 v) = \delta_2(v\delta_1) \\ &= (v\delta_1)\delta_2. \end{aligned}$$

If, however, Δ is noncommutative, this trick will not work.

Definition 7.1.3 Let V be a vector space over Δ. A nonempty subset U of V is called a *subspace* of V if

i) $(U,+)$ is a subgroup of $(V,+)$
ii) $\alpha u \in U$ for all $\alpha \in \Delta$ and $u \in U$.

It is clear that U is a subspace of V provided that U is closed with respect to the operations of addition in V and scalar multiplication of vectors by scalars.

A vector space may consist of one element alone, namely a zero element. Such a vector space, even if regarded as a subspace, will be denoted by 0.

Before we give any examples of vector spaces, we list a number of properties that follow directly from the definitions.

Theorem 7.1.4 Let V be a vector space over Δ.

i) Let 0 denote the zero element of $(V,+)$. Let $\delta \in \Delta$. Then $\delta 0 = 0$.
ii) $0v = 0$, the first 0 denoting the zero of Δ and the second the zero of $(V,+)$.
iii) $-(\delta v) = (-\delta)v = \delta(-v)$, for all $\delta \in \Delta$, $v \in V$.
iv) $\delta v = 0$ if and only if $\delta = 0$ or $v = 0$.

Proof: Exercises.

Examples of vector spaces arise quite naturally and are easy to find. Several of the better known ones are listed.

Example 7.1.5 Let $R^n = \{(a_1,a_2,\cdots,a_n) \mid a_i \in R$, the real numbers$\}$. Here n is fixed. We define addition on R^n by

$$(a_1,a_2,\cdots,a_n) + (b_1,b_2,\cdots,b_n) = (a_1 + b_1,a_2 + b_2,\cdots,a_n + b_n)$$

and we define multiplication of vectors by scalars by

$$\delta(a_1,a_2,\cdots,a_n) = (\delta a_1,\delta a_2,\cdots,\delta a_n), \text{ for } \delta \in R.$$

Then R^n is a vector space over R.

The case for $n = 2$ is already familiar to the reader. We can think of R^2 as denoting all vectors in the Euclidean plane (relative to fixed rectangular coordinate axes) with tails at the origin. Thus, the element (x,y) of R^2 is visualized as in Figure 12. We add two vectors (x_1,y_1) and (x_2,y_2) using the parallelogram method, as in Figure 13. The arrow with head at $(x_1 + x_2,y_1 + y_2)$ is just the sum of the vectors (x_1,y_1) and (x_2,y_2).

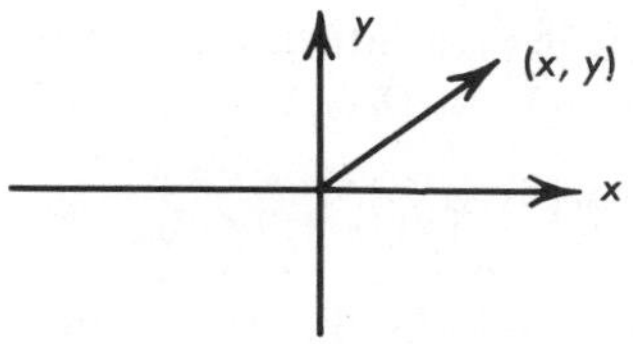

Figure 12

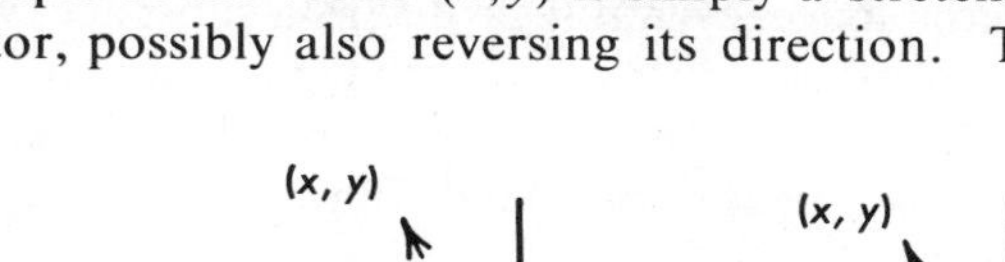

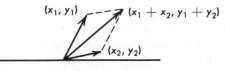

Figure 13

A scalar multiple of the vector (x,y) is simply a stretching or contraction of the vector, possibly also reversing its direction. This is pictured in Figure 14.

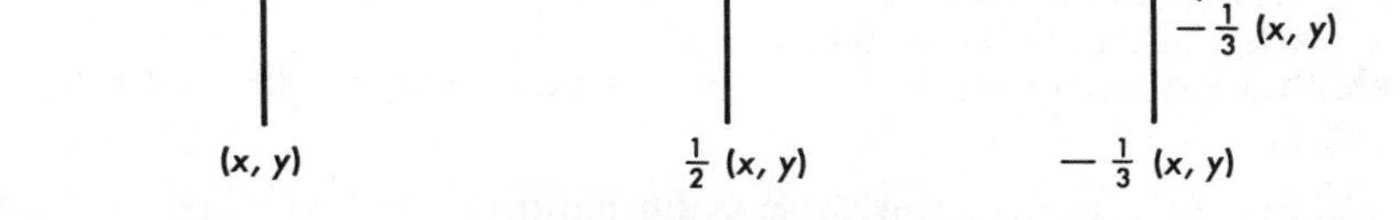

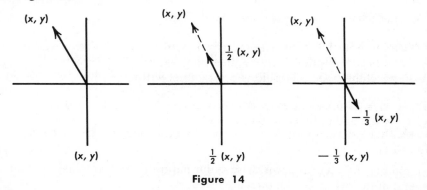

Figure 14

Example 7.1.6 In Example 7.1.5, replace R by any division ring Δ and denote the resulting set of n-tuples by Δ^n. Then Δ^n is a vector space over Δ.

Example 7.1.7 Let V denote any ring and let Δ denote any subdivision ring. Then V is a vector space over Δ if we consider the scalar multiple δv to be the usual product of the two elements δ and v of V. Similarly, if we consider the scalar multiple $v\delta$ as the product of v and δ in V, then V is a right vector space over Δ.

In particular, a division ring Δ can be thought of as a vector space over itself.

Exercises

1. Prove Theorem 7.1.4.
2. Let K be the set of all real numbers. Let C be the set of all functions $f: K \to K$, such that f is continuous. For f_1 and $f_2 \in C$, define $f_1 + f_2$ by

$$(x)(f_1 + f_2) = (x)f_1 + (x)f_2, \text{ for all } x \in K.$$

For $f \in C$ and $\alpha \in K$, define αf by

$$(x)(\alpha f) = \alpha \cdot (xf).$$

Prove that C is a vector space over K.

3. Let $(G, +)$ be an abelian group and suppose there is a prime p such that $px = 0$, for all $x \in G$. Prove that G is a vector space over the field Z_p.
4. Let V be a vector space over Δ. Show that if V_1 and V_2 are subspaces of V, then $V_1 \cap V_2$ is also a subspace of V.

7.2 BASES

Certain important properties of vector spaces can be discovered from the examples of Section 7.1. To illustrate, we can find vectors $e_1, \cdots, e_n$ in Δ^n, which play a special role. For example, putting

$$e_1 = (1,0,\cdots,0),\ e_2 = (0,1,0,\cdots,0), \cdots, e_n = (0,0,\cdots,0,1),$$

we see that any vector $(\delta_1, \delta_2, \cdots, \delta_n)$ can be expressed as a linear combination of $e_1, \cdots, e_n$:

$$(\delta_1, \delta_2, \cdots, \delta_n) = \delta_1(1,0,\cdots,0) + \delta_2(0,1,0,\cdots,0) + \cdots + \delta_n(0,0,\cdots,0,1) = \delta_1 e_1 + \cdots + \delta_n e_n.$$

It is also clear that none of the e_i's is expressible as a linear combination of the remaining e_j's. Other sets of vectors, however, may have the above properties. We leave this to the exercises.

Definition 7.2.1 Let V be a vector space over Δ and let $v_1, v_2, \cdots, v_n \in V$. Then the vector $v = \delta_1 v_1 + \cdots + \delta_n v_n, \delta_1, \delta_2, \cdots, \delta_n \in \Delta$, is called a *linear combination* of the v_i's over Δ. We also say that v is *dependent* on $v_1, \cdots, v_n$.

Definition 7.2.2 Let V be a vector space over Δ. Then the set of vectors $\{v_\alpha \mid \alpha \in \Lambda\}$ (it may happen that $v_\alpha = v_\beta$, for $\alpha \neq \beta$) is *linearly independent* over Δ (or simply, *independent*) if for each finite subset of vectors

$$v_{\alpha_1}, \cdots, v_{\alpha_n} \quad \text{of} \quad \{v_\alpha \mid \alpha \in \Lambda\}, \ \delta_1 v_{\alpha_1} + \cdots + \delta_n v_{\alpha_n} = 0$$

$$\text{implies} \quad \delta_1 = \delta_2 = \cdots = \delta_n = 0.$$

Otherwise, the set $\{v_\alpha \mid \alpha \in \Lambda\}$ (it may happen $v_\alpha = v_\beta$ for $\alpha \neq \beta$) is called *linearly dependent* (or simply, *dependent*).

Strictly speaking, $\{v_\alpha \mid \alpha \in \Lambda\}$ is an indexed set. Thus, the (indexed) set $\{v_1, v_2\}$, where $v_1 = v_2 \neq 0$, is a dependent set, whereas the (indexed) set $\{v_1\}$ is independent. When we speak of a set of vectors $\{v_\alpha\}$, we shall generally have in mind an indexed set and hence allow for repetitions of vectors. This represents a minor, but traditional, abuse of language.

We also observe that ϕ, the empty set, is an independent subset of any vector space. Also if $W = \{v_\alpha \mid \alpha \in \Lambda\}$ is a set of vectors such that $0 \in W$, then W is a dependent set. For suppose that $0 = v_1$. Then $1v_1 = 0$, yet not all the δ_i's are zero.

In case W is a dependent set of nonzero vectors, say $W = \{v_1, \cdots, v_n\}$, then at least one of the v_i's can be written as a linear combination of the others. For we must have

$$\delta_1 v_1 + \cdots + \delta_n v_n = 0, \quad \text{not all} \quad \delta_i = 0, \quad \text{say} \quad \delta_1 \neq 0.$$

Then

$$v_1 = (-\delta_1^{-1}\delta_2)v_2 + (-\delta_1^{-1}\delta_3)v_3 + \cdots + (-\delta_1^{-1}\delta_n)v_n.$$

It is now immediate that an independent set of vectors has no repetitions.

The set of vectors $\{e_1, \cdots, e_n\}$, $e_i = (0, \cdots, 0, \underset{i}{1}, 0, \cdots, 0)$, is an independent set of vectors. Moreover, any vector in Δ^n can be written as a linear combination of $e_1, \cdots, e_n$.

Definition 7.2.3 Let V be a vector space over Δ. Let G be a subset of V, say $G = \{v_\alpha\}$. Then G is said to be a set of *generators* for V, or G *spans* V, if any $v \in V$ is a linear combination of vectors in G.

We shall also consider ϕ to be a spanning set for the vector space 0.

Definition 7.2.4 Let V be a vector space over Δ. A *basis* B for V is a subset of V such that

i) B spans V and

ii) B is an independent set.

As a consequence of these definitions, we obtain the following result:

Theorem 7.2.5 Let B be a basis for a vector space V over Δ. Then, if $v \in V$, $v \neq 0$, there exist unique vectors $v_{\alpha_1}, \cdots, v_{\alpha_m} \in B$ and unique nonzero scalars $\delta_1, \cdots, \delta_m \in \Delta$ such that

$$v = \delta_1 v_{\alpha_1} + \cdots + \delta_m v_{\alpha_m}.$$

Proof: Suppose $v = \delta_1 v_{\alpha_1} + \cdots + \delta_m v_{\alpha_m} = \gamma_1 v_{\beta_1} + \cdots + \gamma_k v_{\beta_k}$. By filling in each expression with $0v_\beta$'s and $0v_\alpha$'s, we may assume that $v = \delta_1 v_{\alpha_1} + \cdots + \delta_n v_{\alpha_n} = \gamma_1 v_{\alpha_1} + \cdots + \gamma_n v_{\alpha_n}$. Then $0 = (\delta_1 - \gamma_1)v_{\alpha_1} + \cdots + (\delta_n - \gamma_n)v_{\alpha_n}$. Since B is an independent set, $\delta_i - \gamma_i = 0$, $i = 1, \cdots, n$, that is, $\delta_i = \gamma_i$, $i = 1, \cdots, n$. This completes the proof.

Definition 7.2.6 A set $H = \{v_\alpha \mid \alpha \in \Lambda\}$ of linearly independent vectors in a vector space V is called a *maximal set of linearly independent vectors* in V if, whenever $H \subset D \subseteq V$ (and D has no repetitions), then D is a dependent set.

Definition 7.2.7 A set G (without repetitions) of generators of V is called a *minimal set of generators* if whenever $H \subset G$, then H is not a set of generators of V.

We are now ready to prove a fundamental theorem relating bases, maximal sets of linearly independent vectors, and minimal sets of generators.

Theorem 7.2.8 Let V be a vector space over a division ring Δ. Let $B \subseteq V$. Then the following three conditions are equivalent:

i) B is a basis for V

ii) B is a minimal set of generators for V

iii) B is a maximal set of linearly independent vectors.

Proof: We will give a cyclic proof, that is, we will show that i) implies ii), ii) implies iii), and iii) implies i). Without loss of generality we may assume that $V \neq 0$. For if $V = 0$, then $B = \phi$ satisfies i), ii), and iii).

i) implies ii). Since B is a basis, B is clearly a set of generators. Now let $H \subset B$ and suppose $b_i \in B$, but $b_i \notin H$. We must show that H is not a set of generators for V. If it were, then there would exist scalars $\delta_1, \cdots, \delta_j$ such that $b_i = \delta_1 b_1 + \cdots + \delta_j b_j$, where $b_1, \cdots, b_j \in H$ and $b_i \neq b_k$,

$k = 1, \cdots, j$. Thus, b_i is represented as a linear combination of vectors of B in two different ways (b_i and $\delta_1 b_1 + \cdots + \delta_j b_j$), contradicting that B is a basis (Theorem 7.2.5). Thus, H does not generate V.

ii) implies iii). First we show that B is a set of independent vectors. Since $V \neq 0$, it is clear that $0 \notin B$ and that $B \neq \phi$. For, if $0 \in B$, we can delete 0 and still have a set of generators. Now, if B is not an independent set, then there exist vectors $b_1, \cdots, b_k$ in B, and scalars $\delta_2, \cdots, \delta_k$ such that $b_1 = \delta_2 b_2 + \cdots + \delta_k b_k$. But then clearly we can delete b_1 from B and still have a set of generators, contradicting the minimality of B. Thus, B is an independent set.

We must show that B is a maximal independent set. Thus, let $B \subset H$ and let $h \in H$, $h \notin B$. Since B is a set of generators, $h = \delta_1 b_1 + \cdots + \delta_k b_k$, for some $\delta_1, \cdots, \delta_k \in \Delta$, $b_1, \cdots, b_k \in B$. Hence, H is a dependent set of vectors. Thus, B is a maximal set of linearly independent vectors.

iii) implies i). Since B is an independent set, we need show only that B generates V. Thus, let $v \in V$. If we cannot write $v = \delta_1 b_1 + \cdots + \delta_k b_k$, for some choice of $\delta_1, \cdots, \delta_k$, $b_1, \cdots, b_k$, then the set $B \cup \{v\}$ is an independent set of vectors, contradicting the maximality of B. Thus, v can be written as a linear combination of elements of B, and B is a basis for V.

We have already observed that Δ^n has a basis with n elements. We have not yet proved, however, that every basis for Δ^n has n elements, but this is indeed the case. In fact, we shall prove in Theorem 7.2.11 that if a vector space V over Δ has one basis with n elements, then every basis has n elements.

Lemma 7.2.9 Let $\{v_1, \cdots, v_k\}$ be a set of k linearly independent vectors. Let $u_1, \cdots, u_{k+1}$ be $k + 1$ vectors, each of which is a linear combination of the v_i's. Then $\{u_1, \cdots, u_{k+1}\}$ is a dependent set of vectors.

Proof: The proof is by induction on k.

Suppose that $k = 1$. Then $u_1 = \alpha_1 v_1$, $u_2 = \alpha_2 v_1$. If either $u_1 = 0$ or $u_2 = 0$, the result is trivial. Otherwise, $u_1 = \alpha_1 \alpha_2^{-1} u_2$, and the result holds.

Suppose now the result holds for all integers k, $k < n$. Then we let

$$u_1 = \alpha_{11} v_1 + \cdots + \alpha_{1n} v_n \tag{1}$$

$$u_2 = \alpha_{21} v_1 + \cdots + \alpha_{2n} v_n \tag{2}$$

$$\vdots$$

$$u_{n+1} = \alpha_{n+1,1} v_1 + \cdots + \alpha_{n+1,n} v_n \qquad (n + 1).$$

Since we can assume that no $u_i = 0$, we may assume $\alpha_{1n} \neq 0$. Then in (1), we can solve for v_n in terms of $u_1, v_1, \cdots, v_{n-1}$. Indeed,

$$v_n = \alpha_{1n}^{-1} u_1 - \alpha_{1n}^{-1} \alpha_{11} v_1 - \alpha_{1n}^{-1} \alpha_{12} v_2 - \cdots - \alpha_{1n}^{-1} \alpha_{1,n-1} v_{n-1}.$$

Substituting this expression for v_n in each of (2), $\cdots$,($n + 1$), we get $u_2, \cdots, u_{n+1}$ written in terms of $v_1, \cdots, v_{n-1}, u_1$, and from these substitutions we have

$$u_2 - \alpha_{2n}\alpha_{1n}^{-1}u_1, u_3 - \alpha_{3n}\alpha_{1n}^{-1}u_1, \cdots, u_{n+1} - \alpha_{n+1,n}\alpha_{1n}^{-1}u_1$$

written as linear combinations of $v_1, \cdots, v_{n-1}$. Since $\{v_1, \cdots, v_{n-1}\}$ is an independent set, by induction we have that the n vectors $u_i - \alpha_{in}\alpha_{1n}^{-1}u_1$, $i = 2, \cdots, n + 1$, are dependent. Thus, there exist scalars, $\beta_2, \cdots, \beta_{n+1}$, not all zero, such that

$$\beta_2(u_2 - \alpha_{2n}\alpha_{1n}^{-1}u_1) + \beta_3(u_3 - \alpha_{3n}\alpha_{1n}^{-1}u_1) + \cdots + \beta_{n+1}(u_{n+1} - \alpha_{n+1,n}\alpha_{1n}^{-1}u_1) = 0$$

But then

$$\beta_2 u_2 + \beta_3 u_3 + \cdots + \beta_{n+1}u_{n+1} + (-\beta_2\alpha_{2n}\alpha_{1n}^{-1} - \cdots - \beta_{n+1}\alpha_{n+1,n}\alpha_{1n}^{-1})u_1 = 0$$

and $\{u_1, \cdots, u_{n+1}\}$ is a dependent set of vectors.

Lemma 7.2.10 Let V be a vector space over Δ and let B be a basis for V. If B has n elements, then any set with more than n vectors is a dependent set.

Proof: Let $B = \{b_1, \cdots, b_n\}$. This is a set of n independent vectors. If E is a set with more than n elements, it has at least $n + 1$ vectors, each of which is a linear combination of the b_i's. By Lemma 7.2.9, these $n + 1$ vectors are dependent, and hence, E is dependent.

Theorem 7.2.11 Let V be a vector space over Δ. If V has one basis B with n elements, then every basis has n elements.

Proof: By Lemma 7.2.10, no basis can have more than n elements. If there is a basis B_1 with m vectors, $m < n$, we simply reverse the roles of B_1 and B in Lemma 7.2.10 and find that B would be dependent. Since this cannot happen, we have that $m = n$.

Corollary 7.2.12 Let B and B' be bases for a vector space V. Then either B and B' are both finite, or both are infinite.

Proof: Exercise.

Given Theorem 7.2.11, it is possible to define the *dimension* of a vector space V in an unambiguous manner.

Definition 7.2.13 Let V be a vector space over a division ring Δ. If V has a basis with n elements, we say that V is *finite dimensional* of *dimen-*

sion n over Δ, and we denote this by $[V:\Delta] = n$. If V does not have a finite basis, we say that V is *infinite dimensional* and write $[V:\Delta] = \infty$.

We note that if $V = 0$, then $[V:\Delta] = 0$ since ϕ is a basis for 0.

It is customary to refer to Theorem 7.2.11 as the *invariance of dimension* theorem for finite dimensional vector spaces.

A simple criterion that a vector space V has a finite basis is given in the next theorem. Before we can prove, however, that every vector space has a basis, we need an axiom of set theory which will be introduced in Section 7.3. A proof that every vector space has a basis will be given in Section 7.4.

Theorem 7.2.14 Let V be a vector space, $V \neq 0$, and let G be a finite set of generators for V. Then V has a finite basis.

Proof: Since $V \neq 0$, there exists a vector $v \in G$, $v \neq 0$. Then $\{v\}$ is an independent set of vectors contained in G. Clearly, since G is finite and since it contains independent subsets, it must contain a maximal independent subset B (possibly G itself). It is easy to see that this set B must be a finite basis.

Theorem 7.2.15 Let V be a vector space, $[V:\Delta] = n$. Let $\{b_1, \cdots, b_k\}$, $k < n$, be a set of linearly independent vectors. Then there exist vectors $h_{k+1}, \cdots, h_n$ such that $\{b_1, \cdots, b_k, h_{k+1}, \cdots, h_n\}$ is a basis for V.

Proof: Let $\mathfrak{F}$ be the collection of all subsets B of V with the following properties:

i) B is an independent set

ii) $B \supseteq \{b_1, \cdots, b_k\}$.

Since V has a basis, say $\{e_1, \cdots, e_n\}$, we see by Lemma 7.2.10, that no B in $\mathfrak{F}$ can have more than n vectors. Also, since $\{b_1, \cdots, b_k\} \in \mathfrak{F}$, $\mathfrak{F} \neq \phi$. Thus, to each set $B \in \mathfrak{F}$, we can assign an integer, $(B)n$, the number of vectors in B, and clearly, $k \leq (B)n \leq n$. Thus, there exists a set $B' \in \mathfrak{F}$ such that $(B)n \leq (B')n$, for all $B \in \mathfrak{F}$. Clearly, B' is a maximal set of linearly independent vectors, whence B' must be a basis by Theorem 7.2.8. Moreover, $(B')n = n$ by Theorem 7.2.11. This completes the proof.

Definition 7.2.16 Let V and U be vector spaces over a division ring Δ. Then V and U are *isomorphic* (as vector spaces) if there exists a function $f: V \xrightarrow[\text{onto}]{1-1} U$ such that

i) $(v_1 + v_2)f = v_1 f + v_2 f$

ii) $(\alpha v)f = \alpha(vf)$, for all v_1, v_2, v in V and all α in Δ.

It is easy to see that V and U are isomorphic vector spaces if and only if $[V:\Delta] = [U:\Delta]$. We leave this for the exercises.

As an application of Theorem 7.2.11 we can now complete the proof of Theorem 6.1.10. Recall that it remained to be proved that in any two canonical decompositions of a finitely generated abelian group, the number of infinite cyclic factors was the same. For convenience we shall rephrase this theorem in additive notation.

Theorem 7.2.17 (Theorem 6.1.10) Let G be a finitely generated abelian group and suppose
i) $G = A_1 \dotplus \cdots \dotplus A_n \dotplus B_1 + \cdots \dotplus B_r$
ii) $G = D_1 \dotplus \cdots \dotplus D_m \dotplus F_1 + \cdots \dotplus F_s$,
where each A_i and D_j is a prime power cyclic group and each B_i and F_j is an infinite cyclic group. Then $r = s$. (The $\dotplus$ is the additive analogue of $\dot{\times}$. All the above groups are written additively.)

Proof: Let $H = \{g \mid kg = 0$, for some integer $k \neq 0\}$. Then $H = A_1 \dotplus \cdots \dotplus A_n = D_1 \dotplus \cdots \dotplus D_m$. It is easy to see that $G/H \simeq B_1 \dotplus \cdots \dotplus B_r \simeq F_1 \dotplus \cdots \dotplus F_s$. Now each B_i (and F_j) is isomorphic to Z, the integers. Thus, by considering Z to be a subset of Q, the field of rational numbers, we may also consider the B_i's and F_j's as subsets of Q, and hence, we may consider that $B_1 \dotplus \cdots \dotplus B_r$ and $F_1 \dotplus \cdots \dotplus F_s$ are subsets of vector spaces V and U over Q, of dimensions r and s, respectively. In addition, the group isomorphism φ between $B_1 \dotplus \cdots \dotplus B_r$ and $F_1 \dotplus \cdots \dotplus F_s$ can be extended to a vector space isomorphism f between V and U by setting $(\alpha_1 x_1 + \cdots + \alpha_r x_r)f = \alpha_1(x_1\varphi) + \cdots + \alpha_r(x_r\varphi)$, where $\alpha_i \in Q$ and $x_i \in B_i$. By Theorem 7.2.11, it follows that $r = s$.

Exercises

1. Let Δ be a division ring.
   a) Let $\gamma_i \neq 0$, $\gamma_i \in \Delta$, $i = 1,2,\cdots,n$.
   Show that the set $\{f_1, f_2, \cdots, f_n\}$, where
   $f_i = (0,\cdots,0,\gamma_i,0,\cdots,0)$, is a basis for Δ^n.
   b) Let $g_1 = (1,0,\cdots,0)$, $g_2 = (1,1,0,\cdots,0)$,
   $\cdots, g_{n-1} = (1,\cdots,1,0)$, $g_n = (1,1,\cdots,1)$.
   Show that $\{g_1,\cdots,g_n\}$ is a basis for Δ^n.
2. Prove the converse of Theorem 7.2.5:
   Let V be a vector space over Δ. Let $B \subseteq V$ and suppose for each $v \in V$, $v \neq 0$, there exists a unique subset $\{b_1,\cdots,b_k\}$ of distinct vectors of B and unique nonzero scalars $\delta_1,\cdots,\delta_k$ of Δ such that
   $$v = \delta_1 b_1 + \cdots + \delta_k b_k.$$
   Prove that B is a basis for V.
3. Let V be a vector space. Let B_1 span V and suppose B_2 is a set such that if $h \in B_1$, then $h = \alpha_1 b_1 + \cdots + \alpha_k b_k$, for some $b_1, \cdots, b_k \in B_2$ and $\alpha_1, \cdots, \alpha_k \in \Delta$. Prove that B_2 also spans V.

*4. Let B be an independent set of vectors of V. Let $B_1 \subseteq B$, $B_1 \neq \phi$. Prove that B_1 is an independent set of vectors.

5. Prove Corollary 7.2.12.

6. In each of the following, let Δ be the field of rational numbers.

   i) Let $V = \Delta^4$. Determine whether $E = \{(1,1,0,1), (1,1,0,0), (1,0,0,1)\}$ is an independent set of vectors. If it is, find a vector v such that $E \cup \{v\}$ is a basis for V. Is the choice of v unique?

   ii) Let $V = \Delta^4$. Let $e_1 = (0,1,0,1)$, $e_2 = (0,0,1,1)$, $e_3 = (1,1,0,0)$, $e_4 = (1,0,0,0)$. Show that $B = \{e_1, e_2, e_3, e_4\}$ is a basis for Δ^4. Moreover, express each of the following as a linear combination of the vectors e_1, e_2, e_3, and e_4:

$$(2, 3, \tfrac{1}{2}, 5), \quad (\tfrac{1}{2}, \tfrac{1}{3}, 0, \tfrac{1}{4}), \quad (1, 2, 3, 4).$$

7. Let V be a vector space over Δ. Let V_1 and V_2 be subspaces of V. Define $V_1 + V_2$ as $\{v_1 + v_2 \mid v_1 \in V_1, v_2 \in V_2\}$. Show that $V_1 + V_2$ is a subspace of V.

8. In 7, assume $[V:\Delta] = n < \infty$. Prove that

   i) $[V_1:\Delta] < \infty, [V_2,\Delta] < \infty$

   ii) $[V_1 + V_2:\Delta] = [V_1:\Delta] + [V_2:\Delta] - [V_1 \cap V_2:\Delta]$

9. Let V be a vector space over Δ, $[V:\Delta] < \infty$. Let V_1, V_2, V_3 be subspaces of V. Define $V_1 + V_2 + V_3$, and prove that $[V_1 + V_2 + V_3:\Delta] = [V_1:\Delta] + [V_2:\Delta] + [V_3:\Delta] - [V_1 \cap V_2:\Delta] - [V_1 \cap V_3:\Delta] - [V_2 \cap V_3:\Delta] + [V_1 \cap V_2 \cap V_3:\Delta]$.

10. Use the invariance of dimension to prove the following: Let C denote the complex numbers and K the real numbers. Prove there is no field H such that $K \subset H \subset C$.

11. Let V and U be finite dimensional vector spaces over Δ. Prove that V and U are isomorphic if and only if $[V:\Delta] = [U:\Delta]$.

12. Complete the details of the proof of Theorem 7.2.16.

7.3 THE AXIOM OF CHOICE AND ZORN'S LEMMA

Let $\mathfrak{F} = \{S_\alpha\}$ be a nonempty collection of pairwise disjoint nonempty sets. In order to form a set S such that $S_\alpha \cap S$ has precisely one element for each $S_\alpha \in \mathfrak{F}$, it would appear that one need merely select one element from each S_α, and gather all the chosen elements into one set S. The question arises, however, whether this can actually be done when $\mathfrak{F}$ has infinitely many elements S_α. The assumption that such a set S exists must be taken as an axiom of mathematics, for the existence of such a set S has been proved to be independent and consistent with the usual axioms for set theory. That is, the existence of S cannot be deduced from the other axioms of set theory, nor is its assumption inconsistent with the other axioms. Thus, we state the following axiom:

Axiom of Choice Let $\{S_\alpha\}$ be a nonempty collection of pairwise disjoint nonempty sets. Then there exists a set S such that $S_\alpha \cap S$ has precisely one element for each S_α in $\{S_\alpha\}$.

The ramifications of this axiom are quite deep and far reaching. In fact, partly due to some of its consequences, this axiom was once the center of a controversy. Today, however, it is almost universally used by mathematicians.[25]

There are several mathematical statements logically equivalent to the axiom of choice. One is that if $\{S_\alpha\}$ is a collection of nonempty sets, disjoint or not, there exists a function γ such that $(\alpha)\gamma \in S_\alpha$, for each index α. (γ is called a *choice function.*) Another of these is a generalization of the principle of mathematical induction, and yet another a generalization of the law of well-ordering. We shall be interested, however, in still another statement equivalent to the axiom of choice, known as Zorn's lemma. It is this form of the axiom of choice that is most frequently used in algebra. Before we can state Zorn's lemma, however, we must introduce some new terminology.

Definition 7.3.1 Let A be a set and let $\leq$ denote a relation on A satisfying

i) $a \leq a$, for all $a \in A$
ii) If $a \leq b$ and $b \leq c$, then $a \leq c$
iii) If $a \leq b$ and $b \leq a$, then $a = b$.

We say that A is a set *partially ordered* by $\leq$, and $\leq$ is called a *partial ordering* of A.

Since a relation on A is simply a subset of $A \times A$, it is clear that there may exist elements $a,b \in A$ such that neither $a \leq b$ nor $b \leq a$ holds (see Exercises 1 and 2).

Definition 7.3.2 Let A be partially ordered by $\leq$. Let $C \subseteq A$ and suppose whenever $a,b \in C$, then either $a \leq b$, or $b \leq a$. Then C is called a *chain* in A. We call $b \in A$ an *upper bound* for the chain C if $c \leq b$, for all $c \in C$.

An element m in A is called a *maximal element of A* if, whenever $m \leq x$, then $x = m$. A may have more than one maximal element, or it may have none. Indeed, it may have infinitely many (see Exercises 5 and 6).

With these definitions, we can now state Zorn's lemma.

[25] The interested reader may find the discussion in Sierpinski [47] quite enjoyable.

Zorn's Lemma Let $A \neq \phi$ be a set partially ordered by $\leq$. Suppose every chain C in A has an upper bound in A. Then A has a maximal element.

Admittedly, the relation between the axiom of choice and Zorn's lemma is not immediate. Nevertheless, each statement implies the other, although we shall not prove this.[26]

To illustrate a standard use of Zorn's lemma, we prove an interesting ring theoretic result.

Theorem 7.3.3 Let R be a ring with 1. Then R contains a maximal ideal.

Proof: Let $\mathfrak{F}$ be the collection of all ideals I_α in R such that $1 \notin I_\alpha$. $\mathfrak{F} \neq \phi$, since $(0) \in \mathfrak{F}$. We partially order $\mathfrak{F}$ by set inclusion, that is, $I_\alpha \leq I_\beta$ if $I_\alpha \subseteq I_\beta$.

Now let $\mathfrak{C}$ be a chain in $\mathfrak{F}$. Then $\mathfrak{C}$ has an upper bound in $\mathfrak{F}$: For let $I = \bigcup_{I_\alpha \in \mathfrak{C}} I_\alpha$ and let $x, y \in I$. Then $x \in I_\alpha$ and $y \in I_\beta$, some $I_\alpha, I_\beta \in \mathfrak{F}$. Since either $I_\alpha \subseteq I_\beta$ or $I_\beta \subseteq I_\alpha$, there is some ideal I_β in $\mathfrak{F}$ such that $x, y \in I_\beta$. Then $x - y \in I_\beta$, and hence, $x - y \in I$. For $x \in I$ and $r \in R$ it is easy to see that $rx \in I$ and $xr \in I$. This shows I is an ideal in R. Also, $1 \notin I$, for if $1 \in I$, then $1 \in I_\alpha$, for some I_α in $\mathfrak{C}$, a contradiction. Thus, $I \in \mathfrak{F}$. But clearly, $I_\alpha \leq I$, for all I_α in $\mathfrak{C}$ and so I is an upper bound of $\mathfrak{C}$ in $\mathfrak{F}$. By Zorn's lemma, $\mathfrak{F}$ must have a maximal element, which we call J.

Even though J is a maximal element in $\mathfrak{F}$, we do not yet know that J is a maximal ideal according to Definition 5.13.1. This is easily seen, however. For if J is not maximal, there is an ideal Q such that $J \subset Q \subset R$. Clearly, $1 \notin Q$, and so $Q \in \mathfrak{F}$. But $J \subset Q$ contradicts the maximality of J in $\mathfrak{F}$, and so J is a maximal ideal.

Exercises

1. Let Z be the set of integers. For $a, b \in Z$, define $a \leq b$ if $a \mid b$. Show that $\leq$ is a partial ordering of Z.

2. Let A be a set. Let $\mathfrak{F}$ be the collection of all subsets of A. Prove that $\mathfrak{F}$ may be partially ordered by letting $X \leq Y$ if $X \subseteq Y$.

*3. Let R be a ring. A subring I of R is called a *left ideal* of R if $rx \in I$, for all $x \in I$, $r \in R$. A left ideal $I \subset R$ is a *maximal left ideal* if, whenever J is a left ideal, $I \subseteq J \subseteq R$, either $J = I$ or $J = R$. Prove that a ring $R \ni 1$ has a maximal left ideal.

4. Let G be a group and suppose there exists a subgroup H and a homo-

[26] Rather, we refer the reader to Kurosh [31], Halmos [16], or Kelley [29], for a proof of the equivalence of these statements.

morphism $f: H \to H$. Prove that there exists a subgroup K of G maximal with respect to these properties:

i) there exists a homomorphism $g: K \to K$

ii) $H \subseteq K$

iii) $f = g \mid H$ (see Example 1.7.13).

Hint: Let (L,h) have the property that $H \subseteq L$, L a subgroup of G, and $h: L \to L$ is a homomorphism such that $f = h \mid H$. Let $\mathfrak{F}$ be the set of all pairs (L,h) and partially order $\mathfrak{F}$ as follows: $(L_1,h_1) \leq (L_2,h_2)$ if $L_1 \subseteq L_2$ and $h_1 = h_2 \mid L_1$.

5. Let A be the set of all points (x,y) in the plane with $y \leq 0$. Partially order A by $(x_1, y_1) \leq (x_2, y_2)$ if $x_1 = x_2$ and $y_1 \leq y_2$. Show that A has infinitely many maximal elements.

6. Prove that the set of real numbers K is partially ordered by the usual $\leq$. Prove that K has no maximal element.

7.4 EXISTENCE OF BASES IN VECTOR SPACES

As we have previously noted, the one main point lacking in our discussion of bases is that we do not yet know that every vector space has a basis. This deficiency is now removed.

Theorem 7.4.1 Let $V \neq 0$ be a vector space over a division ring Δ. Then V has a basis.

Proof: Recall the definition of an independent set of vectors. Let $\mathfrak{F}$ be the family of all independent subsets of V. Clearly, $\mathfrak{F} \neq \phi$, for, if $v \neq 0$, $\{v\}$ is an independent set. We partially order $\mathfrak{F}$ by set inclusion, that is, $B_1 \leq B_2$ if and only if $B_1 \subseteq B_2$. Now let $\mathfrak{C}$ be a chain in $\mathfrak{F}$. Let $B = \bigcup_{B_\alpha \in \mathfrak{C}} B_\alpha$. Then B is also an independent set. For, if it is not, we can find vectors $v_1, \cdots, v_k$ in B that are dependent. But there must be some B_α that contains $v_1, \cdots, v_k$, since B is just a union of a chain of sets. The dependence relation among $v_1, \cdots, v_k$ in B contradicts their independence in B_α. Thus, B is independent and hence B is an upper bound in $\mathfrak{F}$ for $\mathfrak{C}$.

By Zorn's lemma, $\mathfrak{F}$ has a maximal element H. We claim H is a basis for V. To see this, first observe H is an independent set of vectors. Next, let $v \in V$. If v is not a linear combination of vectors of H, then $H \cup \{v\}$ is an independent set, but this contradicts the maximality of H in $\mathfrak{F}$. Thus, H is a maximal linearly independent set of vectors and so H is a basis, by Theorem 7.2.8.

We have proved in the case of a finite dimensional vector space that two bases have the same number of elements. The same theorem holds for infinite dimensional vector spaces, namely, if B_1 and B_2 are bases for V, there exists a function f such that $f:B_1 \xrightarrow[\text{onto}]{1-1} B_2$. The proof of this fact, which we shall not need, involves ideas from cardinal number theory.[27]

We do prove, however, an analogue in the infinite dimensional case to Theorem 7.2.15.

Theorem 7.4.2 Let V be a vector space. Let B_1 be an independent set of vectors in V. Then there exists a set B_2 such that $B_1 \cup B_2$ is a basis for V.

Proof: Again we use Zorn's lemma.

If B_1 is a basis, then $B_2 = \phi$ works. Thus, suppose B_1 is not a basis. Let $\mathfrak{F}$ be the family of subsets B of V such that B is an independent set of vectors and $B_1 \subseteq B$.

By Zorn's lemma, $\mathfrak{F}$ has a maximal element (why?), say M. But then M is a basis for V (why?), and setting $B_2 = M - B_1$, we have the desired set.

The reader should observe that the basic idea used in proving Theorem 7.4.2 is the same one used in proving Theorem 7.2.15.

Exercises

1. Prove that $\sqrt{2}$ and $\sqrt{3}$ may be taken as vectors in some basis for the real numbers as a vector space over the rational numbers.

2. Prove that in Exercise 2, Section 7.1, the polynomial functions defined by $1, x, x^2, \cdots, x^n, \cdots$ are linearly independent and hence may be taken as part of a basis for C over K. Use your knowledge of e^x or $\sin x$ to prove that the set $\{1, x, x^2, \cdots, x^n, \cdots\}$ is not a basis for C.

3. Let G be a group (written additively) such that $2a = 0$, for all $a \in G$. Prove, by considering G a vector space over Z_2, that G has an irredundant set of generators.

4. Prove that for each group G with $|G| > 2$, there exists a nonidentity automorphism.

   Hint: For G nonabelian, or for G abelian but with an element of order different from two, see Exercise 7, Section 4.12. For G abelian with every element ($\neq e$) of order 2, the finite case has been settled in Exercise 19, Section 4.13. Thus, the only remaining case is for G an infinite group, as in Exercise 3 above.

7.5 LINEAR TRANSFORMATIONS

We have already seen the advantages in investigating a class of algebraic structures together with certain functions. For example, our investigation of groups and rings was intimately connected with our study of homomor-

[27] The reader should consult Halmos [16] or Jacobson [23], vol. II.

phisms of groups and rings, respectively. Similarly, there are advantages in studying analogous functions from one vector space to another. Our main interest in introducing these functions will be in later applications.

Definition 7.5.1 Let V and U be vector spaces over Δ. Let $T:V \to U$ satisfy
i) $(v_1 + v_2)T = v_1 T + v_2 T$, for all $v_1, v_2 \in V$
ii) $(\alpha v)T = \alpha(vT)$, for all $\alpha \in \Delta$, $v \in V$.
We call T a *linear transformation* from V to U and we denote the set of all linear transformations from V to U by $\text{Hom}_\Delta(V, U)$.

To illustrate, let K denote the field of real numbers. Then $V = K^2$ and $U = K$ are vector spaces over K and the function $T:V \to U$ defined by $(x,y)T = x$, for all $(x,y) \in V$, is a linear transformation. This linear transformation T is just a *projection* from the Euclidean plane onto the x axis.

As a second illustration, let V be as above and let $S:V \to V$ be defined by $(x,y)S = (-y,x)$. Then S is a linear transformation from V to V, which we recognize as a 90° counterclockwise rotation of the points of the plane.

For a third example, again with $V = K^2$, we see that the function S, defined by $(x,y)S = (3x,3y)$, is also a linear transformation, which, of course, we get simply by stretching each vector in the plane by a factor of 3.

Now let $E = \{e_\alpha\}$ be a basis for a vector space V and let $T \in \text{Hom}_\Delta(V, U)$. Then vT, for any $v \in V$, is completely determined, if we know $e_\alpha T$, for all $e_\alpha \in E$. For if $v \in V$, $v \neq 0$, there exist unique nonzero scalars $\delta_1, \cdots, \delta_k$ and unique vectors $e_{\alpha_1}, \cdots, e_{\alpha_k}$ in E such that $v = \delta_1 e_{\alpha_1} + \cdots + \delta_k e_{\alpha_k}$. Then

$$\begin{aligned} vT &= (\delta_1 e_{\alpha_1} + \cdots + \delta_k e_{\alpha_k})T \\ &= (\delta_1 e_{\alpha_1})T + \cdots + (\delta_k e_{\alpha_k})T, \text{ by i) of Definition 7.5.1} \\ &= \delta_1(e_{\alpha_1}T) + \cdots + \delta_k(e_{\alpha_k}T), \text{ by ii) of Definition 7.5.1.} \end{aligned}$$

Moreover, it is possible to define a linear transformation T' from V to U simply by defining the action of T' on each of the e_α's and extending this definition according to i) and ii) of Definition 7.5.1. That is, for each e_α in E, let $e_\alpha T'$ be any vector of U. Once we have defined $e_\alpha T'$, we define, for $v \in V$, $vT' = (\delta_1 e_{\alpha_1} + \cdots + \delta_k e_{\alpha_k})T' = \delta_1(e_{\alpha_1}T') + \cdots + \delta_k(e_{\alpha_k}T')$. It is easy to verify that T', defined in this manner, is indeed a linear transformation.

We now restrict our attention to the case where V and U are both finite dimensional. Thus, let $\{e_1, \cdots, e_n\}$ be a basis for V and $\{f_1, \cdots, f_m\}$ be a basis for U, and let $T \in \text{Hom}_\Delta(V, U)$. Then for each i, $e_i T$ has a unique representation $e_i T = \alpha_{i1} f_1 + \cdots + \alpha_{im} f_m$, which we shall denote by

$\sum_{j=1}^{m} \alpha_{ij} f_j$. Given the scalars α_{ij}, $i = 1,\cdots,n$ and $j = 1,\cdots,m$, we associate the following rectangular array with T:

$$\begin{bmatrix} \alpha_{11} \cdots\cdots \alpha_{1m} \\ \alpha_{21} \cdots\cdots \alpha_{2m} \\ \vdots \\ \alpha_{n1} \cdots\cdots \alpha_{nm} \end{bmatrix}$$

This array is called an $n \times m$ *matrix with coefficients* in Δ, and we abbreviate it by $[\alpha_{ij}]_{n\times m}$ or by $[\alpha_{ij}]$. Thus, we see that given the basis $\{e_1,\cdots,e_n\}$ for V, $\{f_1,\cdots,f_m\}$ for U, and the linear transformation T, we obtain an $n \times m$ matrix. Conversely, if we are given an $n \times m$ matrix $[\alpha_{ij}]$, we define a linear transformation $T': V \to U$ in terms of the bases $\{e_1,\cdots,e_n\}$ and $\{f_1,\cdots,f_m\}$, as follows: $e_i T' = \sum_{j=1}^{m} \alpha_{ij} f_j$, $i = 1,2,\cdots,n$. Thus, there exists a 1–1 correspondence between the set $\text{Hom}_\Delta(V,U)$ and the set of all $n \times m$ matrices.

We point out that the matrix of a linear transformation T depends on the given bases. Thus, relative to a second choice of bases, T may have an entirely different matrix. To learn of the relationship between these two matrices, the reader should consult one of the references on linear algebra (see also Exercise 17).

We also mention that we have now proved in particular

Theorem 7.5.2 Let V be an n dimensional vector space over a division ring Δ. Then there exists a 1–1 correspondence between the set Δ_n of all $n \times n$ matrices over Δ and the set $\text{Hom}_\Delta(V,V)$.

Usually, when we consider $\text{Hom}_\Delta(V,V)$, $[V:\Delta] = n$, and when we desire matrix representations for the elements of $\text{Hom}_\Delta(V,V)$, we shall let $\{e_1, \cdots,e_n\}$ be a basis for V, and for each T in $\text{Hom}(V,V)$, we shall express $e_i T$ in the form $\sum_{j=1}^{n} \alpha_{ij} e_j$ (that is, $\{e_1,\cdots,e_n\}$ takes the place of $\{f_1,\cdots,f_m\}$ in the discussion preceding Theorem 7.5.2). The correspondence, then, prior to Theorem 7.5.2 (and referred to in that theorem) simply associates T and $[\alpha_{ij}]_{n\times n}$.

Now let W be a vector space of dimension p. Let $T \in \text{Hom}_\Delta(V,U)$, $S \in \text{Hom}_\Delta(U,W)$. Then the composite function $T \circ S$ (denoted TS) is in $\text{Hom}_\Delta(V,W)$, and relative to the bases $\{e_1,\cdots,e_n\}$, $\{g_1,\cdots,g_p\}$ of V and W, TS has an $n \times p$ matrix $[\gamma_{ik}]_{n\times p}$. It is a simple matter to determine $[\gamma_{ik}]_{n\times p}$ if we know $[\alpha_{ij}]_{n\times m}$ and $[\beta_{jk}]_{m\times p}$, the matrices of T and S, respectively, where the bases are $\{e_1,\cdots,e_n\}$ for V, $\{f_1,\cdots,f_m\}$ for U, and $\{g_1,\cdots,g_p\}$ for W.

Thus, let $e_iT = \sum_{j=1}^{m} \alpha_{ij}f_j$ and $f_jS = \sum_{k=1}^{p} \beta_{jk}g_k$. Then

$$\begin{aligned} e_i(TS) &= (e_iT)S = \left(\sum_{j=1}^{m} \alpha_{ij}f_j\right)S \\ &= \sum_{j=1}^{m} \alpha_{ij}(f_jS) = \sum_{j=1}^{m} \alpha_{ij}\left(\sum_{k=1}^{p} \beta_{jk}g_k\right) \\ &= \sum_{j=1}^{m}\sum_{k=1}^{p} \alpha_{ij}\beta_{jk}g_k = \sum_{k=1}^{p}\left(\sum_{j=1}^{m} \alpha_{ij}\beta_{jk}\right)g_k = \sum_{k=1}^{p} \gamma_{ik}g_k. \end{aligned}$$

Thus, the (i,k)th *element*, or *entry*, (the element in the ith row and kth column) of $[\gamma_{ik}]_{n\times p}$ is seen to be $\gamma_{ik} = \sum_{j=1}^{m} \alpha_{ij}\beta_{jk}$. In view of this, we are able to define a multiplication of matrices that will agree with our multiplication of linear transformations. Thus, we define $[\alpha_{ij}]_{n\times m}\cdot[\beta_{jk}]_{m\times p}$ by

$$\begin{bmatrix} \alpha_{11} & \cdots & \alpha_{1m} \\ \alpha_{21} & \cdots & \alpha_{2m} \\ \vdots & & \\ \alpha_{n1} & \cdots & \alpha_{nm} \end{bmatrix} \begin{bmatrix} \beta_{11} & \cdots & \beta_{1p} \\ \beta_{21} & \cdots & \beta_{2p} \\ \vdots & & \\ \beta_{m1} & \cdots & \beta_{mp} \end{bmatrix} = \begin{bmatrix} \gamma_{11} & \cdots & \gamma_{1p} \\ \gamma_{21} & \cdots & \gamma_{2p} \\ \vdots & & \\ \gamma_{n1} & \cdots & \gamma_{np} \end{bmatrix},$$

where γ_{ij} is the product of the ith row of $[\alpha_{ij}]$ by the jth column of $[\beta_{ij}]$, namely $\gamma_{ij} = \alpha_{i1}\beta_{1j} + \alpha_{i2}\beta_{2j} + \cdots + \alpha_{im}\beta_{mj}$.

It is clear that matrices $[\alpha_{ij}]_{n\times q}$ and $[\beta_{ij}]_{r\times p}$ can be multiplied only when $q = r$, that is, when the first matrix has the same number of columns as the second has rows.

To illustrate this operation, we easily see that the product

$$\begin{bmatrix} 1 & 2 & 3 \\ 2 & 1 & 4 \end{bmatrix} \begin{bmatrix} 3 & 1 \\ 2 & 1 \\ 1 & 2 \end{bmatrix}$$

$$= \begin{bmatrix} 1\cdot 3 + 2\cdot 2 + 3\cdot 1 & 1\cdot 1 + 2\cdot 1 + 3\cdot 2 \\ 2\cdot 3 + 1\cdot 2 + 4\cdot 1 & 2\cdot 1 + 1\cdot 1 + 4\cdot 2 \end{bmatrix} = \begin{bmatrix} 10 & 9 \\ 12 & 11 \end{bmatrix}.$$

We can prove, by straightforward calculation, that whenever matrices $[\alpha_{ij}]_{n\times m}$, $[\beta_{jk}]_{m\times p}$, $[\gamma_{k\ell}]_{p\times r}$ are given, the associative law holds:

$$([\alpha_{ij}][\beta_{jk}])[\gamma_{k\ell}] = [\alpha_{ij}]([\beta_{jk}][\gamma_{k\ell}]).$$

It is not necessary, however, to actually perform this calculation. For matrix multiplication has been defined according to the action of linear transformations (which are functions), and since function multiplication is associative, so must be the corresponding matrix multiplication.

Next, let T and S both be in $\text{Hom}_\Delta(V,U)$. It is possible to define a new linear transformation, denoted $T + S$, as follows:

For $x \in V$, put

$$(x)(T + S) = xT + xS.$$

By a straightforward verification, $T + S$ is in $\text{Hom}_\Delta(V,U)$. If $\{e_1,\cdots,e_n\}$ and $\{f_1,\cdots,f_m\}$ are bases for V and U respectively, with $e_iT = \sum_{j=1}^{m} \alpha_{ij}f_j$ and $e_iS = \sum_{j=1}^{m} \beta_{ij}f_j$, then $e_i(T + S) = \sum_{j=1}^{m} (a_{ij} + \beta_{ij})f_j$. Thus, we have the following definition of addition of matrices:

$$\begin{bmatrix} \alpha_{11} & \cdots & \alpha_{1m} \\ \vdots & & \\ \alpha_{n1} & \cdots & \alpha_{nm} \end{bmatrix} + \begin{bmatrix} \beta_{11} & \cdots & \beta_{1m} \\ \vdots & & \\ \beta_{n1} & \cdots & \beta_{nm} \end{bmatrix}$$

$$= \begin{bmatrix} \alpha_{11} + \beta_{11} & \cdots & \alpha_{1m} + \beta_{1m} \\ \vdots & & \vdots \\ \alpha_{n1} + \beta_{n1} & \cdots & \alpha_{nm} + \beta_{nm} \end{bmatrix}$$

We add two matrices only if both have the same number of rows and both have the same number of columns.

We remark that the formulation of TS and $T + S$, in the above discussion, can be made even if none of the vector spaces V, U, and W is finite dimensional. The matrix representation would, of course, be another matter.

Of special interest is the important situation where $V = U$ and we study $\text{Hom}_\Delta(V,V)$. Regardless of the dimension (finite or infinite) of V, the following hold:

1. $\text{Hom}_\Delta(V,V)$ is an additive group, where for $T,S \in \text{Hom}_\Delta(V,V)$,

$T + S$ is defined by

$$x(T + S) = xT + xS, \text{ for all } x \in V.$$

2. $\text{Hom}_\Delta(V, V)$ is closed under multiplication, which is associative.
3. In $\text{Hom}_\Delta(V, V)$, the two distributive laws hold, that is, for $T_1, T_2, T_3 \in \text{Hom}_\Delta(V, V)$,

$$T_1(T_2 + T_3) = T_1T_2 + T_1T_3$$

and

$$(T_1 + T_2)T_3 = T_1T_3 + T_2T_3.$$

The distributive laws are proved by showing that for arbitrary x in V, the left hand side and the right hand side both have the same effect on x.

In the event that V is finite dimensional, 3 shows that the distributive laws hold in the set of $n \times n$ matrices.

We summarize this discussion in

Theorem 7.5.3 Let V be a vector space over a division ring Δ. Then $\text{Hom}_\Delta(V, V)$ is a ring.

Proof: Given above.

Corollary 7.5.4 Let Δ be a division ring. Let Δ_n denote the set of all $n \times n$ matrices with coefficients in Δ. Then Δ_n is a ring, $\Delta_n \cong \text{Hom}_\Delta(v, v)$.

Proof: The correspondence of Theorem 7.5.2 shows that $\Delta_n \cong \text{Hom}_\Delta(v, v)$ and is hence a ring.

These results are the last of the special results we will require from linear algebra. Thus, we shall not pursue this deep and very important field further. We do, however, develop some additional results in linear algebra in the exercises and the reader is urged to attempt these. In addition, he should consult the books listed in the bibliography.

Before proceeding, we give one application of our work on vector spaces, namely, a second proof (see Exercise 15, Section 5.8 for the first proof) that if F is a finite field of characteristic p, then F has p^n elements for some integer $n > 0$. Later, we shall prove that for each prime p and each integer $n > 0$, there exists a field with p^n elements.

Theorem 7.5.5 Let F be a finite field with characteristic p. Then there exists an integer n such that F has p^n elements.

Proof: From Theorem 5.8.10, we have that Z_p (or an isomorphic "copy" of Z_p) is the prime subfield of F. Thus, F can be considered a vector space over Z_p. Since F is finite, it clearly has a finite basis over Z_p, say $e_1, \cdots, e_n$, for some integer $n > 0$. Then any element in F has precisely one representation in the form

$$\alpha_1 e_1 + \cdots + \alpha_n e_n, \quad \alpha_i \in Z_p.$$

Since there are p choices for each α_i, there are clearly $p \cdot p \cdots p = p^n$ elements in F.

Exercises

1. Let K denote the real numbers, and let V be a vector space over K, $[V:K] = 3$. Let $\{e_1, e_2, e_3\}$ be a basis for V and let $T \in \mathrm{Hom}_K(V,V)$ have the following matrix representation:

$$\begin{bmatrix} 1 & 0 & 1 \\ 0 & 1 & 1 \\ 1 & 1 & 0 \end{bmatrix}.$$

Prove that i) $T: V \xrightarrow[\text{onto}]{1-1} V$.

ii) $T^{-1} \in \mathrm{Hom}_K(V,V)$.

Moreover, iii) discover the matrix representation for T^{-1}.

Hint: Let T^{-1} have representation

$$\begin{bmatrix} a_{11} & a_{12} & a_{13} \\ a_{21} & a_{22} & a_{23} \\ a_{31} & a_{32} & a_{33} \end{bmatrix}$$

and use the fact that

$$\begin{bmatrix} 1 & 0 & 1 \\ 0 & 1 & 1 \\ 1 & 1 & 0 \end{bmatrix} \begin{bmatrix} a_{11} & a_{12} & a_{13} \\ a_{21} & a_{22} & a_{23} \\ a_{31} & a_{32} & a_{33} \end{bmatrix} = \begin{bmatrix} 1 & 0 & 0 \\ 0 & 1 & 0 \\ 0 & 0 & 1 \end{bmatrix},$$

the matrix of the identity linear transformation.

2. Let V be a vector space over K, $[V:K] = 2$. Let $T \in \mathrm{Hom}_K(V,V)$ have matrix $\begin{bmatrix} a_{11} & a_{12} \\ a_{21} & a_{22} \end{bmatrix}$ and suppose T^{-1} exists. Find the matrix for T^{-1}.

3. Let V be a vector space over K, the real numbers, with $[V:K] = 2$. Let $T \in \mathrm{Hom}_K(V,V)$ have matrix $\begin{bmatrix} a_{11} & a_{12} \\ a_{21} & a_{22} \end{bmatrix}$. Find a necessary and sufficient condition on the a_{ij}'s so that $T: V \xrightarrow[\text{onto}]{1-1} V$.

Hint: Consider $a_{11}a_{22} - a_{12}a_{21}$.

4. Let V and U be vector spaces over a division ring Δ. Let $T \in \operatorname{Hom}_\Delta(V,U)$ and let $N = \{x \in V \mid xT = 0\}$. Prove that

i) N is a subspace of V

ii) Im T is a subspace of U

iii) $[V:\Delta] = [\operatorname{Im} T:\Delta] + [N:\Delta]$

iv) if $[V:\Delta] = [U:\Delta] = n$, then T is onto if and only if $N = 0$.

5. Let F be a field and let

$$[a_{ij}]_{n\times n} = \begin{bmatrix} a_{11} & \cdots & a_{1n} \\ a_{21} & \cdots & a_{2n} \\ \vdots & & \\ a_{n1} & \cdots & a_{nn} \end{bmatrix}$$

be a matrix with coefficients in F.

Define the *determinant* of $[a_{ij}]$, denoted $\det[a_{ij}]$, as the following finite sum:

$$\sum_{\sigma \in S_n} \operatorname{sgn} \sigma \cdot a_{1,1\sigma} a_{2,2\sigma} \cdots a_{n,n\sigma},$$

where σ varies over all permutations on n letters, and

$$\operatorname{sgn} \sigma = \begin{cases} 1, & \text{if } \sigma \text{ is even} \\ -1, & \text{if } \sigma \text{ is odd} \end{cases}$$

i) Prove that the determinant of $\begin{bmatrix} a_{11} & a_{12} \\ a_{21} & a_{22} \end{bmatrix}$ is $a_{11}a_{22} - a_{12}a_{21}$.

ii) Prove that the determinant of

$$\begin{bmatrix} a_{11} & a_{12} & a_{13} \\ a_{21} & a_{22} & a_{23} \\ a_{31} & a_{32} & a_{33} \end{bmatrix}$$

is $a_{11}a_{22}a_{33} - a_{11}a_{23}a_{32} + a_{21}a_{13}a_{32} - a_{21}a_{12}a_{33} + a_{31}a_{12}a_{23} - a_{31}a_{22}a_{13}$.

6. Let $[a_{ij}] \in F_n$, F a field. Prove that

$$\det[a_{ij}] = \sum_{\sigma \in S_n} \operatorname{sgn} \sigma \cdot a_{1\sigma,1} a_{2\sigma,2} \cdots a_{n\sigma,n}$$

7. Let F be a field and let

$$[a_{ij}] = \begin{bmatrix} a_{11} & a_{12} & \cdots & a_{1n} \\ a_{21} & a_{22} & \cdots & a_{2n} \\ \vdots & & & \vdots \\ a_{n1} & a_{n2} & \cdots & a_{nn} \end{bmatrix} \in F_n.$$

Define A_{ij}, the ijth *cofactor* of $[a_{ij}]$, as follows:

$$A_{ij} = (-1)^{i+j} \det [a_{ij}]_{\hat{i}\hat{j}},$$

where $[a_{ij}]_{\hat{i}\hat{j}}$ is the matrix obtained by crossing out the ith row and jth column of $[a_{ij}]$. Prove that

i) $\det [a_{ij}] = a_{11}A_{11} + a_{21}A_{21} + \cdots + a_{n1}A_{n1}$

ii) $\det [a_{ij}] = a_{i1}A_{i1} + a_{i2}A_{i2} + \cdots + a_{in}A_{in}$, for all i

iii) $\det [a_{ij}] = a_{1i}A_{1i} + a_{2i}A_{2i} + \cdots + a_{ni}A_{ni}$, for all i.

Hint: Examine the cases for $n = 3,4$ first, in order to gain the general idea.

8. Let F be a field and let $[a_{ij}]_{n\times n} \in F_n$. Prove that

$$a_{i1}A_{j1} + a_{i2}A_{j2} + \cdots + a_{in}A_{jn} = 0, \quad \text{for} \quad i \neq j,$$

and
$$a_{1i}A_{1j} + a_{2i}A_{2j} + \cdots + a_{ni}A_{nj} = 0, \quad \text{for} \quad i \neq j.$$

9. Let $[a_{ij}]_{n\times n} \in F_n$, F a field. Let $[b_{ij}]_{n\times n}$ be the same as $[a_{ij}]$, except that two rows are interchanged. Prove that $\det [b_{ij}] = -\det [a_{ij}]$.

Hint: First assume that the two rows are adjacent.

10. Let $[a_{ij}] \in F_n$, and assume two rows of $[a_{ij}]$ are identical. Prove that $\det [a_{ij}] = 0$.

11. Let $[a_{ij}] \in F_n$ and suppose that $\det [a_{ij}] = \alpha \neq 0$. Let $[b_{ij}]$ be the matrix whose ijth entry is

$$b_{ij} = A_{ji} \cdot \alpha^{-1}.$$

Show that

$$[b_{ij}][a_{ij}] = [a_{ij}][b_{ij}] = \begin{bmatrix} 1 & 0 & \cdots & 0 \\ 0 & 1 & \cdots & 0 \\ \vdots & \vdots & \ddots & 0 \\ 0 & 0 & 0 & 1 \end{bmatrix}$$

Hint: Use Exercises 7 and 8.

12. Let V be a vector space over F, a field, with $[V:F] = n$ and with basis $\{e_1,\cdots,e_n\}$. Let $T \in \mathrm{Hom}_F(V,V)$ have matrix $[a_{ij}]$ relative to $\{e_1,\cdots,e_n\}$. Define $\det T$ as $\det [a_{ij}]$. Prove that T has an inverse in $\mathrm{Hom}_F(V,V)$ if and only if $\det T \neq 0$. (It can be shown—Exercise 17—that the value of $\det T$ does not depend on the particular choice of basis used to represent T).

13. Let V be a vector space over a field F, $[V:F] = n$. Let $GL_n(F) = \{T \mid T \in \mathrm{Hom}_F(V,V) \text{ and } \det T \neq 0\}$. Prove that $(GL_n(F), \cdot)$ is a group with respect to multiplication.

Hint: See Exercise 12.

14. Let V be a vector space over a field F, $[V:F] = n$. Let $T \in \mathrm{Hom}_F(V,V)$. Prove that if $\det T \neq 0$, then $\det (T^{-1}) = [\det T]^{-1}$.

15. Let $[a_{ij}] \in F_n$, F a field, and let $[b_{ij}]$ be the matrix identical to $[a_{ij}]$, except that the ith row of $[b_{ij}]$ is $a_{i1} + ta_{k1}, a_{i2} + ta_{k2}, \cdots, a_{in} + ta_{kn}$, $k \neq i$, $t \in F$. Prove that $\det [a_{ij}] = \det [b_{ij}]$.

16. Let V be a vector space over a field F, $[V:F] = n$. Let $S,T \in \mathrm{Hom}_F(V,V)$. Prove that $\det (TS) = \det T \cdot \det S$.

Hint: Let T have matrix $[a_{ij}]$ and S matrix $[b_{ij}]$ and observe that $\det [a_{ij}] \cdot \det [b_{ij}]$

$$= \det \left[\begin{array}{ccc|ccc} a_{11} & & a_{1n} & & & \\ \vdots & & & & 0 & \\ a_{n1} & \cdots & a_{nn} & & & \\ \hline -1 & & & b_{11} & \cdots & b_{1n} \\ & \ddots & 0 & \vdots & & \\ 0 & & -1 & b_{n1} & \cdots & b_{nn} \end{array}\right].$$

This follows without too much trouble from the definition of det.

Number the rows of the big matrix as follows: $1,2,\cdots,n, 1^*,2^*,\cdots,n^*$. By Exercise 15, the value of the determinant is not changed by adding a multiple of a * row to a non * row. Thus, we perform the following n^2 such operations: Add a_{ik} times the row k^* to the ith row. The resulting matrix will be

$$\left[\begin{array}{ccc|ccc} & & & c_{11} & \cdots & c_{1n} \\ & 0 & & \vdots & & \\ & & & c_{n1} & \cdots & c_{nn} \\ \hline -1 & & 0 & b_{11} & \cdots & b_{1n} \\ & \ddots & & \vdots & & \\ 0 & & -1 & b_{n1} & \cdots & b_{nn} \end{array}\right]$$

where c_{ij} is the i,jth element of $[a_{ij}][b_{ij}]$. By direct computation, this new matrix has as its determinant det $([a_{ij}][b_{ij}])$. Try this method with specific 3×3 matrices and 4×4 matrices.

17. Let $T \in \text{Hom}_F(V,V)$, F a field and $[V:F] = n$. Let $\{e_1,\cdots,e_n\}$ and $\{f_1,\cdots,f_n\}$ be two bases for V. Suppose $[a_{ij}]$ and $[b_{ij}]$ are the matrices for T relative to $\{e_1,\cdots,e_n\}$ and $\{f_1,\cdots,f_n\}$, respectively. Let $[c_{ij}]$ be the matrix obtained by writing each e_i as a linear combination of the f_j's. Show that

i) $[c_{ij}][b_{ij}] = [a_{ij}][c_{ij}]$,
ii) $\det [c_{ij}] \neq 0$,
iii) $\det [b_{ij}] = \det [a_{ij}]$.

Hint: Consider $e_iT = [\Sigma c_{ij}f_j]T$ and $e_iT = \Sigma a_{ij}e_j$.

7.6 FIELD EXTENSIONS

We now proceed toward one of our main goals in this chapter: proving the existence of a field with p^n elements, for each prime p and for each integer $n > 0$. To do this, we shall work with field extensions and splitting fields, aided by our earlier study of rings modulo maximal ideals.

Definition 7.6.1 Let F and E be fields, where F is a subfield of E. Then we also call E an *extension field* of F.

For example, the field of real numbers is an extension field of Q, the field of rational numbers, and the field $Q(\sqrt{2})$ (Example 5.4.10) is an extension field of Q.

In Section 5.13, Exercise 4, we showed that if $f(x)$ is irreducible over the field F, then $(f(x))$ is a maximal ideal in $F[x]$, whence by Theorem 5.13.6, $F[x]/(f(x))$ is a field. This fact plays a paramount role in our current discussion, so we include its proof in the next result.

Lemma 7.6.2 Let F be a field and let $f(x) \in F[x]$. Then $f(x)$ is irreducible over F if and only if $F[x]/(f(x))$ is a field.

Proof: Let $f(x)$ be irreducible. We show that the principal ideal $(f(x))$ is maximal in $F[x]$. Thus, let $g(x) \in F[x]$, $g(x) \notin (f(x))$. Since $g(x) \notin (f(x))$, $f(x) \nmid g(x)$, and so, by the irreducibility of $f(x)$, 1 is in the ideal generated by $f(x)$ and $g(x)$. Thus, $F[x]$ is equal to the ideal $(f(x), g(x))$, and $(f(x))$ is maximal. By Theorem 5.13.6, $F[x]/(f(x))$ is a field.

Conversely, if $f(x)$ is not irreducible, then $f(x) = g(x) \cdot h(x)$, and so $g(x) + (f(x))$ is a zero divisor in $F[x]/(f(x))$, contradicting that $F[x]/(f(x))$ is a field.

As an elementary, but illuminating result, we easily prove the next theorem.

Theorem 7.6.3 Let E be an extension field of the field F. Let $\alpha \in E$. Then either α is transcendental over F, or α is algebraic over F. In the latter case, α satisfies an irreducible, monic polynomial $f(x)$ with coefficients in F, and the set of all finite sums of the form

$$(1) \qquad f_0 + f_1\alpha + \cdots + f_k\alpha^k, \quad f_i \in F$$

(the k varies), is a field isomorphic to $F[x]/(f(x))$.

Proof: Either α satisfies a polynomial with coefficients in F, or it does not. In the latter case, α is transcendental over F by Definition 5.9.7. In the former case, α is algebraic over F. In this case, there is a polynomial of least degree which α satisfies, say $f(x) = f_0 + f_1x + \cdots + f_nx^n$, $f_n \neq 0$. By multiplying this by f_n^{-1}, we may assume $f(x)$ is monic. Thus, we have

$$(2) \qquad f_0 + f_1\alpha + \cdots + f_{n-1}\alpha^{n-1} + \alpha^n = 0.$$

Now, $f(x)$ must be irreducible, for otherwise $f(x) = g(x)h(x)$, with $1 \le \deg g(x), \deg h(x) < \deg f(x)$ and $0 = (\alpha)f = (\alpha)g \cdot (\alpha)h$, whence either $(\alpha)g = 0$ or $(\alpha)h = 0$. In either case, α would satisfy a polynomial of degree less than that of $f(x)$, a contradiction.

Now let $F(\alpha)$ be the set of all elements of the form (1). It is easy to see that $F(\alpha)$ is a subring of E. To show that $F(\alpha)$ is a field, we shall show that $F(\alpha)$ is isomorphic to the field $F[x]/(f(x))$. Thus, let $h(x) = h_0 + h_1x + \cdots + h_kx^k \in F[x]$ and let $\varphi: F[x] \to F(\alpha)$ be defined by

$$h(x)\phi = h_0 + h_1\alpha + \cdots + h_k\alpha^k.$$

This is easily seen to be a homomorphism onto the ring $F(\alpha)$. Suppose that $h(x)\phi = 0$. By the division algorithm, there exist polynomials $q(x)$ and $r(x)$ such that

$$h(x) = q(x)f(x) + r(x), \quad \deg r(x) < \deg f(x).$$

Then

$$(\alpha)h = (\alpha)q \cdot (\alpha)f + (\alpha)r$$
$$0 = (\alpha)q \cdot 0 + (\alpha)r,$$

whence $(\alpha)r = 0$. Thus, α satisfies the polynomial $r(x)$. This contradicts our choice of $f(x)$, unless $r(x)$ is the zero polynomial. Hence, $f(x) \mid h(x)$ and we see that $\ker \phi = \{h(x) \in F[x] \mid f(x) \mid h(x)\}$, that is, $\ker \phi = (f(x))$.

Thus, $F(\alpha) \simeq F[x]/(f(x))$, which completes the proof.

Definition 7.6.4 Let E be an extension field of the field F. If $\alpha \in E$ is algebraic over F, we call the field $F(\alpha)$ a *simple algebraic extension* of F, and we say that α has been *adjoined* to F. We call the monic polynomial of Theorem 7.6.3 the *minimal polynomial* of α.

Theorem 7.6.5 Let $F(\alpha)$ be a simple algebraic extension of a field F and let $f(x)$ be the minimal polynomial of α, $\deg f(x) = n$. Then $F(\alpha) = \{a_0 + a_1\alpha + \cdots + a_{n-1}\alpha^{n-1} \mid a_i \in F\}$.

Proof: By Theorem 7.6.3, $F(\alpha) = \{b_0 + b_1\alpha + \cdots + b_k\alpha^k \mid b_i \in F$, and where k varies$\}$. Thus, let $b_0 + b_1\alpha + \cdots + b_k\alpha^k \in F(\alpha)$, and let $h(x) = b_0 + b_1x + \cdots + b_kx^k$. Then $h(x) = q(x)f(x) + r(x)$, $\deg r(x) < n$, by the division algorithm. Then if $r(x) = a_0 + a_1x + \cdots + a_{n-1}x^{n-1}$, $b_0 + b_1\alpha + \cdots + b_k\alpha^k = (\alpha)h = (\alpha)q(a)f + (\alpha)r = (\alpha)q\cdot 0 + (\alpha)r = (\alpha)r = a_0 + a_1\alpha + \cdots + a_{n-1}\alpha^{n-1}$.

Lemma 7.6.6 Let F_1 and F_2 be fields, and let ϕ be an isomorphism from F_1 onto F_2. Then there exists an isomorphism $\Phi: F_1[x] \xrightarrow{\text{onto}} F_2[x]$ such that

$$(a_0 + a_1x + \cdots + a_kx^k)\Phi = a_0\phi + (a_1\phi)x + \cdots + (a_k\phi)x^k.$$

Moreover, $f_1(x)$ is irreducible over F_1 if and only if $(f_1(x))\Phi$ is irreducible over F_2.

Proof: Suppose

$$(a_0 + a_1x + \cdots + a_kx^k)\Phi = (b_0 + b_1x + \cdots + b_kx^k)\Phi.$$

(There is no loss of generality in assuming both of these polynomials have the same degree). Then $a_i\phi = b_i\phi$, $i = 0,\cdots,k$, whence, since ϕ is 1–1, $a_i = b_i$, $i = 0,\cdots,k$. Thus, Φ is 1–1. Also, for

$$c_0 + c_1x + \cdots + c_kx^k \in F_2[x],$$

we have that

$$[c_0\phi^{-1} + (c_1\phi^{-1})x + \cdots + (c_k\phi^{-1})x^k]\Phi = c_0 + \cdots + c_kx^k,$$

so Φ is onto. Using the fact that ϕ is an isomorphism, it is equally easy to show that Φ is an isomorphism. The remark concerning irreducibility also follows without any trouble.

Theorem 7.6.7 Let F_1 and F_2 be isomorphic fields, with ϕ the given isomorphism, and let E_1 and E_2 be extension fields of F_1 and F_2, respectively. Let Φ be defined as in Lemma 7.6.6. Let $\alpha_1 \in E_1$ and $\alpha_2 \in E_2$, and assume α_i is algebraic over F_i, $i = 1,2$. If α_1 satisfies $f_1(x)$ and if α_2 satisfies $f_1(x)\Phi = f_2(x)$, then $F_1(\alpha_1) \cong F_2(\alpha_2)$.

Proof: By Theorem 7.6.3, $F_1(\alpha_1) \cong F_1[x]/(f_1(x))$ and $F_2(\alpha_2) \cong F_2[x]/(f_2(x))$. Thus, it suffices to show that

$$F_1[x]/(f_1(x)) \cong F_2[x]/(f_2(x)).$$

To do this, we consider the composite of the homomorphisms Φ and ν, where ν is the natural homomorphism $F_2[x] \rightarrow F_2[x]/(f_2(x))$. Thus, $F_1[x] \xrightarrow{\Phi} F_2[x] \xrightarrow{\nu} F_2[x]/(f_2(x))$. Then $\Phi \circ \nu$ is a homomorphism, and it is easy to see that its kernel is $(f_1(x))$. Since $F_1[x]/\ker(\Phi \circ \nu) \cong \operatorname{Im}(\Phi \circ \nu)$, we have the desired result: $F_1[x]/(f_1(x)) \cong F_2[x]/(f_2(x))$.

So far we have assumed that F is a subfield of E, examined elements α algebraic over F, found irreducible polynomials $f(x)$, and lastly observed that $F(\alpha) \cong F[x]/(f(x))$. Since it is our desire to create an extension field from a given field in which a given irreducible polynomial will have a root, we now suppose that F is a field with $f(x)$ irreducible over F. We shall show how F can be considered a subfield of $F[x]/(f(x)) = E$ and how $f(x)$ will have a root in E.

Theorem 7.6.8 Let F be a field and let $f(x)$ be irreducible over F. Then $E = F[x]/(f(x))$ is an extension field of F and $f(x)$ has a root in E.

Proof: We have already seen that $F[x]/(f(x))$ is a field, where x is an indeterminate. Let $\phi: F \rightarrow F[x]/(f(x))$ be defined by $a\phi = a + (f(x))$, for all $a \in F$. This is clearly an embedding of F in $F[x]/(f(x)) = E$, and in this sense F is a subfield of E.

Next, let ξ denote the coset $x + (f(x))$ in E. We show that ξ satisfies the polynomial $f(x)$. Let

$$\begin{aligned} f(x) &= a_0 + a_1 x + \cdots + a_n x^n. \text{ Then} \\ (\xi)f &= a_0 + a_1\xi + a_2\xi^2 + \cdots + a_n\xi^n \\ &= a_0 + a_1[x + (f(x))] + \cdots + a_n[x + (f(x))]^n \\ &= a_0 + a_1 x + \cdots + a_n x^n + (f(x)) \\ &= f(x) + (f(x)) = (f(x)), \end{aligned}$$

which is the zero element of E. This completes the proof.

In the situation of Theorem 7.6.8, we see that it is possible to denote the field E by $F(\xi)$. Thus, our earlier notation (Theorem 7.6.3) carries over.

Given a field F and a polynomial $f(x)$, not necessarily irreducible, it is important that we be able to find an extension field E of F such that $f(x)$ factors completely into linear factors over E. Our technique in finding E is relatively simple. We need only apply Theorem 7.6.8 repeatedly.

To illustrate the idea, let Q denote the rational number system and let

$f(x) = (x^2 - 2)(x^2 - 3)$. We first form $Q[x]/(x^2 - 2) = E_1$ and observe that over E_1, $f(x) = (x + \sqrt{2})(x - \sqrt{2})(x^2 - 3)$. We then form $E_1[x]/(x^2 - 3) = E_2$ and observe that over E_2,

$$f(x) = (x + \sqrt{2})(x - \sqrt{2})(x + \sqrt{3})(x - \sqrt{3}).$$

Thus, $Q(\sqrt{2}, \sqrt{3}) = (Q(\sqrt{2}))(\sqrt{3})$ is the smallest field E in which $f(x)$ has a complete factorization into linear factors.

Definition 7.6.9 Let F be a field and let E be an extension field of F. Let $f(x)$ be a polynomial with coefficients in F. Suppose that $f(x) = a_0(x - \alpha_1)\cdots(x - \alpha_n)$, $a_0 \in F$, $\alpha_i \in E$, is a complete factorization of $f(x)$ into linear factors over E, and suppose that whenever $f(x)$ can be so factored in any field E' such that $F \subseteq E' \subseteq E$, then $E' = E$. Then E is called a *splitting field* for $f(x)$ over F. (F is called the *base* field).

Note that if $f(x)$ can be completely factored into linear factors over F, then F itself is the splitting field for $f(x)$. In a sense, E is the "smallest" field containing F in which $f(x)$ factors completely.

It is our goal to prove that every polynomial over a field F has a splitting field, and that any two splitting fields are isomorphic.

We remark that a splitting field depends *both* on $f(x)$ and F, the base field. That is, we must keep in mind the original coefficient field F for $f(x)$. Thus, if we take F as the rational numbers, then the real numbers are not a splitting field for $(x - 1)(x - 2)$ (as are the rational numbers); whereas if we take F as the real numbers, then F is a splitting field for $(x - 1)(x - 2)$.

Theorem 7.6.10 Let $f(x) \in F[x]$, F a field. Then there exists a splitting field E for $f(x)$.

Proof: We first prove by induction on $\deg f(x)$ that there exists at least one extension field of F in which $f(x)$ factors completely into linear factors. It will then follow easily that a splitting field exists.

First, if $\deg f(x) = 1$, then $f(x)$ factors into linear factors over F itself. Thus, assume that if $\deg g(x) < n$, then there exists a field H, $F \subseteq H$, such that $g(x)$ factors completely into linear factors over H. Thus, let $\deg f(x) = n$ and suppose $f(x) = f_1(x)\cdots f_m(x)$, each $f_i(x)$ irreducible. We may assume without loss of generality that $\deg f_i(x) > 1$, $i = 1,\cdots,m$. Then $f_1(x)$ has at least one root in $F[x]/(f_1(x)) = E_1$ and $f(x)$ can be written $f(x) = (x - \xi_1)g(x)$, where $\xi_1 \in E_1$ and $g(x) \in E_1[x]$. Clearly, $\deg g(x) < n$, and so by our induction hypothesis, there exists an extension field H of E_1 over which $g(x)$, and hence $f(x)$, factors completely into linear factors.

Now to get the splitting field, we let $\{H_\alpha\}$ be the collection of all subfields H_α of H in which $f(x)$ factors completely. Clearly, $\bigcap H_\alpha = E$ is the desired splitting field.

Theorem 7.6.11 Let ϕ be an isomorphism from F_1 onto F_2, F_i a field, $i = 1,2$. Let Φ be the isomorphism from $F_1[x]$ onto $F_2[x]$ defined in Lemma 7.6.6. Let $f_1(x) \in F_1[x]$ and $f_2(x) = f_1(x)\Phi \in F_2[x]$. Let E_i be a splitting field for $f_i(x)$, $i = 1,2$. Then there exists an isomorphism $\psi: E_1 \xrightarrow{\text{onto}} E_2$ such that $\psi \mid F_1 = \phi$.

Proof: We first show that any irreducible factor $g(x)$ of $f_1(x)$ over F_1 has a root in E_1. For let $f_1(x) = (x - \xi_1)\cdots(x - \xi_n)$ be the factorization of $f_1(x)$ over E_1, and let $f_1(x) = g(x)h(x)$, $g(x)$ irreducible over F_1, $g(x) \in F_1[x]$ and $h(x) \in F_1[x]$. Since $F_1 \subseteq E_1$, $(x - \xi_1)\cdots(x - \xi_n) = g(x)h(x)$ are two factorizations of $f_1(x)$ over E_1. Since Euclid's lemma holds in $E_1[x]$ and since $E_1[x]$ is a UFD (Theorem 5.16.7), it follows that for at least one i, $x - \xi_i \mid g(x)$, whence ξ_i is a root for $g(x)$ in E_1.

We now prove the theorem by induction on the number of roots that $f_1(x)$ has outside of F_1 (but in E_1). If $f_1(x)$ has no roots outside of F_1, then $f_1(x)$ factors completely into linear factors over F_1, whence $E_1 = F_1$. Then $f_2(x)$ factors completely over F_2, whence $E_2 = F_2$ and the theorem is true in this case.

Thus, assume that if $f_1(x)$ has fewer than n roots outside of F_1, then the theorem is true. Now we suppose that $f_1(x)$ has n roots outside of F_1. We factor $f_1(x)$ into polynomials irreducible over F_1, thus:

$$f_1(x) = g_1(x)\cdots g_m(x).$$

This factorization induces a factorization of $f_2(x)$ over F_2: $f_2(x) = h_1(x)\cdots h_m(x)$, where each $h_i(x)$ corresponds to $g_i(x)$ under $\Phi: F_1[x] \to F_2[x]$. Also, each $h_i(x)$ is irreducible. Since $f_1(x)$ has $n > 1$ roots outside of F_1, at least one of the $g_i(x)$'s has degree >1, say $\deg g_1(x) > 1$.

By our opening remark, $g_1(x)$ has a root, say ξ, in E_1. By Theorem 7.6.3, $F_1[x]/(g_1(x)) \simeq F_1(\xi)$. Also, $h_1(x)$ has a root η in E_2 and $F_2[x]/(h_1(x)) \simeq F_2(\eta)$. But by Theorem 7.6.7, $F_1(\xi) \simeq F_2(\eta)$ under an extension ϕ' of ϕ.

We now consider $f_1(x)$ as a polynomial over $F_1(\xi)$ and $f_2(x)$ as a polynomial over $F_2(\eta)$. We observe that E_1 is a splitting field for $f_1(x)$ over $F_1(\xi)$ and that $f_1(x)$ has fewer than n roots outside of $F_1(\xi)$. We also make the same observations concerning E_2, $f_2(x)$, and $F_2(\eta)$. By our induction hypothesis (with $F_1(\xi)$ and $F_2(\eta)$ now considered the base fields), ϕ', and hence ϕ, can be extended to an isomorphism ψ between E_1 and E_2, and the theorem is proved.

Before terminating this section, we mention that without too much more work, we could discuss Galois theory and, in particular, prove the fundamental theorem of Galois theory. Several of the references in the bibliography contain this very important area of algebra. The work by Artin [2], which many of the other sources follow, is especially recommended.

Exercises

1. Prove Lemma 7.6.6.
2. Complete the proof of Theorem 7.6.7.
3. Let $x^3 - 2 \in Q[x]$, Q the field of rational numbers. Find an extension field in which $x^3 - 2$ has a solution.
4. Let $x^3 + 1 \in Q[x]$. Find a splitting field for $x^3 + 1$.
5. Let $f(x)$ be irreducible over a field F. Let ξ_1 and ξ_2 be distinct roots of $f(x)$ in a splitting field. Show that $F(\xi_1) \simeq F(\xi_2)$.
6. Let $(x^2 + b_1x + c_1)(x^2 + b_2x + c_2)$ be a polynomial over K, the field of real numbers, where each quadratic factor is irreducible over K and where the four roots of the polynomial in C, the complex number system, are distinct. Let ξ_1, ξ_1' be the roots of the first factor, and ξ_2, ξ_2' the roots of the second. Show that $K(\xi_1, \xi_2) = K(\xi_1', \xi_2')$.
7. Let E be an extension field of the field F. As a vector space, E has a basis over F. Show that if $[E:F] < \infty$, then every element in E is algebraic over F.

7.7 FINITE FIELDS

In this section we shall prove that for each prime power p^n, $n > 0$, there exists a field with p^n elements. In addition, we shall also prove that the multiplicative group of such a field is cyclic.

Let E be an extension field of the field F, and let $\alpha_1, \alpha_2, \cdots, \alpha_n \in E$. Then the intersection of all the subfields of E containing all finite sums of the form $\Sigma a_i \alpha_1^{e_{1i}} \cdots \alpha_n^{e_{ni}}$, $a_i \in F$, $e_{jk} \in Z$, is a subfield of E and an extension field of F which we shall denote by $F(\alpha_1, \cdots, \alpha_n)$.

Theorem 7.7.1 Let p be a prime and n an integer, $n > 0$. Then there exists a field with p^n elements. Moreover, any two fields with p^n elements are isomorphic.

Proof: We consider the polynomial $x^{p^n} - x$ over Z_p. Then there is a splitting field E for $x^{p^n} - x$ over Z_p. Moreover, $E = Z_p(\xi_1, \xi_2, \cdots, \xi_m)$, where the ξ_i's are all of the roots of $x^{p^n} - x$ in E. We show that E has precisely p^n elements.

Thus, let ξ_1 and ξ_2 be roots of $x^{p^n} - x$. Then $\xi_1^{p^n} - \xi_1 = 0$ and $\xi_2^{p^n} - \xi_2 = 0$. Since E has characteristic p, we have, by Exercise 13, Section 5.8, that $(\xi_1 - \xi_2)^{p^n} = \xi_1^{p^n} - \xi_2^{p^n} = \xi_1 - \xi_2$, so $\xi_1 - \xi_2$ is also a root of $x^{p^n} - x$. Assuming that $\xi_1 \neq 0$, we see that $(\xi_1^{-1})^{p^n} = (\xi_1^{p^n})^{-1} = \xi_1^{-1}$, so that ξ_1^{-1} satisfies $x^{p^n} - x = 0$. Thus, the set of all solutions to $x^{p^n} - x = 0$ forms a subfield of E, and hence is equal to E, by the definition of a splitting field.

If E has fewer than p^n elements, then $x^{p^n} - x$ has a multiple root in E, say ξ. Thus, in E, $f(x) = x^{p^n} - x = (x - \xi)^m g(x)$, where $m > 1$. We let $f'(x)$ denote the *formal derivative* of $f(x)$, determined according to the rules of elementary calculus. Then, on one hand, $f'(x) = p^n x^{p^n - 1} - 1 = -1$, since p is the characteristic of E. On the other, $f'(x) = (x - \xi)^m g'(x) + m(x - \xi)^{m-1} g(x) = (x - \xi)^{m-1}[(x - \xi)g'(x) + mg(x)]$. Thus, on the one hand, $f'(x)$ has no roots in E, while on the other hand, ξ is a root of $f'(x)$ if $m > 1$. Thus, $m = 1$ and $x^{p^n} - x$ has no multiple roots in E. Thus, $x^{p^n} - x$ has precisely p^n roots in E, that is, E has p^n elements.

It finally remains to prove that any two fields with p^n elements are isomorphic. Suppose E_1 and E_2 are both fields with p^n elements. Let $Z_p{}^1$ and $Z_p{}^2$ be the prime subfields of E_1 and E_2, respectively. We know that $Z_p{}^1 \cong Z_p{}^2$. Now in E_i, the nonzero elements form a multiplicative group $E_i{}^* = E_i - \{0\}$, and since $E_i{}^*$ has $p^n - 1$ elements, each element in E_i satisfies $x^{p^n - 1} - 1 = 0$ and hence satisfies $x^{p^n} - x = 0$. Since all p^n elements of E_i satisfy $x^{p^n} - x = 0$, $x^{p^n} - x$ factors completely into linear factors in E_i. Thus, E_i is a splitting field for $x^{p^n} - x$. Since $Z_p{}^1 \cong Z_p{}^2$, we can extend this isomorphism to one between E_1 and E_2, by Theorem 7.6.11. This completes the proof of Theorem 7.7.1.

Definition 7.7.2 A field with p^n elements is called a *Galois field*,[28] and is denoted by $\mathrm{GF}(p^n)$.

Theorem 7.7.3 The multiplicative group of $\mathrm{GF}(p^n)$ is cyclic.

Proof: It suffices to prove that $\mathrm{GF}(p^n)^* = \mathrm{GF}(p^n) - \{0\}$ has one element of order $p^n - 1 = m$. In a finite abelian group G, if a has order r and b has order s, then there is an element c in G whose order is lcm $[r, s]$ (see Exercise 11, Section 4.7). Thus, since there is a finite number of orders of elements of G, there is an element of G whose order is the lcm of all the orders. Let this order be m'. We consider $x^{m'} - 1$. Since each $\alpha \in \mathrm{GF}(p^n)^*$ satisfies $x^r - 1$, where $r \mid m'$, α satisfies $x^{m'} - 1$. Thus, $x^{m'} - 1$ has m roots, where $m' \leq m$. Since $x^{m'} - 1$ can have no more than m' roots in a field, it follows that $m = m'$. Thus, $\mathrm{GF}(p^n)^*$ is cyclic.

Knowing that $\mathrm{GF}(p^n)^*$ is cyclic, we can easily find a necessary and sufficient condition for $\mathrm{GF}(p^n)$ to have subfields, and we can determine these subfields precisely.

Lemma 7.7.4 Let F' be a subfield of $\mathrm{GF}(p^n)$. Then there exists an integer m such that F' has p^m elements, and $m \mid n$.

Proof: Since $\mathrm{GF}(p^n)$ has characteristic p, so does F', and hence F' has p^m elements for some integer $m > 0$. Next, we consider $\mathrm{GF}(p^n)$

[28] In honor of Evariste Galois.

as a vector space over F', by letting the scalar product αx, $\alpha \in F'$, $x \in \mathrm{GF}(p^n)$, be the same as the product αx in $\mathrm{GF}(p^n)$. Since $\mathrm{GF}(p^n)$ is finite, it has a finite basis over F', say $e_1, \cdots, e_s$. Then $\mathrm{GF}(p^n)$ has $(p^m)^s = p^{ms}$ elements, whence $ms = n$ and $m \mid n$.

Theorem 7.7.5 $\mathrm{GF}(p^n)$ has a subfield F' with p^m elements if and only if $m \mid n$. Moreover, F' is unique.

Proof: If $\mathrm{GF}(p^n)$ has a subfield with p^m elements, then $m \mid n$ by Lemma 7.7.4.

Conversely, let $m \mid n$. Then $\mathrm{GF}(p^n)^*$ has

$$p^n - 1 = p^{sm} - 1 = (p^m - 1)(p^{(s-1)m} + p^{(s-2)m} + \cdots + 1)$$

elements, where $n = sm$. Since

$$p^m - 1 \mid p^n - 1$$

and since $\mathrm{GF}(p^n)^*$ is cyclic, it has a unique cyclic subgroup F'^* with $p^m - 1$ elements, and say with generator b. Then for any integer k, $(b^k)^{p^m - 1} - 1 = 0$, whence $(b^k)^{p^m} - b^k = 0$. Thus, each element in F'^* satisfies $x^{p^m} - x = 0$, and so each of the p^m elements in $F' = F'^* \cup \{0\}$ satisfies $x^{p^m} - x = 0$. In addition, since the characteristic of $\mathrm{GF}(p^n)$ is p, $(b^{k_1} + b^{k_2})^{p^m} = (b^{k_1})^{p^m} + (b^{k_2})^{p^m} = b^{k_1} + b^{k_2}$, whence $b^{k_1} + b^{k_2}$ satisfies $x^{p^m} - x = 0$. Since F' is closed under addition and multiplication, it is easy to see that F' is a subfield of $\mathrm{GF}(p^n)$. Since F'^* is the unique subgroup of $\mathrm{GF}(p^n)$ with $p^m - 1$ elements, it follows that F' is unique, for the existence of another field F'' with p^m elements would imply that there is a second subgroup of $\mathrm{GF}(p^n)^*$ with $p^m - 1$ elements. (We could also argue the uniqueness of F' by counting the number of solutions to $x^{p^m} - x = 0$).

Exercises

1. Prove that there exists an irreducible polynomial of degree n over Z_p, p a prime, for each integer $n > 0$.

   Hint: Let b generate $\mathrm{GF}(p^n)^*$. Look at the minimal polynomial of b.

2. Let $f(x)$ be irreducible over Z_p, p a prime, $\deg f(x) = n$. Prove that $Z_p[x]/(f(x))$ has p^n elements.

3. Let $f_1(x)$ and $f_2(x) \in Z_p[x]$, p a prime, be two irreducible polynomials of degree n. Let ξ_i be a root of $f_i(x)$ in a splitting field E_i for $f_i(x)$, $i = 1,2$. Prove that $Z_p(\xi_1) \simeq Z_p(\xi_2)$.

4. Find a second degree polynomial irreducible over Z_3. Write out the multiplication table for $\mathrm{GF}(3^2)$.

5. For what finite fields F and E is the multiplicative group of F isomorphic to the additive group of E.

Note: This problem is essentially equivalent to determining all primes of the form $2^p - 1$. Consult a text on number theory for a discussion of these *Mersenne* primes.

6. Let $f(x) \in F[x]$, $f(x)$ irreducible. Let α be a root of $f(x)$ in some splitting field E of $f(x)$. Show that the minimal polynomial of α over F is $f(x)$.

7. In Exercise 6, show that if $H = \{g(x) \mid g(x) \in F[x], (\alpha)g = 0\}$, then H is the principal ideal $(f(x))$ in $F[x]$.

8. Let $f(x)$ be irreducible of degree m over Z_p, p a prime. Show that $f(x) \mid x^{p^m} - x$.

9. Let $f(x)$ be an irreducible polynomial over a field with characteristic 0. Show that the roots of $f(x)$, in any splitting field, are distinct.

Hint: If $f(x)$ has multiple roots, use Exercise 7 to show that $f(x) \mid f'(x)$.

10. Let F be any field and let G be a finite multiplicative subgroup of F^*. Prove that G is cyclic.

7.8 A THEOREM OF WEDDERBURN AND A THEOREM OF JACOBSON

We now have enough mathematical machinery at hand to prove the theorem of Wedderburn[29] stated in Chapter 5, namely, a finite division ring is a field. Throughout this section, we shall write *char* F for the characteristic of F.

Theorem 7.8.1 Let F be a finite field with p^n elements and let $\alpha \in F$. Then there exist elements μ and ν in F such that $\alpha = \mu^2 + \nu^2$.

Proof: If $\alpha = 0$, then $\mu = \nu = 0$ satisfies the conclusion of the theorem.

[29]The proof we give is based on, and closely follows, the proof given by I. N. Herstein in the *American Mathematical Monthly*, (68) 1961, pp. 249–251. Its chief advantage is that it is especially elementary. A second advantage of this proof is that it permits us to easily prove a famous theorem of Jacobson. The proof of the general case of Jacobson's theorem that we present was given by Herstein in the *Duke Mathematical Journal*, (21) 1954, pp. 45–48. Herstein's proof of Wedderburn's Theorem starts essentially with Lemma 7.8.5.

A more traditional and shorter proof of Wedderburn's Theorem can be found in Barnes [4], p. 177, or Herstein [18], pp. 319–320. The proof given in these books, however, requires the concept of cyclotomic polynomials. This interesting and important topic is discussed in these sources and in many of the other references in the bibliography that treat field theory.

We now distinguish two cases: char $F = 2$ and char $F = p > 2$.

I. char $F = 2$. Then every element of F satisfies the equation $x^{2^n} - x = 0$. Thus, if $\alpha \in F$, $\alpha = \alpha^{2^n} = (\alpha^{2^{n-1}})^2$. Clearly, $\mu = \alpha^{2^{n-1}}$ and $\nu = 0$ satisfy the theorem.

II. char $F = p > 2$. Let $F^* = F - \{0\}$ and let $h: F^* \to F^*$ be defined by $\alpha h = \alpha^2$. Since F^* is commutative, h is easily seen to be a homomorphism from the group F^* to the group F^*. The kernel of h is

$$\ker h = \{\alpha \in F^* \mid \alpha^2 = 1\}.$$

Thus, $\ker h = \{1, -1\}$, and since char $F \neq 2$, $-1 \neq 1$, and so $\ker h$ has two elements. This shows that for each $\beta \in \operatorname{Im} h$, there exist exactly two elements in F^*, α_1, α_2, such that $\alpha_1{}^2 = \alpha_2{}^2 = \beta$. Thus, precisely half of the elements of F^* are squares. Denote these elements $\beta_1, \cdots, \beta_k$, where $k = (p^n - 1)/2$. Let $y \in F^*$, y not a square, and let $S = \{y - \beta_i \mid i = 1, \cdots, k\}$. If for no i is $y - \beta_i$ a square, then the set S of k distinct elements must coincide with the k nonsquares in F^*. Thus, $y \in S$, and so $y = y - \beta_i$, for some i. But this implies that $\beta_i = 0$, which is a contradiction. Thus, for some i, $y - \beta_i = \beta_j$, a square, and $y = \beta_i + \beta_j$ is the sum of two squares. This completes the proof of the theorem.

Corollary 7.8.2 Let F be a field with p^n elements and let $\alpha \in F$, $\alpha \neq 0$. Then there exist elements ξ and η such that $1 + \xi^2 - \alpha\eta^2 = 0$.

Proof: Exercise.

Lemma 7.8.3 Let D be a division ring. Let $C = \{c \in D \mid cx = xc$, all $x \in D\}$ (C is called the *center* of D). Then C is a field.

Proof: C contains the elements 0 and $1 \neq 0$ of D. Thus, C has at least two elements. The rest of the verification that C is a field is left as an exercise.

Lemma 7.8.4 Let D be a division ring, char $D = p > 0$. Then D contains a unique prime subfield Z_p' which is isomorphic to Z_p. Moreover, $Z_p' \subseteq C$, the center of D.

Proof: This is left as an exercise.

We now come to the first lemma of substance. This lemma is what makes Herstein's proof work.

Lemma 7.8.5 Let D be a division ring, char $D = p > 0$, with center C. Let $a \in D$, $a \notin C$. Suppose $a^{p^h} = a$, for some integer $h > 0$. Then there exists an element $x \in D$ such that

i) $xax^{-1} \neq a$

ii) $xax^{-1} \in Z_p'(a)$, the extension field of Z_p' obtained by adjoining a.

Proof: We define a function $f: D \to D$ by putting $xf = xa - ax$, for all $x \in D$. Since a is algebraic over Z_p', we know that $Z_p'(a)$ is a finite field, by Theorem 7.6.3, and its proof. Thus, $Z_p'(a)$ has p^m elements for some $m > 0$. Now let $b \in Z_p'(a)$. Then $b^{p^m} - b = 0$. (1)

Next, we can prove by induction that

$$xf^n = xa^n - naxa^{n-1} + \frac{n(n-1)}{2}a^2xa^{n-2} + \cdots + (-1)^n a^n x.$$

For $n = p$, all the coefficients become 0, since the characteristic is p (see Exercise 13, Section 5.8), except for the first and last terms. Thus,

$$xf^p = xa^p + (-1)^p a^p x = \begin{cases} xa^p - a^p x, & \text{if } p \text{ is odd} \\ xa^p + a^p x = xa^p - a^p x, & \text{if } p = 2, \text{ since char } D = 2 \text{ implies } 1 = -1. \end{cases}$$

Similarly, it is easy to show that

$$xf^{p^m} = xa^{p^m} - a^{p^m}x = xa - ax = xf,$$

since (1) implies $a^{p^m} = a$.

Thus, we see that the function $f^{p^m} = f$.

Now let $\lambda \in Z_p'(a)$. Then

$$\begin{aligned}(\lambda x)f &= (\lambda x)a - a(\lambda x) = \lambda[xa - ax] \\ &= \lambda(xf), \quad \text{since} \quad \lambda \in Z_p'(a), \text{ a field.}\end{aligned}$$

Letting I denote the identity map on D, and letting λI denote the map defined by $(x)\lambda I = \lambda x$, we see that the composite $f \circ (\lambda I) = (\lambda I) \circ f$, for all $\lambda \in Z_p'(a)$. Since all elements of $Z_p'(a)$ satisfy the polynomial $z^{p^m} - z$, we find that $z^{p^m} - z = (z - \lambda_1)(z - \lambda_2)\cdots(z - \lambda_{p^m})$, where the λ_i are all the distinct p^m elements of $Z_p'(a)$. Using the fact that $f \circ (\lambda_i I) = (\lambda_i I) \circ f$, for all $\lambda_i \in Z_p'(a)$, we can easily show that the zero map θ ($a\theta = 0$, for all $a \in D$) satisfies

$$\theta = f^{p^m} - f = (f - \lambda_1 I) \circ (f - \lambda_2 I) \circ \cdots \circ (f - \lambda_{p^m} I)$$

where $$(x)(f - \lambda I) = xf - \lambda x.$$

Now let $\lambda_1 = 0$ (one of the λ_i's must be zero), and suppose for each $\lambda_i \neq 0$, $(x)(f - \lambda_i I) \neq 0$, all $x \in D$, $x \neq 0$. Then

$$(x)[(f - \lambda_2 I) \circ \cdots \circ (f - \lambda_{p^m} I)] \neq 0,$$

for all $x \in D, x \neq 0$. But since $\theta = f^{p^m} - f = f \circ (f - \lambda_2 I) \circ \cdots \circ (f - \lambda_{p^m} I)$, it follows that $xf = 0$, for all $x \in D$.

Thus, $0 = xf = xa - ax$, whence $xa = ax$, for all $x \in D$. Thus, $a \in C$, contradicting the hypothesis. Thus, there is a $\lambda_i \neq 0$, $\lambda_i \in Z_p'(a)$, and there is an $x \neq 0$ in D such that

$$(x)(f - \lambda_i I) = 0, \text{ that is, } xa - ax - \lambda_i x = 0,$$

$xa - ax = \lambda_i x$, whence $xax^{-1} - a = \lambda_i$ and $xax^{-1} = a + \lambda_i \neq a$, since $\lambda_i \neq 0$. Since $\lambda_i \in Z_p'(a)$, $xax^{-1} \in Z_p'(a)$. This completes the proof of Lemma 7.8.5.

Lemma 7.8.6 Let D be a division ring with center C, and char $D = p > 0$. Let $a \in D$, $a \notin C$. Suppose $a^{p^n} = a$, for some integer $n > 0$. Then there exists an element $x \in D$ and an integer i such that $xax^{-1} = a^i \neq a$.

Proof: Let a have order t in the group D^*. Then the roots of the polynomial $z^t - 1$ in $Z_p'(a)$ are $1, a, \cdots, a^{t-1}$. Since $xax^{-1} \in Z_p'(a)$, and since xax^{-1} clearly satisfies $z^t - 1 = 0$, it follows that $xax^{-1} = a^i$, for some i. By Lemma 7.8.5, $a^i \neq a$.

Lemma 7.8.7 Let D be a finite division ring such that every proper subdivision ring of D is commutative. Let a and $b \in D$ satisfy $ab \neq ba$, but $b^s a = ab^s$, for some s. If $N(b^s) = \{x \in D \mid xb^s = b^s x\}$, then $N(b^s) = D$, that is, $b^s \in C$, the center of D.

Proof: It is easy to verify that $N(b^s)$ is a division ring. If $N(b^s) \neq D$, then $N(b^s)$ is commutative by hypothesis. But clearly

$$a, b \in N(b^s),$$

and since $ab \neq ba$, $N(b^s)$ is not commutative. Thus, $N(b^s) = D$.

Lemma 7.8.8 Let D be a finite division ring, $D \neq C$, its center. Then there exists an element a and an integer $r > 0$ with these properties:

i) $a \in D, a \notin C$
ii) $a^r \in C$
iii) If $b \in D, b \notin C$ and $b^s \in C$, then $r \leq s$
iv) r is a prime.

Proof: $D^* = D - \{0\}$ is a multiplicative group, say with m elements. Then $d^m = 1$, for each $d \in D^*$, whence for each d in D^*, there exists a least integer $(d)m$ such that $d^{(d)m} \in C$. Since $D \neq C$, there exists an element $a \in D^*$, $a \notin C$, and we can choose a and $(a)m$ to have properties i), ii), iii). If $r = (a)m$ is not prime, then $r = m_1 m_2$, $1 < m_i < r$, $i = 1,2$, whence $a^{m_1} \notin C$, yet $(a^{m_1})^{m_2} \in C$, contradicting our choice of r. Thus, r is a prime.

Lemma 7.8.9 Let D be a division ring with center C, and let r be a prime. Suppose $\lambda \in C, \lambda \neq 1$ and $\lambda^r = 1$. Then if $y \in D$ satisfies $y^r = 1$, then $y = \lambda^i$, for some i, and $C(y) = C$.

Proof: $C(y)$ is an algebraic extension of C. Now since r is a prime, $\lambda^0, \lambda^1, \cdots, \lambda^{r-1}$, are all distinct and satisfy $z^r - 1 = 0$. Since $z^r - 1 = 0$ has at most r roots in $C(y)$, and since $y^r - 1 = 0$, clearly, $y = \lambda^i$, for some i. Thus, $y \in C$ and $C(y) = C$.

Lemma 7.8.10 Let G be a group with center C. Let $ba^{-1}b^{-1} = \lambda^{-1}a^{-1}$, for some $\lambda \in C$. Then

i) $ba^{-m}b^{-1} = \lambda^{-m}a^{-m}$

ii) $b^n a^{-m} b^{-n} = \lambda^{-mn}a^{-m}$

Proof: We leave this as an exercise.

Lemma 7.8.11 Let D be a division ring, with char $D \neq 2$ and suppose there exist $a_1, b_1 \in D$ such that

i) $a_1 b_1 = -b_1 a_1 \neq b_1 a_1$

ii) $a_1{}^2 = b_1{}^2 = \alpha \neq 0$

iii) there exist $\xi, \eta \in C$, the center of D, such that

$$1 + \xi^2 - \alpha\eta^2 = 0.$$

Then $a_1 + \xi b_1 + \eta a_1 b_1 = 0$.

Proof: $(a_1 + \xi b_1 + \eta a_1 b_1)^2$

$$= a_1{}^2 + \xi^2 b_1{}^2 + \eta^2 a_1 b_1 a_1 b_1 + \xi a_1 b_1 + \xi b_1 a_1$$
$$+ \eta a_1{}^2 b_1 + \eta a_1 b_1 a_1 + \xi\eta b_1 a_1 b_1 + \xi\eta a_1 b_1{}^2$$
$$= \alpha + \xi^2\alpha + \eta^2[a_1(-a_1 b_1)b_1] = \alpha[1 + \xi^2 - \alpha\eta^2] = 0.$$

Since D is a division ring, $a_1 + \xi b_1 + \eta a_1 b_1 = 0$.

Theorem 7.8.12 Wedderburn A finite division ring D is a field.

Proof: Clearly, if D has two elements, D is isomorphic to Z_2 and therefore it is a field.

If the theorem is not true for all finite division rings D, let D be chosen so that D has minimal order among the noncommutative division rings. Thus, every division ring with fewer elements than D is commutative. We shall show that this assumption about D leads to a contradiction.

Since D is not a field, by Lemma 7.8.8, there exists an element $a \in D$ and an integer r satisfying the conclusions of that Lemma. Since $a \notin C$, by Lemmas 7.8.5 and 7.8.6, there exist $x \in D$ and an integer i such that $xax^{-1} = a^i \neq a$, and clearly $x \notin C$. Since r is a prime, by Exercise 5, Section 4.5, and by Corollary 2.14.2, $x^{r-1}ax^{-(r-1)} = a^{i^{r-1}} = a^{1+ru} = a \cdot a^{ru} = \lambda a$, since $a^{ru} = \lambda$, for some $\lambda \in C$.

By our choice of a and r, $x^{r-1} \notin C$. By Lemma 7.8.7, with $x = b$ and $r - 1 = s$, we see that $x^{r-1}a \neq ax^{r-1}$. Thus, $x^{r-1}ax^{-(r-1)} = \lambda a$, with $\lambda \in C, \lambda \neq 1$.

Now let $b = x^{r-1}$. Note that $ba \neq ab$. Then $bab^{-1} = \lambda a$, and since $a^r \in C$,

$$a^r = ba^rb^{-1} = (bab^{-1})^r = (\lambda a)^r = \lambda^r a^r, \text{ whence } \lambda^r = 1.$$

Thus, $b^r = \lambda^r b^r = \lambda^r(a^{-1}ba\lambda^{-1})^r = (a^{-1}ba)^r = a^{-1}b^ra$, whence $b^ra = ab^r$. By Lemma 7.8.7, $b^r \in C$.

Since $C^* = C - \{0\}$ is cyclic (Theorem 7.7.3), say with generator γ, and since a^r and b^r are in C, there exist integers n and m such that $a^r = \gamma^n$, $b^r = \gamma^m$. Moreover, $r \nmid n$ and $r \nmid m$. For, suppose $n = kr$. Then $a^r = \gamma^n = \gamma^{kr}$, whence $a^r(\gamma^{-k})^r = 1$ and, since $\gamma \in C$, $(a\gamma^{-k})^r = 1$. By Lemma 7.8.9, $a\gamma^{-k} = \lambda^i$, whence $a = \lambda^i\gamma^k \in C$, a contradiction.

Now let $a_1 = a^m$ and $b_1 = b^n$. Then $a_1{}^r = a^{mr} = \gamma^{mn} = b^{nr} = b_1{}^r$. Also, $a_1b_1a_1{}^{-1}b_1{}^{-1} = a^mb^na^{-m}b^{-n}$

$$= a^m[b^na^{-m}b^{-n}] = a^m(\lambda^{-mn}a^{-m}) \quad \text{(by Lemma 7.8.10)}$$

$$= \lambda^{-mn} = \mu \in C. \text{ Thus,}$$

$$(*) \quad a_1b_1 = \mu b_1a_1, \quad \text{with } \mu \neq 1.$$

To see $\mu \neq 1$, suppose $\mu = 1$. Then $\lambda^{-mn} = 1$, whence $r \mid mn$, which is a contradiction, since $r \nmid m$ and $r \nmid n$, and since r is prime. In addition, $\mu^r = (\lambda^{-mn})^r = (\lambda^r)^{-mn} = 1$.

Next, using (*), we get

$$(b_1{}^{-1}a_1)^r = \mu^{-(1+2+\cdots+(r-1))}b_1{}^{-r}a_1{}^r$$
$$= \mu^{-r(r-1)/2}, \quad \text{since } a_1{}^r = b_1{}^r.$$

We are about ready to get a contradiction that will establish the theorem.

Case I: r is odd. Then $\mu^{-r(r-1)/2} = 1$, since $\mu^r = 1$, and so $(b_1{}^{-1}a_1)^r = 1$. But by Lemma 7.8.9, $b_1{}^{-1}a_1 = \lambda^i$, for some i, whence $a_1 = \lambda^ib_1$, but then $a_1b_1 = b_1a_1$, a contradiction, and the theorem is proved if $r > 2$.

Case II: $r = 2$. Since $\mu^2 = 1$, $\mu \neq 1$, necessarily $\mu = -1$. But then $a_1b_1 = -b_1a_1 \neq b_1a_1$, by (*). Thus, char $D \neq 2$. By Corollary 7.8.2, with $\alpha = a_1{}^2 = b_1{}^2 \in C$, there exist $\xi, \eta \in C$ such that $1 + \xi^2 - \alpha\eta^2 = 0$. By Lemma 7.8.11, $(a_1 + \xi b_1 + \eta a_1b_1) = 0$. But then

$$0 = a_1(a_1 + \xi b_1 + \eta a_1b_1) + (a_1 + \xi b_1 + \eta a_1b_1)a_1 = 2a_1{}^2 = 2\alpha \neq 0,$$

since char $D \neq 2$. This contradiction establishes the theorem in case $r = 2$, and the proof of Wedderburn's theorem is concluded.

Now that we have Wedderburn's theorem, by using it and Lemma 7.8.7, we can give a proof of Jacobson's theorem. We can do this in two steps, first doing the special case of Jacobson's theorem for division rings

Lemma 7.8.13 **Jacobson** Let D be a division ring such that for every $x \in D$, there exists an integer $(x)n > 1$ such that $x^{(x)n} = x$. Then D is a field.

Proof: First we prove that char D is a prime p. If char $D = 2$, there is nothing to prove. Thus, assume char $D \neq 2$. We must prove char $D \neq 0$. Let $a \neq 0$, $a \in D$. Then by assumption $2a \neq 0$. By hypothesis, there exist integers $n > 1$ and $m > 1$ such that $a^n = a$ and $(2a)^m = 2a$. Then with $q = (n-1)(m-1) + 1$, it follows that $q > 1$, $a^q = a$ and $(2a)^q = 2a$. Thus, $(2^q - 2)a = 0$, whence there exists a least positive integer p such that $pa = 0$. This shows that char D is a prime, say p.

Since $a^n = a$, a is algebraic over Z'_p, the prime subfield of D, and so $Z'_p(a)$ is a finite field, say with p^h elements. Thus, $a^{p^h} = a$. If $a \notin C$, the center of D, then the conditions of Lemma 7.8.6 hold, and so there exist an element $b \in D$ and an integer i such that

$$bab^{-1} = a^i \neq a. \tag{1}$$

By considering $Z'_p(b)$, we find that

$$b^{p^k} = b,$$

for some integer k. Now we let F be the set of all finite sums of the form

$$\sum_{\lambda=0}^{p^h-1} \sum_{\tau=0}^{p^k-1} c_{\lambda\tau} a^\lambda b^\tau,$$

where $c_{\lambda\tau} \in Z'_p$. Then clearly, $F \subseteq D$, F is finite, F is closed under addition, and by (1), F is closed under multiplication. (We use the relation $ba = a^i b$ in bringing the a's together and the b's together in an arbitrary product.) Thus, F is a finite ring. Since $F \subseteq D$, the cancellation laws hold, whence $F^* = F - \{0\}$ is a group. Thus, F is a finite division ring, whence by Wedderburn's theorem, F is commutative. Since $a,b \in F$, $ab = ba$, contradicting that $bab^{-1} = a^i \neq a$. Thus, D must be commutative and the lemma is proven.

We will prove the general case of Jacobson's theorem via a sequence of lemmas. We first make some definitions.

Definition 7.8.14 Let R be a ring. An element $a \in R$ is called *nilpotent* if there exists an integer $n > 1$ such that $a^n = 0$. An element $e \in R$ is called *idempotent* if $e^2 = e$.

A *right* (*left*) *ideal* I of R is a subring of R such that $xr \in I (rx \in I)$ for all $x \in I, r \in R$.

Clearly, a two-sided ideal is also a right ideal.

Lemma 7.8.15 Let R be a ring with identity 1 and no right ideals other than (0) and R. Then R is a division ring.

Proof: It suffices to show that $R^* = R - \{0\}$ is a group with respect to multiplication. Since 1 is a right identity for R^*, we need only show every $x \in R^*$ has a right inverse. Thus, let $x \in R^*$. Then $xR = \{xr \mid r \in R\}$ is a right ideal, and since $x1 \in xR$, $xR \neq (0)$. Thus, $xR = \{xr \mid r \in R\} = R$. Clearly, there exists $y \in R^*$ such that $xy = 1$. It is easy to see that R^* is closed. Thus, R is a division ring.

Definition 7.8.16 Let R be a ring. A right ideal $I \neq R$ of R is called a *maximal* right ideal if whenever $I \subseteq J \subseteq R$, and J is a right ideal, either $J = I$ or $J = R$.

Lemma 7.8.17 Let R be a ring with 1 and let I be a right ideal of R, $I \neq R$. Then there exists a maximal right ideal J of R such that $I \subseteq J$.

Proof: Clearly, $1 \notin I$. Now let $\mathfrak{F}$ be the collection of all right ideals K of R such that i) $I \subseteq K$ and ii) $1 \notin K$. $\mathfrak{F} \neq \phi$, since $I \in \mathfrak{F}$. By applying Zorn's lemma to $\mathfrak{F}$, we can establish the existence of the desired maximal right ideal (see the proof of Theorem 7.3.3 and Exercise 3, Section 7.3).

We now proceed to the proof of Jacobson's theorem.

Definition 7.8.18 A ring R is called a *J-ring* if for each $x \in R$, there exists an integer $(x)n > 1$ such that $x^{(x)n} = x$.

Lemma 7.8.19 Let R be a J-ring. Then every right ideal I of R is a two-sided ideal of R.

Proof: We first observe that R has no nonzero nilpotent elements. For if $x \neq 0$, then $x^{(x)n} = x$ implies that $x^m \neq 0$, all $m > 1$. Next, let e be an idempotent. Then for any $x \in R$, $(xe - exe)^2 = 0 = (ex - exe)^2$. Thus, $xe - exe = 0 = ex - exe$ and so $xe = ex$, that is, e commutes with every element of R.

Now let $a \in I$ and suppose $a^n = a$, for some integer $n > 1$. Then $(a^{n-1})^2 = a^{2n-2} = a^n a^{n-2} = aa^{n-2} = a^{n-1}$, so a^{n-1} is idempotent. Thus, for any $r \in R$, $ra = ra^n = ra^{n-1}a = a^{n-1}ra = ar'$, where $r' = a^{n-2}ra \in R$. (We interpret a^0 as 1.) Since $ar' \in I$, so does ra and so I is a two-sided ideal.

We observe that in view of Lemma 7.8.19, right (left) and two-sided ideals are the same thing in a J-ring. Thus, I is a maximal right ideal if and only if I is a maximal two-sided ideal.

Lemma 7.8.20 Let R be a J-ring with identity 1. Then for all $x, y \in R$, $xy - yx$ is in the intersection of the maximal ideals of R.

Proof: By Lemma 7.8.17, R has maximal ideals. Let I be such a maximal ideal. Then the quotient ring R/I has an identity, and since I is a maximal right ideal of R, R/I has no right ideals other than (0) and R/I. Thus, by Lemma 7.8.15, R/I is a division ring. Since R is a J-ring, it is easy to see that R/I is a J-ring. Then, by Lemma 7.8.13, R/I is commutative. From this it follows that $xy - yx \in I$, for all $x, y \in R$. The conclusion of the Lemma is now immediate.

Lemma 7.8.21 Let R be a J-ring with identity 1. Then R is commutative.

Proof: Suppose $x \neq 0$ is in every maximal ideal of R. Now some power of x is an idempotent, say $x^{n-1} = e \neq 0$ (see proof of Lemma 7.8.19), and e must also be in every maximal ideal of R. Now $1 - e$ cannot be in any proper right ideal of R, for if it were, $1 - e$ would be in a maximal (right) ideal K, by Lemma 7.8.17, and since $e \in K$, $e + (1 - e) = 1$ would be in K, whence $K = R$, a contradiction. Since $(1 - e)R \neq 0$ and since $(1 - e)R$ is a right ideal, it now follows that $(1 - e)R = R$, whence $(1 - e)r = e$, for some $r \in R$. Thus, $0 = e(1 - e)r = e$, a contradiction. Thus, x cannot be in every maximal ideal in R and the intersection of all the maximal ideals of R is (0). Thus, by Lemma 7.8.20, $xy - yx \in (0)$, all $x, y \in R$, that is, $xy = yx$, all $x, y \in R$.

We now prove Jacobson's theorem in full generality.

Theorem 7.8.22 ***Jacobson*** If R is a J-ring, then R is commutative.

Proof: Let e be any idempotent in R. In the proof of Lemma 7.8.19, we observed that $xe = ex$, for all $x \in R$. Thus, $eR = Re = T$ is also a J-ring, but T has an identity, namely e. By Lemma 7.8.21, T is commutative. Hence, for all $x, y \in R$, $xye = xye^2 = (xe)(ye) = (ye)(xe) = yxe$, that is, $(xy - yx)e = 0$. Since $(xy - yx)^s = (xy - yx)$, for some s, $(xy - yx)^{s-1}$ is an idempotent e_1. Thus,

$$0 = (xy - yx)e_1 = (xy - yx)^s = xy - yx, \text{ that is, } xy = yx.$$

This completes the proof of the theorem.

Exercises

1. Prove Corollary 7.8.2.
2. Complete the proof of Lemma 7.8.3.
3. Prove Lemma 7.8.4.
4. Prove Lemma 7.8.10.
5. Prove that every finite field is a J-ring.
6. Prove without Wedderburn's theorem that every finite division ring is a J-ring.

Note: Since we used Wedderburn's theorem to prove that J-rings are commutative, this will not give us a new proof of Wedderburn's Theorem.

*7. Let Δ be a division ring. Show that for $n > 1$, (0) is the only maximal two-sided ideal of Δ_n. (This shows that the hypothesis of Lemma 7.8.15 concerning right ideals is essential.)

Hint: It is enough to show that if A is a nonzero two-sided ideal of Δ_n, then $A = \Delta_n$. To do this, let

$$E_{ij} = i \begin{bmatrix} 0 & \cdots \overset{j}{} & 0 \\ 0 & & 0 \\ \vdots & 1 & \vdots \\ 0 & \cdots & 0 \end{bmatrix},$$

that is, E_{ij} is the matrix with 1 in the i,j position and 0 everywhere else. Show that if $[\beta_{ij}] = [\beta]$ has the element b in the k, ℓ position, then $E_{ik}[\beta]E_{\ell j}$ has b in the i,j position and 0 everywhere else.

Now complete the proof by showing that by properly multiplying this matrix on the left and the right, and by adding resulting matrices, any matrix in Δ_n can be obtained.

8. Let R be a ring with identity 1 and an idempotent e, $e \neq 0,1$. Prove that $1 - e$ is also an idempotent (see Exercise 5, Section 5.14).
9. Let R be a ring such that $a^2 = a$, for all $a \in R$. Prove, without using Jacobson's theorem, that R is commutative.

Hint: show char $R = 2$.

7.9 MODULES: BASIC NOTIONS

We wish to show that, with the material already developed, it is possible to study in some detail certain exciting aspects of ring theory. We have therefore chosen to develop a number of ideas concerning rings with descending chain conditions. Our choice of studying this branch of ring theory is based on several reasons. First, these rings are important in the study of group representation theory, an area of mathematics important for both mathematical purposes and physical applications. Secondly, these rings exhibit part of the role that linear algebra plays in ring theory. Thirdly, these rings have a connection with a relatively new but important branch of mathematics, known as homological algebra. Two homological algebra concepts are introduced in the last section of this text. Finally, we study these rings because the theory concerning them is both elegant and easily accessible.

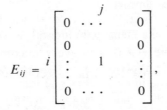

We begin by introducing the concept of a module. These objects are the natural generalization of vector spaces. Now, however, instead of the scalars being in a division ring, we allow them to be elements of an arbitrary ring.

Definition 7.9.1 Let R be a ring and let $(M,+)$ be an abelian group. Then M is called an *R-module* (or *right R-module*) if there exists a mapping $f: M \times R \to M$, with $(m,r)f$ written as mr, such that

i) $m_1(r_1 + r_2) = m_1r_1 + m_1r_2$

ii) $(m_1 + m_2)r_1 = m_1r_1 + m_2r_1$

iii) $m_1(r_1r_2) = (m_1r_1)r_2$, for all $m_1, m_2 \in M$, $r_1, r_2 \in R$.

If, in addition, R has an identity 1 and $m1 = m$, for all $m \in M$, then M is called a *unital* R-module.

A parallel concept, of equal importance, is that of *left R-module.*

Definition 7.9.2 Let R be a ring and let $(M,+)$ be an abelian group. Then M is called a *left R-module* if there exists a mapping $g: R \times M \to M$, with $(r,m)g$ written as rm, such that

i) $(r_1 + r_2)m_1 = r_1m_1 + r_2m_1$

ii) $r_1(m_1 + m_2) = r_1m_1 + r_1m_2$

iii) $(r_1r_2)m_1 = r_1(r_2m_1)$, for all $m_1, m_2 \in M$, $r_1, r_2 \in R$.

If $R \ni 1$ and $1m = m$, for all $m \in M$, we call M a *unital* left R-module.

Henceforth, we shall agree to the following convention. If R is a ring with identity, then all R-modules and left R-modules are assumed to be unital, and we shall simply say "R-module M," or "left R-module M," with unital understood.

It is immediate that a left vector space V over a division ring Δ is a left Δ-module. Also, if R is a ring and if $f: R \times R \to R$ is defined by $(a,b)f = ab$, the ring product, then either R can be considered as a left R-module ${}_RR$ or R can be considered as a right R-module R_R.

Definition 7.9.3 Let M be an R-module. Let $(N,+)$ be a subgroup of $(M,+)$. We call N an *R-submodule* of M if $nr \in N$, for all $n \in N$, $r \in R$.

A similar definition can be made for left R-modules. Clearly, a submodule N of a module M is a module in its own right.

For the sake of convenience, we shall use the symbol 0 in several different ways: the additive identity of the module M, the zero-module (that is, the module with only one element), the zero element of the ring R, and the integer zero. It will always be clear from the context as to what role any particular 0 plays.

Although we have defined left and right ideals in Definition 7.8.14, we now redefine them in terms of modules.

Definition 7.9.4 Let R be a ring and consider R as the left R-module ${}_RR$. A *left ideal* L of R is a left R-submodule of ${}_RR$.

A similar definition works for right ideals, namely, J is a *right ideal* of R if J is a submodule of R_R.

It is easy to see that I is a two-sided ideal of R if and only if I is both a left ideal and a right ideal.

We agree to another convention. When we use the word "ideal," without modifying it by "left" or "right," then it shall be interpreted as "two-sided ideal."

Thus, it is easy to prove that the matrix ring Δ_n, (Δ a division ring and $n \geq 2$), has only two ideals, (0) and Δ_n, whereas it has additional right ideals and left ideals. For example, the set of matrices of the form

$$\begin{bmatrix} a_{11} & a_{12} \cdots a_{1n} \\ 0 & 0 \cdots 0 \\ \vdots & \\ 0 & 0 \cdots 0 \end{bmatrix}, a_{ij} \in \Delta,$$

is a right ideal in Δ_n, but not an ideal.

Definition 7.9.5 Let R be a ring. Then R is said to satisfy the *descending chain condition* (DCC)[30] *on right ideals* if whenever $I_1 \supsetneqq I_2 \supsetneqq I_3 \supsetneqq \cdots \supsetneqq I_n \supsetneqq \cdots$ is a descending chain of right ideals, there exists an integer N such that $I_k = I_N$, for $k \geq N$.

A similar definition can be made for the *ascending chain condition* (ACC) (reverse the inclusion signs). We assume this to have been done. Also, similar definitions can be made concerning left ideals and two-sided ideals.

Equivalent to the DCC is the *minimum condition.* We shall, at times, want to use these two conditions interchangeably.

Definition 7.9.6 Let R be a ring, and let $\{I_\alpha\}$ be a nonempty collection of right ideals in R. Then I is called *minimal* with respect to the collection $\{I_\alpha\}$ if

i) $I \in \{I_\alpha\}$

ii) whenever $I_\beta \in \{I_\alpha\}$ and $I_\beta \subseteq I$, then $I_\beta = I$.

Definition 7.9.7 The ring R is said to satisfy the *minimum condition on right ideals* if every nonempty collection $\{I_\alpha\}$ of right ideals has a minimal element.

Theorem 7.9.8 Let R be a ring. Then the following two conditions on the right ideals of R are equivalent:

i) DCC

ii) Minimum condition.

[30] Many authors use the terms *Artinian* and *Noetherian* in place of DCC and ACC, respectively. This is in honor of the late Emil Artin and the late Emy Noether.

Proof: First we show that i) implies ii). Let $\{I_\alpha\}$ be a nonempty collection of right ideals, and suppose $\{I_\alpha\}$ has no minimal element. Then let $I_1 \in \{I_\alpha\}$. Since I_1 is not minimal, there exists $I_2 \in \{I_\alpha\}$ such that $I_1 \supset I_2$. Again, there exists $I_3 \in \{I_\alpha\}$ such that $I_1 \supset I_2 \supset I_3$. Continuing, we get an infinite descending chain, all of whose inclusions are proper, contradicting the DCC. Thus, $\{I_\alpha\}$ has a minimal element.

To show that ii) implies i), let $I_1 \supseteq I_2 \supseteq I_3 \supseteq \cdots$ be a descending chain of right ideals. By (ii), the collection $\{I_\alpha\}$ has a minimal member, say I_N. It is clear that $I_k = I_N$, all $k \geq N$.

A definition similar to that of 7.9.7 can be made for *maximum condition*, and we can prove that a ring R satisfies the ACC if and only if it satisfies the maximum condition.

Intimately related to the DCC is the idea of a minimal right ideal. The following definition should be compared with that of maximal ideal in Definition 5.13.1. Moreover, the reader should define minimal ideal and maximal right ideal.

Definition 7.9.9 The right ideal I of a ring R is called a *minimal right ideal* if

i) $I \neq 0$

ii) whenever $I \supseteq J \supseteq 0$, J a right ideal, then either $J = I$ or $J = 0$.

It is left for the exercises to prove that if a ring $R \neq 0$ satisfies the DCC on right ideals, then R has a minimal right ideal.

Although we have discussed DCC and ACC on right ideals, we have not considered many examples. Clearly, any division ring or field satisfies both the ACC and DCC on right ideals. A similar statement holds for matrix rings Δ_n over a division ring (this is left for the exercises). The integers Z satisfy the ACC, but not the DCC, and hence the ACC does not imply the DCC, even if the ring has an identity. If, however, R has 1, and if R satisfies the DCC on right ideals, then R will necessarily satisfy the ACC on right ideals. This theorem, due to Hopkins, will be proved toward the end of the chapter. Rings satisfying the DCC but not the ACC do exist, however, and we now give such an example.

Let p be a prime and let

$$Z_p(\infty) = \{a/p^n \mid n = 0,1,2,\cdots, a \in Z, 0 \leq a < p^n\}.$$

In $Z_p(\infty)$, define addition by $a/p^n + b/p^m = c/p^j$, where $j = \max(n,m)$ and c is the least positive residue modulo p^j congruent to $p^{j-n}a + p^{j-m}b$. $a/p^n + b/p^m$ is that rational number congruent to $(p^m a + p^n b)/p^{n+m}$ modulo 1. Define the product xy as zero, for all $x, y \in Z_p(\infty)$. It is easy to verify that $Z_p(\infty)$ is a ring with DCC but not ACC.

A number of ideas we have already seen in our study of groups and rings have important analogues in the study of modules. Since the proofs of the analogous theorems are so very similar to those given earlier, we shall leave them as exercises. Thus, we shall conclude this section by listing several definitions and theorems.

First, we point out that for the remainder of the section R will denote a ring. Also, it is now that we shall make an exception to the rule given in Section 1.7 that if $f: M \to N$, we write xf, where $x \in M$. We shall define a special type of function mapping the module M to the module N, and for a function f of this type, we shall denote the image of x under f by $f(x)$, for $x \in M$. If M is a left R-module, we shall continue to write xf, where $x \in M$.

Definition 7.9.10 Let M and N be R-modules. An *R-homomorphism* (or *module homomorphism*) is a function $f: M \to N$ such that

i) $f(x + y) = f(x) + f(y)$, for all $x,y \in M$

ii) $f(xr) = [f(x)]r$, for all $x \in M, r \in R$.

In case M and N are left R-modules, i) and ii) become

i′) $(x + y)f = xf + yf$, all $x,y \in M$

ii′) $(rx)f = r[xf]$, all $x \in M, r \in R$.

We note that we write the symbol for an R-homomorphism to the side of $x, x \in M$, opposite to which we write the elements of R. Thus, ii) and ii′) appear as a type of associative law.

Definition 7.9.11 Let $f:M \to N$ be an R-homomorphism from the R-module M to the R-module N. We call f an *R-isomorphism* (or a *module isomorphism*) if f is 1–1 and onto N. We say that M and N are *R-isomorphic* and write $M \simeq N$.

Note that a vector space isomorphism between vector spaces over a division ring Δ is simply a Δ-isomorphism between left Δ-modules.

Definition 7.9.12 Let f be an R-homomorphism from M to N. We define the *kernel of* f, denoted $\ker f$, as $\{x \in M \mid f(x) = 0\}$..

Definition 7.9.13 Let N be a submodule of the R-module M. Then the set $\{m + N \mid m \in M\}$ is called the *quotient module* M/N, where $(m + N)r = mr + N$, for all $r \in R$ and $m \in M$, and $(m_1 + N) + (m_2 + N) = (m_1 + m_2) + N$, for all $m_1, m_2 \in M$.

It is easy to see that M/N is actually an R-module. With all these definitions, the next theorem is easy to prove.

Theorem 7.9.14 Let M and N be R-modules and let $f: M \to N$ be a R-homomorphism. Then,

i) Im f is a submodule of N

ii) $\ker f$ is a submodule of M

iii) $M/\ker f \simeq \operatorname{Im} f$ as R-modules
iv) f is 1–1 if and only if $\ker f = 0$, the zero submodule of M
v) $M \simeq N$ if and only if f is onto and $\ker f = 0$.

Proof: Exercise.

The notions of direct product of groups and direct sum of rings also carry over to modules.

Definition 7.9.15 Let M and N be R-modules.

Then the *direct sum* of M and N, denoted $M \oplus N$, is $\{(m,n) \mid m \in M, n \in N\}$, where for (m_1,n_1) and $(m_2,n_2) \in M \oplus N$, and $r \in R$, $(m_1,n_1) + (m_2,n_2) = (m_1 + m_2, n_1 + n_2)$ and $(m_1,n_1)r = (m_1 r, n_1 r)$.

Theorem 7.9.16

i) Let M and N be R-modules. Then $M \oplus N$ is an R-module.
ii) Let M be an R-module. Let N_1 and N_2 be submodules such that
  a) $N_1 \cap N_2 = 0$
  b) if $m \in M$, then there exist $n_1 \in N_1$ and $n_2 \in N_2$ such that $m = n_1 + n_2$.
  Then $M \simeq N_1 \oplus N_2$.

Proof: Exercise.

Definition 7.9.17 Let M be an R-module, with submodules N_1 and N_2 such that

i) $M = N_1 + N_2 = \{n_1 + n_2 \mid n_1 \in N_1 \text{ and } n_2 \in N_2\}$
ii) $N_1 \cap N_2 = 0$. Then we say M is the *internal direct sum* of N_1 and N_2 and we write $M = N_1 \dotplus N_2$.

Note that by Theorem 7.9.16, if $M = N_1 \dotplus N_2$, then $M \simeq N_1 \oplus N_2$. Of course, the ideas of direct sum and internal direct sum of modules can be extended to the direct sum of n modules, for any integer n (see Exercise 16).

Lastly, we come to the analogue of composition series and the Jordan-Hölder theorem for modules.

Definition 7.9.18 Let M be an R-module. Then N is said to satisfy the *descending chain condition* (DCC) on submodules if whenever $M_1 \supseteq M_2 \supseteq M_3 \supseteq \cdots \supseteq M_n \supseteq \cdots$, for submodules M_i of M, then there exists an integer N such that $M_k = M_N$, for all $k \geq N$. We define *ascending chain condition* (ACC) analogously.

Definition 7.9.19 Let M be an R-module. Then M is said to satisfy the *minimum condition* on submodules if whenever $\mathcal{S} = \{M_\alpha\}$ is a nonempty collection of submodules of M, there exists a submodule $N \in \mathcal{S}$ such that $M_\alpha \subseteq N$, $M_\alpha \in \mathcal{S}$, implies $M_\alpha = N$. The module N is called a *minimal* element of $\mathcal{S}$. We define *maximum condition* and *maximal* element analogously.

As with left (right, two-sided) ideals, it is easy to show that a module M satisfies the DCC(ACC) on submodules if and only if it satisfies the minimum (maximum) condition on submodules. We leave this to the reader.

Definition 7.9.20 Let M be an R-module. A *normal series* for M is a collection $\{M_0 = M, M_1, \cdots, M_n = 0\}$ of submodules of M such that $M = M_0 \supset M_1 \supset \cdots \supset M_n = 0$. (The n may vary from normal series to normal series. Observe that here (see Section 6.3) all inclusions are proper). We call n the *length* of the normal series. The quotient modules M_i/M_{i+1} are called the *factors* of the normal series.

A normal series $\{N_0 = M, N_1, \cdots, N_m = 0\}$ for M is called a *refinement* of the normal series $\{M_0 = M, \cdots, M_n = 0\}$ if each M_i is also an N_j. A *composition series* for M is a normal series that has no nontrivial refinement, that is, there exists no submodule N of M that can be inserted properly between any M_i and M_{i+1}.

Two normal series for M are called *equivalent* if they have the same length and if the factors of one can be paired with the factors of the other into isomorphic pairs. That is, $\{M_0, \cdots, M_n\}$ and $\{N_0, \cdots, N_n\}$ are equivalent normal series for M if there is a function

$$g\colon \{M_i/M_{i+1}\} \to \{N_i/N_{i+1}\}$$

such that $M_i/M_{i+1} \cong (M_i/M_{i+1})g$.

By modifying the techniques of Section 6.3, primarily the proofs and statements of the Zassenhaus lemma (6.3.12) and the Jordan-Hölder theorem (6.3.15), we can easily prove the next two theorems. We leave the proofs to the reader.

Theorem 7.9.21 Let M be an R-module. Then any two normal series of M have equivalent refinements.

Proof: Exercise.

Theorem 7.9.22 Jordan-Hölder Let M be an R-module. If M has a composition series, then any normal series can be refined to a composition series of M. Moreover, any two composition series have the same length.

Proof: Exercise.

Now we are able to state a theorem that shows the connection between composition series and the chain conditions. This theorem will be valuable in our later work.

Theorem 7.9.23 Let M be an R-module. Then M has a composition series if and only if M satisfies both the ACC and DCC on submodules.

Proof: Suppose, first, that M has a composition series of length n. If either the ACC or DCC fails, we can get a normal series of length $n + 1$. Any refinement of this normal series clearly has length $\geq n + 1$, so in particular, refining this normal series to a composition series (Theorem 7.9.22) leads to a composition series of length $\geq n + 1$, contradicting, by Theorem 7.9.22, the existence of a composition series of length n. Thus, both the ACC and DCC must hold.

Conversely, suppose that the ACC and DCC, and hence the maximum and minimum conditions, hold. If $\mathcal{S}$ is the collection of all proper submodules of $M_0 = M$, $\mathcal{S}$ has a maximal element (by the ACC), say M_1. Similarly, if $M_1 \neq 0$, there exists a proper submodule of M_1, say M_2, maximal with respect to being a proper submodule. Continuing, we get $M = M_0 \supset M_1 \supset M_2 \supset \cdots$. By the DCC, this chain must be finite, say $M = M_0 \supset M_1 \supset \cdots \supset M_n = 0$, and clearly $\{M_0, M_1, \cdots, M_n\}$ is a composition series for M.

The concepts of normal series and composition series for modules also apply to the ideals of a ring R. For example, the right ideals of R can be considered submodules of the right R-module R_R. Thus, when we later speak of a composition series for the ring R, we shall be speaking of a composition series for the R-module R_R. Of course, Theorems 7.9.21, 7.9.22, and 7.9.23 also hold in this situation.

We conclude this section with a theorem which we shall need shortly.

Theorem 7.9.24 Let R_1 and R_2 be rings with DCC (ACC) on right ideals. Then $R_1 \oplus R_2$ also has DCC (ACC) on right ideals.

Proof: We prove the theorem for DCC and leave the case of ACC to the exercises. Thus, let $I_1 \supseteq I_2 \supseteq I_3 \supseteq \cdots$ be a descending chain of right ideals in $R_1 \oplus R_2$. Let $A_i = \{a_i \mid (a_i, b_i) \in I_i\}$. Then each A_i is a right ideal in R_1 and also $A_1 \supseteq A_2 \supseteq \cdots$. By the DCC in R_1, there exists an integer N such that $A_N = A_{N+1} = \cdots$.

Now for $i \geq N$, let $B_i = \{b_i \mid (0, b_i) \in I_i\}$. Then B_i is a right ideal in R_2 and $B_N \supseteq B_{N+1} \supseteq \cdots$. By the DCC in R_2, there exists an integer M such that $B_M = B_{M+1} = \cdots$. We claim that $I_M = I_{M+1} = \cdots$. To show this, let $(a_M, b_M) \in I_M$. Since $A_N = A_{M+1}$, there exists $(a_M, c_M) \in I_{M+1} \subseteq I_M$. Therefore, $(a_M, b_M) - (a_M, c_M) \in I_M$, whence $(0, b_M - c_M) \in I_M$. Thus, $b_M - c_M \in B_M = B_{M+1}$ and so $(0, b_M - c_M) \in I_{M+1}$. Since $(a_M, c_M) \in I_{M+1}$, $(a_M, c_M) + (0, b_M - c_M) = (a_M, b_M) \in I_{M+1}$. This shows that $I_M \subseteq I_{M+1}$. But since $I_{M+1} \subseteq I_M$, we now have that $I_M = I_{M+1}$ and so $R_1 \oplus R_2$ satisfies the DCC on right ideals.

Exercises

1. Prove Theorem 7.9.14.
2. Prove Theorem 7.9.16.
3. Prove Theorem 7.9.21 and 7.9.22.
4. Let R be a ring. Prove that the ACC and maximum condition on right ideals are equivalent.
5. Prove that R has a minimal right ideal I if R satisfies the minimum condition on right ideals.
6. In 5, replace "minimal" by "maximal" and "minimum" by "maximum."
7. Show that $Z_p(\infty)$ satisfies the DCC but not the ACC on right ideals.
8. Let F_1 and F_2 be fields. Prove that $F_1 \oplus F_2$ satisfies the DCC and the ACC on right ideals.

*9. Let Δ be a division ring. Show that Δ_n, the ring of all $n \times n$ matrices over Δ, satisfies the ACC and the DCC on right ideals.

Hint: By Theorem 7.9.23 it is enough to show that Δ_n has a composition series on right ideals. To show this, let

$$E_i = i\begin{bmatrix} 0 & \cdots & i & & \\ \cdot & 0 & & & \\ \cdot & & 1 & & \\ \cdot & & & 0 & \\ 0 & \cdots & & & 0 \end{bmatrix},$$

that is, E_i is the matrix with 1 in the i,i position and 0 everywhere else. Show that $E_i\Delta_n$ is a minimal right ideal of Δ_n. Then show that $\Delta_n = B_n \supset B_{n-1} \supset \cdots \supset B_0 = 0$ is a composition series for Δ_n, where $B_i = (E_1 + \cdots + E_i)\Delta_n, i > 0$, and $B_0 = 0$.

10. Let R be a principal ideal domain. We know that R satisfies the ACC. Show that for any ideal $I \neq (0)$ in R, R/I satisfies both the ACC and the DCC.

    Hint: Examine the ring $Z/(m)$, Z the integers, $m > 0$.
11. Is it true that if R has DCC on right ideals, then every subring has DCC on right ideals? Give an example to support your conclusion.
12. Let R_1 and R_2 be rings satisfying the ACC on right ideals. Prove that $R_1 \oplus R_2$ also satisfies the ACC.
13. Let I be a minimal right ideal in a ring R. Prove that

$I^2 = \left\{\sum_{\text{finite}} i_\alpha i_\beta \mid i_\alpha, i_\beta \in I\right\}$ is a right ideal and that either $I^2 = I$ or $I^2 = 0$.

14. Let R be a ring with DCC on right ideals. Let I be a right ideal in R. Prove that $I^n = I^{n+1} = I^{n+2} = \cdots$, for some n. Here

$$I^k = \left\{\sum_{\text{finite}} i_{\alpha_1} i_{\alpha_2} \cdots i_{\alpha_k} \mid i_{\alpha_j} \in I\right\} = I^{k-1}I.$$

15. Let M be an R-module. Let N_1 and N_2 be submodules. Prove that $N_1 \cap N_2$ is a submodule of M and $N_1 + N_2 = \{n_1 + n_2 \mid n_1 \in N_1, n_2 \in N_2\}$ is a submodule.
16. a) Let $N_1, N_2, \cdots, N_k$ be k R-modules. Define $N_1 \oplus N_2 \oplus \cdots \oplus N_k$ and prove that it is an R-module.
    b) Let M be an R-module and let $N_1, N_2, \cdots, N_k$ be submodules of M such that for each m in M, there is one and only one way of writing $m = n_1 + n_2 + \cdots + n_k$, where $n_i \in N_i$, $i = 1,2,\cdots,k$. Prove that if $k = 2$, then $M = N_1 \dotplus N_2$.
    Under the conditions of b), we say that M is the *internal direct sum* of $N_1, N_2, \cdots, N_k$ and we write $M = N_1 \dotplus N_2 \dotplus \cdots \dotplus N_k$.
    c) Let M be an R-module and let $N_1, N_2, \cdots, N_k$ be submodules satisfying
    i) $M = N_1 + \cdots + N_k = \{n_1 + \cdots + n_k \mid n_i \in N_i, i = 1,\cdots,k\}$.
    ii) $(N_1 + \cdots + N_j) \cap N_{j+1} = 0$, for $j = 1,\cdots,k-1$, where $N_1 + \cdots + N_j = \{n_1 + \cdots + n_j \mid n_i \in N_i, i = 1,\cdots,j\}$. Show that $M = N_1 \dotplus \cdots \dotplus N_k$ and that $M \simeq N_1 \oplus \cdots \oplus N_k$.
17. Let M be a right R-module and suppose M has property C: For each submodule N_1 of M, there exists a submodule N_2 of M such that $M = N_1 \dotplus N_2$. Prove that each submodule N of M also has property C.

    Hint: Let $N \subseteq M$, $N_1 \subseteq N$. Then there exists N' and N_1' such that $M = N \dotplus N'$, and $M = N_1 \dotplus N_1'$. Examine $N_1 \dotplus (N \cap N_1')$.
18. Let R be a commutative ring without zero divisors and with DCC on ideals. Prove that R is a field.

    Hint: It is necessary to show that $R^* = R - \{0\}$ is a group with respect to multiplication. Thus, let $a,b \in R$ and show that $ax = b$ has a solution in R. Consider the descending chain $aR \supseteq a^2R \supseteq a^3R \supseteq \cdots$.
19. Let R be a ring without zero divisors and with DCC on right ideals. Prove that R is a division ring.

    Hint: Use the chain $aR \supseteq a^2R \supseteq \cdots$ to show that there exists an element $e \in R$ such that $a^{n+1}e = a^n a$, some n. Show that this element e is a two-sided identity for R. Then show that any nonzero element in R has a two-sided inverse relative to e. (See Exercise 11, Section 5.4).
20. Let R be a commutative ring. Let I be an ideal in R. Let $A(I) = \{x \in R \mid xa = 0, \text{ all } a \in I\}$, and assume that $A(A(I)) = I$, for all

ideals I in R. Show that if J is a minimal ideal in R, then $A(J)$ is a maximal ideal.

21. In 20, interchange the role of maximal and minimal.
22. Let p be a prime, and let

$$Q_p = \{a/p^m \mid a \in Z,\ m \geq 0\}.$$

Define addition on Q_p to be the usual addition of rational numbers. Define multiplication by putting $xy = 0$, for all $x, y \in Q_p$. Show that Z is an ideal in Q_p and show that the quotient ring Q_p/Z is isomorphic to $Z_p(\infty)$. (In this exercise, Z denotes the additive group of integers with multiplication defined by $xy = 0$, for all $x,y \in Z$).

23. Let M be an R-module. Prove that if N_1 and N_2 are submodules of M, then $(N_1 + N_2)/N_2$ is R-isomorphic to $N_1/(N_1 \cap N_2)$. Note that this is the module analogue of Theorem 4.10.12, the second isomorphism theorem.
24. Let M be an R-module and let N be a submodule of M. Suppose that N and M/N satisfy the DCC (ACC) on submodules. Prove that M satisfies the DCC (ACC) on submodules.

    Hint: Use Exercise 23.
25. Use Exercise 24 to obtain a second proof of Theorem 7.9.24.

7.10 IRREDUCIBLE MODULES AND SCHUR'S LEMMA

In Section 7.5, we considered the ring $\text{Hom}_\Delta(V, V)$ where V was a vector space over Δ, a division ring. It is an easy matter to extend these considerations to modules, which we do here. Thus, if R is a ring and M and N are R-modules, then we shall denote the set of all R-homomorphisms by $\text{Hom}_R(M,N)$. This notation will be used whether M and N are both (right) R-modules or both left R-modules.

When M and N are left vector spaces over a division ring Δ, we have the situation $\text{Hom}_\Delta(M,N)$, the set of all linear transformations from the vector space M to the vector space N. In the vector space case, $\text{Hom}_\Delta(M,M)$ turned out to be a ring (Theorem 7.5.2). It is also true, as we show here, that $\text{Hom}_R(M,M)$ is a ring, whether M is an R-module or a left R-module. We give a proof for just one of these cases.

Theorem 7.10.1 Let M be an R-module. For $f,g \in \text{Hom}_R(M,M)$, define $f + g$ by $(f + g)(x) = f(x) + g(x)$, for all x in M, and define fg by $(fg)(x) = f(g(x))$. Then $\text{Hom}_R(M,M)$ is a ring with identity.

Proof: Clearly, the function $1_M : M \to M$, defined by

$$1_M(x) = x, \quad \text{all } x \in M,$$

is an identity for $\mathrm{Hom}_R(M,M)$. Also, $\theta: M \to M$, defined by $\theta(x) = 0$, all x in M, is a zero element for $(\mathrm{Hom}_R(M,M),+)$, and $-f$, defined by $(-f)(x) = -(f(x))$, is an additive inverse for f.

All that really needs to be shown now are the two distributive laws. Thus, for $x \in M$, and for f, g, and h in $\mathrm{Hom}_R(M,M)$, we have

$$[(f+g)h](x) = (f+g)(h(x)) = f(h(x)) + g(h(x)),$$

whence $(f+g)h = fh + gh$. It is also easy to show that $h(f+g) = hf + hg$, and so $\mathrm{Hom}_R(M,M)$ is a ring.

It is true, of course, that the analogous theorem holds when M is a left R-module.

Theorem 7.10.2 Let M be a left R-module. Then $\mathrm{Hom}_R(M,M)$ can be made into a ring with identity.

Proof: Exercise.

The next theorem will be of great importance in characterizing simple rings with DCC on right ideals. The reader should note that a vector space V over Δ can be considered a right $\mathrm{Hom}_\Delta(V,V)$-module.

Theorem 7.10.3 Let M be a right (left) R-module. Then M can be made into a left (right) $\mathrm{Hom}_R(M,M)$-module.

Proof: Let M be a right R-module. Then for $f \in \mathrm{Hom}_R(M,M)$, $x \in M$, we define a module multiplication $f \circ x$ to be $f(x)$. It is immediate that this definition makes M a left $\mathrm{Hom}_R(M,M)$-module.

We leave all the verifications for the reader.

Definition 7.10.4 Let M be an R-module. We say that M is an *irreducible* R-module if

i) $M \neq 0$ and $M \supseteq N \supseteq 0$, N an R-submodule, implies $N = M$ or $N = 0$, and

ii) $mr \neq 0$, for some $m \in M$, $r \in R$.

If we set MR equal to the set of all finite sums of the form $m_1 r_1 + \cdots + m_k r_k$, where k varies and $m_i \in M$, $r_i \in R$, then ii) is equivalent to $MR \neq 0$.

Examples of irreducible modules are

i) a one-dimensional right vector space

ii) the right ideal

$$I = \left\{ \begin{bmatrix} a_{11} & \cdots & a_{1n} \\ 0 & & 0 \\ \vdots & & \\ 0 & & 0 \end{bmatrix} \middle| \; a_{ij} \in \Delta, \text{ a division ring} \right\} \text{ in } \Delta_n$$

iii) a minimal right ideal I in a ring R such that $IR \neq 0$.

Theorem 7.10.5 Let M be an irreducible R-module and let N be an R-module. Let $\alpha \in \mathrm{Hom}_R(M,N)$ and suppose $\alpha(m) \neq 0$, for at least one $m \in M$. Then $\alpha(M) = \{\alpha(m) \mid m \in M\}$ is an irreducible submodule of N, and α is 1–1.

Proof: First we show that $\alpha(M)$ is a submodule of N. Clearly, $\alpha(m_1) + \alpha(m_2) = \alpha(m_1 + m_2)$ and $[\alpha(m)]r = \alpha(mr)$, so $\alpha(M)$ is a submodule of N.

Next, let N' be a submodule of $\alpha(M)$ and let $T = \{m \in M \mid \alpha(m) \in N'\}$. If $N' \neq 0$, then $T \neq 0$, and since T is a submodule of the irreducible module M, $T = M$. Thus,

$$\alpha(M) = \alpha(T) \subseteq N' \subseteq \alpha(M),$$

so $\alpha(M)$ satisfies i) of Definition 7.10.5.

Also, $\alpha(M)R = \alpha(MR) = \alpha(M) \neq 0$, so ii) of Definition 7.10.4 is satisfied and $\alpha(M)$ is irreducible.

Finally, let $U = \{m \in M \mid \alpha(m) = 0\}$. It is easy to show that U is an R-submodule of M, whence either $U = M$ or $U = 0$. If $U = M$, then $\alpha(M) = \alpha(U) = 0$, a contradiction. Thus, $U = 0$. By Theorem 7.9.14, α is 1–1.

Theorem 7.10.6 Let M be an irreducible R-module, and let N be an R-module. Let $\alpha \in \mathrm{Hom}_R(N,M)$, $\alpha \neq 0$, the zero homomorphism. Then α is onto.

Proof: Since $\alpha(N)$ is a submodule of M, by the irreducibility of M, $\alpha(N) = M$ and α is onto.

Theorems 7.10.5 and 7.10.6 together are known as Schur's lemma. Also known as Schur's lemma is Theorem 7.10.7.

Theorem 7.10.7 Let M be an irreducible R-module. Then $\mathrm{Hom}_R(M,M)$ is a division ring.

Proof: Let $\alpha \in \mathrm{Hom}_R(M,M)$, $\alpha \neq 0$. By Theorems 7.10.5 and 7.10.6, α is 1–1 and onto. Thus, $\alpha^{-1}: M \to M$ exists. It is necessary to show that $\alpha^{-1} \in \mathrm{Hom}_R(M,M)$. To this end, let $m_1 \in M$ and observe that there exists a unique $m_2 \in M$ such that $\alpha(m_2) = m_1$. Then for any $r \in R$,

$$\alpha^{-1}(m_1 r) = \alpha^{-1}[\alpha(m_2)r] = \alpha^{-1}[\alpha(m_2 r)] = m_2 r = [\alpha^{-1}(m_1)]r.$$

Also, for m and n in M, there exist unique m' and n' in M such that $\alpha(m') = m$ and $\alpha(n') = n$. Then $\alpha^{-1}(m + n) = \alpha^{-1}(\alpha(m') + \alpha(n'))$ $= \alpha^{-1}(\alpha(m' + n')) = m' + n' = \alpha^{-1}(m) + \alpha^{-1}(n)$, and so

$$\alpha^{-1} \in \mathrm{Hom}_R(M,M).$$

Clearly, the nonzero elements of $\mathrm{Hom}_R(M,M)$ form a multiplicative group, so $\mathrm{Hom}_R(M,M)$ is a division ring.

Corollary 7.10.8 Let M be an irreducible R-module. Then M is a left vector space over the division ring $\Delta = \mathrm{Hom}_R(M,M)$.

Proof: $\mathrm{Hom}_R(M, M) = \Delta$ is a division ring by Schur's lemma. By Theorem 7.10.3, M is a left Δ-module, that is, M is a left vector space over Δ.

Definition 7.10.9 Let M be an R-module. For $a \in R$, we define the function $a_r: M \to M$ by $ma_r = ma$, all $m \in M$.

Note: We do not claim $a_r \in \mathrm{Hom}_R(M,M)$. In general, this will not be the case.

We denote the set $\{a_r \mid a \in R\}$ by R_r.

As a Corollary to Schur's lemma, we can prove the following:

Corollary 7.10.10 Let M be an irreducible R-module, and let $\Delta = \mathrm{Hom}_R(M,M)$. Then $R_r \subseteq \mathrm{Hom}_\Delta(M,M)$.

Proof: Let $a \in R$. We must show that $a_r \in \mathrm{Hom}_\Delta(M,M)$. Thus, if we let $\delta \in \Delta$ and $m \in M$, we have

$$\begin{aligned}[\delta m]a_r &= [\delta(m)]a_r = [\delta(m)]a \\ &= \delta(ma) \quad (\text{since } \delta \in \mathrm{Hom}_R(M,M)) \\ &= \delta(ma_r), \quad \text{so } a_r \in \mathrm{Hom}_\Delta(M,M).\end{aligned}$$

We shall later examine a situation in which

i) R_r will be a subring of $\mathrm{Hom}_\Delta(M,M)$, R_r ring isomorphic to R

ii) $R_r \cong \mathrm{Hom}_\Delta(M,M)$ as rings. Meanwhile, we can at least show that R_r is a subring of $\mathrm{Hom}_\Delta(M,\mathrm{M})$ and R_r is a ring homomorphic image of R.

Corollary 7.10.11 Let M be an irreducible R-module. Then R_r is a ring which is a ring homomorphic image of R.

Proof: That R_r is a ring is easy to show, and the proof is left as an exercise. Now let $\gamma: R \to R_r$ be defined by $(a)\gamma = a_r$, all $a \in R$. Then, for $m \in M$, $(m)(ab)_r = mab = (ma_r)b_r = (m)(a_r \circ b_r)$, so $(ab)_r = a_r \circ b_r$, and, indeed, R_r is a homomorphic image of R.

We observe that if for all $a \neq 0$, the function a_r is also not the zero function, that is, $(M)a_r \neq 0$, then R and R_r will be isomorphic. To see this, we simply note that if the function a_r equals the function b_r, then $(a - b)_r = 0_r$, whence $a - b = 0$, that is, $a = b$. This shows that the mapping in Corollary 7.10.11 is 1–1 under the condition of this paragraph.

Exercises

1. Prove Theorem 7.10.2.
2. Prove Theorem 7.10.3.
3. Complete the proof of Corollary 7.10.11.
4. Let M be an R-module, and let N be an irreducible R-submodule of M. Prove that if N' is a submodule of M and if $N \cap N' \neq 0$, then $N \subseteq N'$.
5. Let M be an n-dimensional vector space over Δ. Then $\text{Hom}_\Delta(M, {}_\Delta\Delta)$ is called the *dual space of* M and is denoted by M^*. Show that M^* can be considered a right vector space over Δ, and that $\dim M^* = n$.

Hint: For $\alpha \in M^*$, $\delta \in \Delta$, $m \in M$, put $(m)(\alpha\delta) = (m\alpha)\delta$. This makes M^* a right Δ-module. Let $m_1, \cdots, m_n$ be a basis for M. Show that the n elements $f_i \in M^*$ such that

$$m_j f_i = \delta_{ji} = \begin{cases} 1 & i = j \\ 0 & i \neq j \end{cases} \quad \text{form a basis for } M^*$$

6. Under the hypotheses of 5, let $M^{**} = \text{Hom}_\Delta(M^*, \Delta_\Delta)$. Show that $M^{**} \simeq M$ as left Δ-modules. Indeed, show that there exists a "natural" isomorphism, namely, for $m \in M$, let m correspond to $\hat{m}$, where $\hat{m}(f) = (m)f$, all $f \in M^*$, and show $\hat{m} \in M^{**}$.
7. Let G be a group with no nontrivial proper normal subgroups. Let α be a homomorphism $G \to G$. Show that either $(g)\alpha = e$, the identity, for all $g \in G$, or α is an automorphism.
8. Let M be an irreducible R-module. Show that if $x \neq 0$, $x \in M$, then $xR = M$, where $xR = \{xr \mid r \in R\}$.

7.11 THE RADICAL

In attempting to gain information about a ring R and R-modules, it is helpful to use a certain ideal N in R called the radical of R. Although there are several different ways of defining the radical,[31] all of the useful definitions agree in the presence of the DCC on right ideals. The definition we give will be in terms of nilpotent ideals.

Definition 7.11.1 Let R be a ring and let I_1 and I_2 be two right (left, two-sided) ideals in R. Then the *sum* of I_1 and I_2 is defined as

$$\{i_1 + i_2 \mid i_1 \in I_1, i_2 \in I_2\}$$

and is denoted $I_1 + I_2$.

[31] Let R be a ring. Let $\{I_\alpha\}$ be the collection of all ideals I_α in R such that I_α annihilates an irreducible R-module M_α, that is, $M_\alpha I_\alpha = 0$. Then $\bigcap I_\alpha$ is called the *Jacobson radical* of R, denoted $J(R)$. To see that $J(R)$ coincides with the radical of Definition 7.11.8 in the presence of the DCC, consult, for example, Herstein [19], or Jacobson [24]. Jacobson [24] defines many other radicals.

Clearly, $I_2 + I_1 = I_1 + I_2$ and $I_1 + I_2$ is also a right (left, two-sided) ideal in R.

Not only does this definition generalize to the sum of n ideals, but we can also define the sum of infinitely many ideals.

Definition 7.11.2 Let $\{I_\alpha\}$ be a collection of right (left, two-sided) ideals in a ring R. Then the *sum* of these ideals, denoted ΣI_α, is the set of all finite sums of the form $i_{\alpha_1} + i_{\alpha_2} + \cdots + i_{\alpha_k}$, where $i_{\alpha_j} \in I_{\alpha_j}$. (The I_{α_j}'s and the k vary from element to element in ΣI_α).

Again, ΣI_α is a right (left, two-sided) ideal.

Definition 7.11.3 Let R be a ring and let I be a right (left, two-sided) ideal. Then I is called *nilpotent* if there exists an integer n such that $a_1 a_2 \cdots a_n = 0$, for all choices of n elements $a_1, a_2, \cdots, a_n$ in I.

We see that if $I^n = \{$ finite sums of elements $a_{i_1} a_{i_2} \cdots a_{i_n} \mid a_{i_j} \in I\}$, then I is nilpotent if and only if $I^n = 0$, for some n. In addition, if I is nilpotent, then every element in I is nilpotent, since $a^n = 0$, for all $a \in I$. It can be shown, however, that there are rings R and ideals I such that every element of I is nilpotent, but I itself is not nilpotent.

As examples of nilpotent ideals, we see that the ideal generated by m in the ring Z_{m^n} is nilpotent. Also, if

$$R = \left\{ \begin{bmatrix} a_{11} & a_{12} & \cdots & a_{1n} \\ 0 & a_{22} & \cdots & a_{2n} \\ 0 & 0 \; a_{33} & \cdots & a_{3n} \\ \vdots & & & \\ 0 & 0 & \cdots 0 & a_{nn} \end{bmatrix} \;\middle|\; a_{ij} \in \Delta, \text{ a division ring} \right\},$$

then

$$I = \left\{ \begin{bmatrix} 0 & a_{12} & \cdots & a_{1n} \\ 0 & 0 \; a_{23} & \cdots & a_{2n} \\ \vdots & & & \\ & & & a_{n-1,n} \\ 0 & \cdots & \cdots & 0 \end{bmatrix} \;\middle|\; a_{ij} \in \Delta \right\} \text{ is a nilpotent ideal}$$

in R.

Theorem 7.11.4 Let R be a ring, and let I_1 and I_2 be two nilpotent right (left) ideals. Then $I_1 + I_2$ is a nilpotent right (left) ideal.

Proof: The proof is for right ideals. A similar proof works for the case of left ideals.

Suppose any product of n_j elements of I_j is zero, $j = 1,2$. Let $m = n_1 + n_2 - 1$, and consider a product of m elements of $I_1 + I_2$, say

$$(a_1 + b_1)(a_2 + b_2)\cdots(a_m + b_m),$$

$a_i \in I_1$, $b_i \in I_2$. Expanding by the distributive laws, we obtain a sum of elements such that each summand is the product of a_i's and b_i's. Such a product must contain at least n_1 a_i's or n_2 b_i's. We note that whenever a_i is followed by a product of b_i's, say $a_\ell b_{k_1}\cdots b_{k_j} = c$, then $c \in I_1$, and so a string of m a_i's and b_i's can be regarded as a string of at least n_1 consecutive a_i's or at least n_2 consecutive b_i's. Thus, such a product is zero.

Corollary 7.11.5 Let R be a ring and let $I_1, I_2, \cdots, I_n$ be nilpotent right (left) ideals in R. Then ΣI_α is a nilpotent right (left) ideal in R.

Proof: Exercise.

Definition 7.11.6 Let R be a ring and let S_1 and S_2 be subsets of R. Define the *product* $S_1 S_2$ as

$$\{s_{11}s_{21} + s_{12}s_{22} + \cdots + s_{1k}s_{2k} \mid s_{1i} \in S_1, s_{2i} \in S_2, \text{ and where } k \text{ varies}\}.$$

If S_2 is a right ideal, it is easy to see that $S_1 S_2$ is a right ideal. Similarly, if S_1 is a left ideal, then $S_1 S_2$ is a left ideal.

Theorem 7.11.7 Let I be a nilpotent right (left) ideal in a ring R. Then RI (IR) is a nilpotent ideal in R.

Proof: Since I is a right ideal, so is RI, and, since R is a left ideal, so is RI. Thus, RI is an ideal. If $I^n = 0$, then

$$(RI)^n = R(IR)^{n-1}I \subseteq R(I)^{n-1}I = RI^n = 0.$$

Definition 7.11.8 Let R be a ring with DCC on right ideals. Let $\{I_\alpha\}$ be the collection of all nilpotent right ideals of R. Then $N = \Sigma I_\alpha$ is called the *radical* of R.

We shall show that N possesses the following properties:

1) N is a nilpotent ideal
2) N contains all nilpotent left ideals, as well as all nilpotent right ideals; thus N is the unique ideal of R maximal with respect to being nilpotent.

Theorem 7.11.9 Let R be a ring with DCC on right ideals, and let N be the radical of R. The N is nilpotent.

Proof: Clearly, N is a right ideal, so $N \supseteq N^2 \supseteq N^3 \supseteq \cdots$ is a descending sequence of right ideals. By the DCC, there exists an integer k

such that $N^k = N^{k+1} = \cdots = N^{2k}$. Thus, $N^k = N^k \cdot N^k$. If $N^k = 0$, the proof is finished. Otherwise, there exist right ideals I (for example N^k) such that $IN^k \neq 0$. By the minimum condition (equivalent to the DCC) there exists a right ideal I_0 minimal with respect to the property $IN^k \neq 0$.

Since $I_0 N^k \neq 0$, there exists an element $x \in I_0$, $x \neq 0$, such that $xN^k \neq 0$. But then $(xN^k)N^k = xN^{2k} = xN^k \neq 0$, so by the minimality of I_0, $xN^k = I_0$. (Note that since $x \in I_0$, $xN^k \subseteq I_0$.) Thus, there exists an element $y \in N^k$ such that $xy = x$. Now $y \in N$, so y also is contained in the sum of finitely many nilpotent right ideals. By Corollary 7.11.5, y is nilpotent, that is, $y^m = 0$, for some integer m. But then, $xy = x$ implies $xy^n = x$, all n, whence $0 = xy^m = x \neq 0$, a contradiction. This contradiction shows $N^k = 0$ and N is nilpotent.

Theorem 7.11.10 Let R be a ring. Let N be the sum of all nilpotent right ideals of R. Then N contains all nilpotent left ideals of R also.

Proof: Let I be a nilpotent left ideal. By Theorem 7.11.7, IR is also nilpotent, whence $I + IR$ is also nilpotent by Theorem 7.11.4. But $I + IR$ is clearly a right ideal, so $I + IR \subseteq N$, whence $I \subseteq N$.

We summarize Theorems 7.11.9 and 7.11.10 in the next theorem, which implies that properties 1) and 2) given prior to Theorem 7.11.9 hold.

Theorem 7.11.11 Let R be a ring with DCC on right ideals. Let N be the radical of R. Then

i) N is a nilpotent ideal
ii) N is the sum of all nilpotent left ideals
iii) N is the unique ideal of R maximal with respect to being nilpotent.

Proof:

i) By Theorem 7.11.9, N is a nilpotent right ideal. Since $RN + N$ is a nilpotent right ideal, $RN + N \subseteq N$, whence $RN \subseteq N$, that is, N is also a left ideal, whence N is an ideal.
ii) By Theorem 7.11.10, N contains all nilpotent left ideals of R. Since N is also a nilpotent left ideal, N is clearly the sum of all nilpotent left ideals.
iii) This follows from the definition of N and ii).

We note that if R has DCC on left ideals, then we could define the radical of R as the sum of the nilpotent left ideals, and prove that it is equal to the sum of the nilpotent right ideals. That is, if R has either DCC on right ideals or DCC on left ideals, then we get the same radical whether we define it as the sum of the nilpotent right ideals or the nilpotent left ideals. We implicitly use this fact in Section 7.15.

Now let R be a ring with DCC on right ideals and let N be the radical of R. Since N is an ideal in R, we may form the quotient ring R/N and it is easy to see that R/N also has DCC on right ideals. We shall prove that the radical of R/N is the zero element of R/N.

Theorem 7.11.12 Let R be a ring with DCC on right ideals. Then the radical of R/N is zero.

Proof: Let I' be a nilpotent right ideal of R/N and let $I = \{r \in R \mid r + N \in I'\}$. Then I is a right ideal in R.

Since I' is nilpotent, and since N is nilpotent, there exist integers m,n such that

i) $(I')^m = 0$ in R/N, that is,
$(r_1 + N)\cdots(r_m + N) = N$, where $r_1,\cdots,r_m \in I$

ii) $N^n = 0$.

Now let $r_1,\cdots,r_{mn} \in I$. Then $a_1 = r_1\cdots r_m \in N$, $a_2 = r_{m+1}\cdots r_{2m} \in N$, $\cdots,a_n = r_{(n-1)m+1}\cdots r_{nm} \in N$, whence the product $a_1\cdots a_n$ of these n elements of N is zero, that is, $r_1\cdots r_{mn} = 0$, and so $I^{mn} = 0$. Since I is nilpotent, $I \subseteq N$, and so I' equals zero in R/N. Thus, R/N has radical zero.

Definition 7.11.13 Let R be a ring with DCC on right ideals. We say R is *semisimple* if the radical of R is 0.

We see immediately that if R has DCC on right ideals, then R/N is semisimple by Theorem 7.11.12. Moreover, it is easy to prove that a direct sum of finitely many matrix rings over division rings, say $\Delta_{n_1}{}^{(1)} \oplus \Delta_{n_2}{}^{(2)} \oplus\cdots \oplus \Delta_{n_k}{}^{(k)}$, where $\Delta^{(i)}$ is a division ring, is a semisimple ring. This includes, therefore, all division rings and fields. We shall prove later that this type of ring includes all semisimple rings.

Theorem 7.11.14 Let $\Delta^{(i)}$ be a division ring, $i = 1,\cdots,k$. Let $n_1,\cdots,n_k$ be integers that are greater than 0. Then

$$S = \Delta_{n_1}{}^{(1)} \oplus\cdots\oplus \Delta_{n_k}{}^{(k)}$$

is semisimple.

Proof: By Theorem 7.9.24 and Exercise 9, Section 7.9, the ring S satisfies the DCC on right ideals. Thus, we need only show that the radical N of S is zero. If $N \neq 0$, there exists an element $(a_1,\cdots,a_i,\cdots,a_k)$ in N, $a_i \neq 0$. Since N is a two-sided ideal in S,

$$(0,\cdots,0,b_i,0,\cdots,0)(a_1,\cdots,a_i,\cdots,a_k)(0,\cdots,0,c_i,0,\cdots,0)$$

is in N, for all $b_i,c_i \in \Delta_{n_i}{}^{(i)}$. Thus N contains all the elements of the form $(0,\cdots,0,b_ia_ic_i,0,\cdots,0)$. Since $\Delta_{n_i}{}^{(i)}$ has no proper two-sided ideals, S contains the set $T = \{(0,\cdots,0,x_i,0,\cdots,0) \mid x_i \in \Delta_{n_i}{}^{(i)}\}$. But this ideal T of S is contained in the radical of S, and T is clearly not nilpotent, contradicting that N is nilpotent. Thus $N = 0$ and the proof is completed.

Before leaving this section, we point out that the notion of a semisimple ring can be defined even for rings that do not have DCC on right ideals.[32]

[32] If the Jacobson radical of R is 0, one often says that R is semisimple. In this sense, Z, the ring of integers, is semisimple, although Z is not semisimple in the sense we use this term in this book.

However, in this book, whenever we say R is semisimple, we assume that R has DCC on right ideals.

Exercises

1. Prove Corollary 7.11.5.
2. Let K be the real numbers. Show that the set of nilpotent elements in K_3 (3×3 matrices) does not form an ideal in K_3.
3. Let R be a commutative ring. Show that the set of nilpotent elements in R forms an ideal.

*4. **i)** Let R be a ring with DCC on right ideals and with radical N. Prove that R/N has DCC on right ideals.
  ii) Let R be a ring with DCC on right ideals. Prove that any ring homomorphic image of R has DCC on right ideals.

5. Let R be a ring with DCC on right ideals. Let V be an irreducible right R-module and let N be the radical of R. Prove that $VN = 0$.
6. Let N be the radical of a ring R with DCC on right ideals. Show that if $a \in N$, there exists $b \in N$ such that

$$a + b + ab = 0.$$

Hint: Let $(1 + b) = 1/(1 + a)$ (symbolically) and expand $1/(1 + a)$ in a power series.

7. Determine the radical of each of the following rings:
   i) Z_4
   ii) Z_6
   iii) $Z_{p_1p_2}$, where p_1 and p_2 are distinct primes
   iv) $Z_{p_1^{\alpha_1}p_2^{\alpha_2}}$, where p_1 and p_2 are distinct primes and $\alpha_1 \geq 1$, $\alpha_2 \geq 1$.
8. Find a necessary and sufficient condition on m so that Z_m has a nonzero radical.
9. Find all idempotent elements e (that is, $e^2 = e$) in each of the following:
   i) Z_6
   ii) Z_8
   iii) Z_{10}
10. Let R be a ring. A right ideal I is called *nil* if, for each $x \in I$, x is nilpotent. Prove that if R is a ring with DCC on right ideals, then every nil right ideal is nilpotent.

7.12 SEMISIMPLE AND SIMPLE RINGS (WITH DCC)

We are now well on our way to characterizing semisimple rings in terms of matrices. In this section we shall show how this problem is reduced to that of characterizing simple rings (with DCC), which, as we shall see, are of the form Δ_n, where Δ is a division ring. Recall that our definition of a semisimple ring is a ring with DCC on right ideals and with radical zero.

Definition 7.12.1 Let R be a ring, $R \neq 0$, such that

i) R has no nontrivial proper two-sided ideals and

ii) $R^2 \neq 0$.

Such a ring R is called *simple*.

Recall that the term ideal, when standing alone, means two-sided ideal.

Theorem 7.12.2 Let R be a simple ring with DCC on right ideals. Then N, the radical of R, is zero.

Proof: Since N is an ideal of R, either $N = R$ or $N = 0$. Since N is nilpotent, $N = R$ implies $R^n = 0$, for some n, contradicting that $R^2 = R(R^2 \neq 0$ implies $R^2 = R$, since R^2 is an ideal). Thus, $N = 0$.

Corollary 7.12.3 A simple ring with DCC on right ideals is semisimple.

Proof: Immediate.

We observe that if Δ is a division ring, then $\Delta_n \oplus \Delta_m$ is semisimple, but not simple. The two direct summands, Δ_n and Δ_m, however, are simple. We also point out that a simple ring R may have a right ideal I, where $I \neq R$ and $I \neq 0$. For example, this is true in Δ_n, if $n \geq 2$.

Theorem 7.12.4 Let R be a ring with DCC on right ideals, $R \neq 0$. Then R contains a minimal right ideal.

Proof: Let $\mathcal{S}$ be the collection of all nonzero right ideals. By the minimum condition, $\mathcal{S}$ has a minimal element I, which is easily seen to be a minimal right ideal.

Theorem 7.12.5 Let R be a ring, $R \neq 0$. Then a minimal right ideal I is either nilpotent or an irreducible R-module.

Proof: $I^2 \subseteq I$, so either $I^2 = 0$, and I is nilpotent, or $I^2 = I$. Since $I^2 = I$ implies $IR \neq 0$, I is an irreducible R-module in the latter case.

Lemma 7.12.6 Let R be a semisimple ring.

i) If $x \in R$ and $Rx = 0$, then $x = 0$.

ii) If $x \in R$ and $xR = 0$, then $x = 0$.

Proof:

i) Let $S = \{x \in R \mid Rx = 0\}$. If x_1 and $x_2 \in S$, then $R(x_1 + x_2) = 0$; so $x_1 + x_2 \in S$. If $r \in R$, $x \in S$, then $R(xr) = (Rx)r = 0r = 0$, so $xr \in S$. Thus, S is a right ideal in R. Clearly, $RS = 0$, so $S^2 = SS \subseteq RS = 0$.

Thus, S is a nilpotent right ideal. Since the radical of R is zero, $S = 0$, that is, $Rx = 0$ implies $x = 0$.
ii) The proof is similar to that of i).

Theorem 7.12.7 Let R be a semisimple ring. Then
i) R has minimal right ideals
ii) No minimal right ideal is nilpotent
iii) If I is a minimal right ideal of R, there exists an idempotent element $e \in I (e^2 = e \neq 0)$ such that $I = eR$.

Proof: i) and ii) follow from Theorem 7.12.4 and the definition of semisimplicity.

To prove iii), let I be a minimal right ideal of R. Since I is not nilpotent, $I^2 \neq 0$, and so $I^2 = I$, since I is minimal. Thus, there exists an element $x \in I$ such that $xI \neq 0$, whence $xI = I$, again by the minimality of I. Clearly there is an element $e \in I$ such that $xe = x$. We show that $e^2 = e$ and that $I = eR$.

If $e^2 \neq e$, then $e^2 - e \neq 0$. By Lemma 7.12.6, $(e^2 - e)R \neq 0$, and since $e^2 - e \in I$, we have that $0 \neq (e^2 - e)R \subseteq I$, so $(e^2 - e)R = I$. But then $I = xI = x(e^2 - e)R = (xe^2 - xe)R = 0$, since $xe^2 = xe$, contradicting that $I \neq 0$. Thus, $e^2 - e = 0$, that is $e^2 = e$. Finally, since $e \neq 0$, $eR \neq 0$, and again since $e \in I$, $eR \subseteq I$, whence $eR = I$.

As a result of Theorem 7.12.7, we can now prove the striking result that a semisimple ring has an identity. We first prove a technical lemma.

Lemma 7.12.8 Let R be a semisimple ring. Let e be a nonzero idempotent in R, that is, $e^2 = e \neq 0$. Let $R_1 = \{ex - x \mid x \in R\}$. Then
i) $R = R_1 \dotplus eR$ (internal direct sum of right ideals)
ii) If $R_1 \neq 0$, there exists a minimal right ideal fR of R contained in R_1, and $ef = fe = 0, f^2 = f \neq 0$
iii) $e + f$ is an idempotent.

Proof:
i) Let $x \in R$. Then $x = (e(-x) - (-x)) + ex \in R_1 + eR$. If $y \in R_1 \cap eR$, then, on the one hand, $y = ex - x$, whence $ey = ex - ex = 0$, while on the other hand, $y = er$, whence $ey = e^2r = er = y$. Thus, $y = 0$ and $R_1 \cap eR = 0$. By Theorem 7.9.16 and Definition 7.9.17, $R = R_1 \dotplus eR$.
ii) By the DCC, R_1 has a minimal right ideal of R, and by Theorem 7.12.7, that right ideal has the form $f'R$, $(f')^2 = f' \neq 0$. In i), we saw that $eR_1 = 0$, so in particular, $ef' = 0$. Now let $f = f' - f'e$. Then

$$\begin{aligned} f^2 &= (f' - f'e)(f' - f'e) \\ &= (f')^2 - f'ef' - (f')^2e + f'ef'e = f' - f'e = f. \end{aligned}$$

Also, $f \in f'R$, so $ef = 0$, and $fe = (f' - f'e)e = f'e - f'e^2 = f'e - f'e = 0$. Finally, $f'R \supseteq fR = (f' - f'e)R$
$\supseteq (f' - f'e)f'R = f'R,$

so
$$fR = f'R.$$

iii) $(e + f)^2 = (e + f)(e + f) = e^2 + ef + fe + f^2 = e + 0 + f = e + f.$

Theorem 7.12.9 Let R be a semisimple ring. Then R has an identity element.

Proof: Let e_1R, $e_1^2 = e_1 \neq 0$, be a minimal right ideal. By Lemma 7.12.8, $R = R_1 \dotplus e_1R$, where $R_1 = \{e_1x - x \mid x \in R\}$. Then it is easy to verify, using Lemma 7.12.8 and the technique of the proof of Lemma 7.12.8, that, if $R_1 \neq 0$, $R = R_2 \dotplus e_2R \dotplus e_1R$, with $e_1e_2 = e_2e_1 = 0$, $e_2^2 = e_2 \neq 0$, $e_2 \in R_1$, $(e_1 + e_2)^2 = e_1 + e_2$, $R_2 = \{e_2x - x \mid x \in R_1\}$. Also, if $x \in e_2R \dotplus e_1R$, then $x = e_2r_2 + e_1r_1$ and $(e_2 + e_1)x = (e_2 + e_1)(e_2r_2 + e_1r_1) = e_2r_2 + e_1r_1 = x$ whence $e_2R \dotplus e_1R = (e_2 + e_1)R$. In addition, if $x \in R_1$, then $e_1x = 0$, so $R_2 = \{(e_2 + e_1)x - x \mid x \in R_1\} = \{(e_2 + e_1)x - x \mid x \in R\}$. Thus,

$$R = R_2 \dotplus e_2R \dotplus e_1R = R_2 \dotplus (e_2 + e_1)R.$$

By repeated application of the lemma, we get $R = R_n \dotplus e_1R \dotplus \cdots \dotplus e_nR = R_n \dotplus (e_1 + e_2 + \cdots + e_n)R$, where $e_i^2 = e_i$, $e_ie_j = 0$, $i \neq j$. Since $R_1 \supset R_2 \supset R_3 \supset \cdots$, the DCC implies that for some n, $R_n = 0$, whence, there exists an n such that $R = e_1R \dotplus e_2R \dotplus \cdots \dotplus e_nR = (e_1 + \cdots + e_n)R$, $e_ie_j = 0$, $i \neq j$, and $e_i^2 = e_i$, with e_iR a minimal right ideal of R.

Letting $e = e_1 + \cdots + e_n$, it is easy to see that e is a left identity of R. All that remains, then, is to show that e is a right identity. Thus, let $r \in R$. Then $(r - re)R = (r - re)eR = (re - re)R = 0$. By Lemma 7.12.6, $r - re = 0$, whence $r = re$, and the proof is completed.

Next, we show that a semisimple ring is the direct sum of simple rings with DCC on right ideals. The only additional equipment needed is the following lemma.

Notice that we need not assume in the lemma that R is semisimple or even has DCC.

Lemma 7.12.10 Let R be a ring and let eR and fR be two minimal right ideals of R, $e^2 = e$, $f^2 = f$. Then eR and fR are R-isomorphic if and only if $fReR \neq 0$.

Proof: Suppose $eR \simeq fR$, with φ an R-isomorphism of eR onto fR. Then $\varphi e = \varphi(ee) = (\varphi e)e = fse$, for some $s \in R$. Since $e \neq 0$, $\varphi e \neq 0$, whence $fse \neq 0$. Clearly, this implies $fReR \neq 0$.

Conversely, suppose $fReR \neq 0$. Then $fse \neq 0$, for some $s \in R$. Define $\varphi: eR \to fR$ by $\varphi(er) = fser$. Then φ is an R-homomorphism. Moreover, $\text{Im}\,\varphi = fseR \neq 0$, since $fse \neq 0$. Since fR is a minimal right ideal,

$fseR = fR$, so φ is onto. Finally, $\ker\varphi = \{x \in eR \mid fsx = 0\}$. But $\ker\varphi$ is an R-ideal contained in the minimal right ideal eR. Thus, either $\ker\varphi = 0$ or $\ker\varphi = eR$. If $\ker\varphi = eR$, then φ is not onto, so $\ker\varphi = 0$ and φ is 1–1. (Compare this proof with that of Theorem 7.10.5. Actually, we could use Theorem 7.10.5 to prove this result, but give the proof here in full detail to emphasize this technique.)

Theorem 7.12.11 Let R be a semisimple ring. Then R is the direct sum of simple rings, and each of these simple rings has DCC on right ideals.

Proof: In the proof of Theorem 7.12.9, we saw that $R = e_1R \dotplus e_2R \dotplus \cdots \dotplus e_nR$, where each e_iR is a minimal right ideal, $e_i^2 = e_i$, $e_ie_j = 0$, $i \neq j$, and $e_1 + e_2 + \cdots + e_n$ is the identity of R. By a suitable rearrangement and renumbering of the e_iR, we have that $R = e_{11}R \dotplus e_{12}R \dotplus \cdots \dotplus e_{1n_1}R \dotplus e_{21}R \dotplus \cdots \dotplus e_{2n_2}R \dotplus \cdots \dotplus e_{m1}R \dotplus \cdots \dotplus e_{mn_m}R$, where $e_{ij}R \simeq e_{k\ell}R$ if and only if $i = k$.

$$\text{Let } A_i = e_{i1}R \dotplus \cdots \dotplus e_{in_i}R = \sum_{j=1}^{n_i} \dotplus\, e_{ij}R.$$

As we shall show, each A_i is a simple ring with DCC on right ideals.

To do this, let eR be a minimal right ideal, $e^2 = e$. If $A_ieR = 0$, $i = 1, \cdots, m$, then $ReR = 0$; but then, since $R \ni 1$, $eR = 0$, contradicting that eR is a minimal (and hence nonzero) right ideal. Thus, there exists an e_{ij} such that $e_{ij}ReR \neq 0$. By Lemma 7.12.10, $eR \simeq e_{ij}R$. If, for some $k \neq i$, $e_{k\ell}ReR \neq 0$, then $e_{k\ell}R \simeq eR$, whence $e_{k\ell}R \simeq e_{ij}R$, which contradicts that $e_{k\ell}R \simeq e_{ij}R$ if and only if $i = k$. Thus, $A_ieR \neq 0$, but $A_keR = 0$, $k \neq i$. Since $1 \in A_1 + \cdots + A_m$, we see that

$$eR = 1 \cdot eR \subseteq (A_1 + \cdots + A_m)eR = A_ieR \subseteq A_i,$$

since A_i is a sum of right ideals.

We have thus proved that A_i is the sum of all minimal right ideals isomorphic, as R-modules, to $e_{i1}R$.

In addition, our proof also shows that $A_iA_j = 0$, $i \neq j$. For otherwise, $e_{i\ell}Re_{jk}R \neq 0$, for some ℓ and k, whence $e_{i\ell}R \simeq e_{jk}R$, a contradiction for $i \neq j$.

To show that A_i satisfies the DCC on right A_i-ideals, let $I_1 \supseteq I_2 \supseteq I_3 \supseteq \cdots$ be a descending chain of right A_i-ideals. Then $I_kA_j = 0$, $j \neq i$, since $A_iA_j = 0$, and so $I_1 \supseteq I_2 \supseteq \cdots$ is a descending chain of R-ideals. But the DCC in R implies this chain must be finite, whence the DCC holds in A_i.

Our last task is to show that A_i has no nonzero proper two-sided ideals. Thus, let T be a nonzero two-sided ideal in A_i. Since $A_iA_j = A_jA_i = 0$, $j \neq i$, it is clear that $A_jT = TA_j = 0$, $j \neq i$. Also, $A_iT \subseteq T$ and

$TA_i \subseteq T$. Thus, T is a two-sided ideal in R and, in particular, a right ideal in R. Thus, T contains a minimal right ideal eR, $e^2 = e$. From remarks already made, it is easy to see that $eR \cong e_{ik}R$, $k = 1,\cdots,n_i$. Thus, $e_{ik}ReR \neq 0$, $k = 1,\cdots,n_i$, and since $e_{ik}R$ is a minimal right ideal, we have that $e_{ik}ReR = e_{ik}R$. But since T is a two-sided ideal, and $eR \subseteq T$, $e_{ik}ReR \subseteq T$. Thus, $e_{ik}R \subseteq T$, $k = 1,\cdots,n_i$, and so finally $A_i \subseteq T$. This shows that A_i is simple and the proof is complete.

The proof of Theorem 7.12.11 also shows that each A_i is a two-sided ideal in R. It is a relatively simple matter to prove the uniqueness of the components in the decomposition: $R = A_1 \dotplus \cdots \dotplus A_m$, where each A_i is both a two-sided ideal in R and a simple ring.

Theorem 7.12.12 Let R be a semisimple ring with DCC on right ideals. Then the decomposition of Theorem 7.12.11 is unique, that is, if $R = B_1 \dotplus \cdots \dotplus B_p$ is a second internal direct sum of R, where each B_i is both a simple ring and a two-sided ideal in R, then $p = m$ and we can rearrange the B_i's so that $B_1 = A_1,\cdots,B_m = A_m$.

Proof: Since $R \ni 1$, $B_i(A_1 + \cdots + A_m) \neq 0$. Suppose $B_iA_j \neq 0$. Since B_i and A_j are both two-sided ideals, $B_iA_j \subseteq B_i$ and $B_iA_j \subseteq A_j$. Moreover, B_iA_j is a two-sided ideal in both B_i and A_j. (Why?) Thus, since both B_i and A_j are simple, we have that $B_i = B_iA_j = A_j$. This completes the proof.

Theorem 7.12.13 Let R be a simple ring with DCC on right ideals. Then any two minimal right ideals are isomorphic.

Proof: In the proof of Theorem 7.12.11, were R simple, it would turn out that $R = A_1$. But then every minimal right ideal must be isomorphic to $e_{11}R$ and the theorem is proved.

Definition 7.12.14 Let M be a module and let $\{M_\lambda\}$ be a collection of submodules of M. We say that M is the *sum of the submodules* M_λ if for each $m \in M$, there exists a finite collection of subscripts $\lambda_1,\cdots,\lambda_k$ and elements $m_{\lambda_i} \in M_{\lambda_i}$, $i = 1,\cdots,k$, such that $m = m_{\lambda_1} + \cdots + m_{\lambda_k}$. We write $M = \Sigma M_\lambda$.

Theorem 7.12.15 Let M be an R-module, where R is semisimple. Then M is the sum of irreducible submodules.

Proof: We know that $1 = e_1 + \cdots + e_n$, where each e_i is idempotent and e_iR is a minimal right ideal. Let $v \in M$. Then $v = v\cdot 1 = ve_1 + \cdots + ve_n$. Suppose $ve_i \neq 0$. Then $ve_iR \neq 0$, and using past techniques, we can show that $ve_iR \cong e_iR$, as R-modules. Since e_iR is irreducible, so is ve_iR. Thus, $v \in \Sigma ve_iR \subseteq M$, and M is clearly a sum of irreducible submodules.

Later we shall show that if R is a ring with 1 such that every R-module is the sum of irreducible submodules, then R is semisimple.

Theorem 7.12.16 Let R be a ring with 1 and with DCC on right ideals. Let N be the radical of R and let M be an R-module. Then $MN = 0$ if and only if M is the sum of irreducible submodules.

Proof: If M is the sum of irreducible submodules, then any $m \in M$ is in $\sum_{k=1}^{n} M_k$, where the M_k are irreducible. Now $M_k N = M_k$ or $M_k N = 0$. If $N^j = 0$, then $M_k N = M_k$ implies $M_k = 0$, a contradiction. Thus, $M_k N = 0$, whence $mN = 0$, and so $MN = 0$.

Conversely, suppose $MN = 0$. Then we can consider M as an R/N-module, by putting $m(r + N) = mr$, for all $r \in R$. Now R/N is semisimple, and so by Theorem 7.12.15, M is the sum of irreducible R/N-modules. Now let $\overline{M}$ be an irreducible R/N-module. Then since $\overline{M}N = 0$, $\overline{M}$ is an R-module, where we put $mr = m(r + N)$. Moreover, $\overline{M}$ has no nonzero proper R-submodules, since this would induce proper nonzero R/N-submodules. Thus, $\overline{M}$ is an irreducible R-module and the proof is completed.

Exercises

1. Let Δ be a division ring. Prove that Δ_n is simple.
   Hint: See Exercise 7, Section 7.8.
2. Let R be a semisimple ring, and suppose $R = A_1 \dot{+} \cdots \dot{+} A_m$ is the decomposition of Theorem 7.12.11. Let $\{I_\alpha\}$ be a set of minimal right ideals of R, no two of which are isomorphic as R-modules. Prove that
   i) there exists such a set $\{I_\alpha\}$ with m elements
   ii) no such set $\{I_\alpha\}$ can have more than m elements.
3. Let R be a ring with 1 and suppose $R = R_1 \dot{+} \cdots \dot{+} R_n$, where each R_i is a two-sided ideal in R. Prove that each R_i has an identity.
4. Let R be a ring with DCC on right ideals. Prove that, up to isomorphism, there are just a finite number of irreducible R-modules.
   Hint: See Theorems 7.12.15 and 7.12.16 and Exercise 2.
5. Let Δ be the real numbers. Show that for any real number b, $e = \begin{bmatrix} 1 & 0 \\ b & 0 \end{bmatrix}$ and $f = \begin{bmatrix} 0 & 0 \\ -b & 1 \end{bmatrix}$ are idempotents in Δ_2. Show also that $e\Delta_2$ and $f\Delta_2$ are minimal right ideals in Δ_2, and that $\Delta_2 = e\Delta_2 \dot{+} f\Delta_2$, with $1 = e + f$ and $ef = fe = 0$. Thus conclude that since $1 = e' + f'$, $e'f' = f'e' = 0$, where $e' = \begin{bmatrix} 1 & 0 \\ 0 & 0 \end{bmatrix}$, $f' = \begin{bmatrix} 0 & 0 \\ 0 & 1 \end{bmatrix}$, that the decomposition of a simple ring as a direct sum of minimal right ideals is not unique.

7.13 WEDDERBURN'S THEOREM

Now that we know that a semisimple ring is the direct sum of simple rings with DCC on right ideals, it will be a relatively easy matter to characterize semisimple rings in terms of matrices. Indeed, we need only get such a characterization of simple rings with DCC. This will be done in Wedderburn's theorem. Recall that a simple ring with DCC on right ideals is also a semisimple ring (Corollary 7.12.13) and hence has an identity 1.

Theorem 7.13.1 Let R be a simple ring with DCC on right ideals. Then there exists an irreducible R-module.

Proof: By Theorem 7.12.7, R has a minimal right ideal eR. Since $eR \cdot R = eR$, eR is an irreducible R-module.

Theorem 7.13.2 Let R be a simple ring with DCC on right ideals. Let $eR = I$ be a minimal right ideal in R. Then $\mathrm{Hom}_R(I,I)$ is a division ring Δ.

Proof: This follows from Schur's lemma (Theorem 7.10.7).

It will be most helpful if we can write Δ in terms of elements of R. Happily, this can be accomplished.

Theorem 7.13.3 Let R be a simple ring and let I be a minimal right ideal of R, with $I = eR$, e an idempotent. Then the division ring $\mathrm{Hom}_R(I,I) \simeq eRe$ (as rings).

Proof: Let $\delta \in \mathrm{Hom}_R(I,I)$. Since $I = eR$, any $x \in eR$ has the form er, for some $r \in R$. Since $\delta(x) = \delta(er) = [\delta(e)]r$, we know how δ acts on I once we know $\delta(e)$. Now $e = ee$, so $\delta(e) = \delta(ee) = [\delta(e)]e$. But $\delta(e) \in eR$, so there exists an $s \in R$ such that $\delta(e) = es$. Thus, $\delta(e) = ese$ and so $\delta(x) = [\delta(e)]r = eser$, for all $r \in R$. Hence, for each $\delta \in \mathrm{Hom}_R(I,I)$, we can find an $s \in R$ so that the action of δ on I is just left multiplication by ese.

If $t \in R$, *we define* $\delta'(er)$ to be $eter$, for all $r \in R$. It is easily seen that $\delta' \in \mathrm{Hom}_R(I,I)$. Now let $\varphi:\mathrm{Hom}_R(I,I) \to eRe$ be defined by $(\delta)\varphi = \delta(e)e$. We leave the proof that φ is a ring isomorphism to the Exercises.

There will be times when it is more convenient to work with eRe rather than directly with $\mathrm{Hom}_R(I,I)$. Thus, we shall use eRe and $\mathrm{Hom}_R(I,I)$ interchangeably.

We point out that it is also possible to prove that eRe is a division ring as follows: Clearly, e is an identity for eRe. Also, since eR is a minimal right ideal, $eReR = eR$, that is, $eReeR = eR$, whence, $eReeRe = eRe$. But now we see immediately that the nonzero elements of eRe form a multiplicative group, whence eRe is a division ring. We have given the proof using Schur's lemma in order to indicate one of the many applications of the ideas presented in Section 7.10.

Theorem 7.13.4   Let R be a simple ring with DCC on right ideals and let eR and fR be minimal right ideals, with e and f idempotents. Then eRe and fRf are ring isomorphic.

   Proof: Let $I_1 = eR$ and $I_2 = fR$. By Theorem 7.13.3, it suffices to show that $\Delta_1 = \mathrm{Hom}_R(I_1, I_1)$ and $\Delta_2 = \mathrm{Hom}_R(I_2, I_2)$ are ring isomorphic. Thus, let ν be the R-isomorphism from I_1 onto I_2, which exists by Theorem 7.12.13. Then ν^{-1} is an R-isomorphism from I_2 onto I_1. We now define the ring isomorphism τ from Δ_1 to Δ_2 as follows: $(\delta_1)\tau = \nu^{-1}\delta_1\nu$, for all $\delta_1 \in \Delta_1$. From the string: $I_2 \xrightarrow{\nu^{-1}} I_1 \xrightarrow{\delta_1} I_1 \xrightarrow{\nu} I_2$, we see easily that $(\delta_1)\tau \in \Delta_2$. Also, it is easy to see that τ is a ring homomorphism. To show that it is onto, we see that $\nu\delta_2\nu^{-1} \in \Delta_1$, for $\delta_2 \in \Delta_2$ and that $(\nu\delta_2\nu^{-1})\tau = \delta_2$.

   Finally, using the fact that ν is 1–1 and that $\delta \neq 0$ is 1–1, it is easy to see that τ is 1–1. This completes the proof.

We shall now characterize simple rings with DCC on right ideals in terms of matrix rings over a division ring.

Theorem 7.13.5   Wedderburn   Let R be a simple ring with DCC on right ideals. Then $R \cong \mathrm{Hom}_\Delta(M, M)$ (as rings) for some finite dimensional vector space M over a division ring Δ. Moreover, if $R \cong \Delta_n \cong \Delta'_m$, then $n = m$ and $\Delta \cong \Delta'$.

   Proof: *I. Existence of M and Δ:* By Theorem 7.13.1, there exists a minimal right ideal $I = eR$, $e^2 = e$. By Theorem 7.13.2, $\mathrm{Hom}_R(I, I) = \Delta$, a division ring, and so $M = eR$ is a vector space over Δ. By Corollary 7.10.11,

$$R_r = \{a_r \mid a \in R \text{ and } a_r : M \to M \text{ is defined by } ma_r = ma\}$$

is a subring of $\mathrm{Hom}_\Delta(M, \mathrm{M})$. We wish to show that $R_r = \mathrm{Hom}_\Delta(M, M)$.[33]

Since $R \ni 1$ and $ReR \neq 0$, the two-sided ideal ReR must equal R and so $1 \in ReR$. Thus, there exist elements a_i and b_i in R, $i = 1, \cdots, k$, such that $1 = a_1eb_1 + \cdots + a_keb_k = \sum_{i=1}^{k} a_ieb_i$. Now let $\varphi \in \mathrm{Hom}_\Delta(M, M)$ and let $x \in M = eR$. Then $x = er$, for some $r \in R$, and we have

$$x\varphi = (er)\varphi = (er \cdot 1)\varphi = (er \cdot \Sigma a_ieb_i)\varphi = (\Sigma era_ieb_i)\varphi.$$

Now $era_ie \in eRe = \mathrm{Hom}_R(M, M) = \Delta$, so there exist $\delta_i \in \Delta$ such that

$$\Sigma era_ie \cdot eb_i = \Sigma \delta_i(eb_i).$$

---

[33] The proof we give of this is due to D. W. Henderson, *American Mathematical Monthly*, vol. 72 (1965), pp. 385–386.

Thus,

$$\begin{aligned}(\Sigma era_i e \cdot eb_i)\varphi = (\Sigma\delta_i(eb_i))\varphi &= \Sigma\delta_i[(eb_i)\varphi\,] \text{ (since } \varphi \in \mathrm{Hom}_\Delta(M,M))\\ &= \Sigma era_i e[(eb_i)\varphi]\\ &= er\,\Sigma a_i e(eb_i)\varphi = x(\Sigma a_i e(eb_i)\varphi).\end{aligned}$$

Thus, denoting $\Sigma a_i e(eb_i)\varphi$ by t, we see that $x\varphi = xt = xt_r$, for some $t \in R$ and so $\varphi \in R_r$. Thus, $R_r = \mathrm{Hom}_\Delta(M,M)$. Now for $s \neq 0$, $eRs \neq 0$: for $eRs = 0$ implies $eRsR = 0$, whence, since $RsR = R$, $eR = 0$, a contradiction. Thus, we have $R \simeq R_r = \mathrm{Hom}_\Delta(M,M)$.

Next we show that M is finite dimensional over Δ. If it is not, by Theorem 7.4.1, M has an infinite basis $B = \{x_\alpha\}$ and we can extract an infinite subset $x_1, x_2, \cdots, x_n, \cdots$ from B. Now we let U_n be the set of all linear transformations T such that $x_i T = 0$, $i = 1,2,\cdots,n$, where T is defined arbitrarily on the other basis elements. Then $U_1 \supset U_2 \supset U_3 \supset \cdots$, for there exists a $T \in U_n$ such that $x_{n+1}T \neq 0$, that is $T \notin U_{n+1}$. In addition, each U_i is a right ideal in $\mathrm{Hom}_\Delta(M,M) \simeq R$, so this chain contradicts the DCC on right ideals in R. Thus, $[M:\Delta] = n < \infty$. It is now clear from Section 7.5 that $R \simeq \Delta_n$.

II. *Uniqueness:* It remains to prove that if $R \simeq \Delta_n \simeq \Delta'_m$, then $n = m$ and $\Delta \simeq \Delta'$. In Δ_n we let E_i be the matrix with 0 everywhere except in the i,i position, where 1 appears. It is easy to show that $E_i\Delta_n$ is an irreducible Δ_n-module (a minimal right ideal). Thus, if we let $M_k = E_1\Delta_n + \cdots + E_k\Delta_n$, we see that $\Delta_n = M_n \supset M_{n-1} \supset \cdots \supset M_1 = E_1\Delta_n \supset M_0 = 0$ is a composition series for Δ_n of length n. By the Jordan-Hölder theorem (Theorem 7.9.22), we see that any composition series for R must have length n. Clearly, this now implies that $m = n$. Now let E'_1 be the matrix over Δ' with 0 everywhere, except 1 in the 1,1 position. Then $(E'_1)^2 = E'_1$ and $E'_1\Delta'_n$ is a minimal right ideal in $\Delta'_n \simeq R$. Now, $E'_1\Delta'_n$ and $E_1\Delta_n$ correspond to minimal right ideals in R, and so by Theorem 7.12.13, $E'_1\Delta'_n$ and $E_1\Delta_n$ correspond to isomorphic minimal right ideals in R, say eR and fR, respectively. But then it is easy to see that

$$\Delta' \simeq E'_1\Delta'_nE'_1 \simeq eRe \simeq fRf \quad \text{(by Theorem 7.13.4)} \simeq E_1\Delta_nE_1 \simeq \Delta,$$

and this concludes the proof.

We can now give an immediate characterization of a semisimple ring in terms of matrix rings.

Theorem 7.13.6 Wedderburn Let R be a semisimple ring. Then there exist division rings $\Delta^{(i)}$, $i = 1,\cdots,m$, and integers n_i, $i = 1,\cdots,m$, such that $R \simeq \Delta_{n_1}{}^{(1)} \oplus \cdots \oplus \Delta_{n_m}{}^{(m)}$.

Proof: In the notation of Theorem 7.12.11, $R = A_1 \dotplus \cdots \dotplus A_m$, and each $A_i \simeq \Delta_{n_i}{}^{(i)}$ by Theorem 7.13.5.

One observation at this time is quite pertinent. In Theorem 7.12.11, we saw that $A_1 = e_{11}R \dotplus \cdots \dotplus e_{1n_1}R$. By Wedderburn's theorem, $A_1 \simeq \Delta_n$, for some n. But this n is clearly equal to n_1, as the Jordan-Hölder theorem shows. Indeed, it is not hard to see that if $eR \simeq fR$, where the e and f are idempotents and eR and fR are minimal right ideals, then $[eR:eRe] = [fR:fRf]$, where R is a semisimple ring.

We conclude this section by giving some standard terminology that we have not so far employed.

Idempotents e and f are called *orthogonal* if $ef = fe = 0$. We say that $e \neq 0$ is a *primitive* idempotent if e cannot be written $e = e_1 + e_2$, where e_1 and e_2 are nonzero orthogonal idempotents. Thus, all of the e_{ij} used in Theorem 7.12.11 were primitive idempotents and any two of them were orthogonal. We also discovered that if R is semisimple, then the identity is the sum of *mutually* orthogonal primitive idempotents.

Exercises

1. Complete the details of the proof of Theorem 7.13.3.
2. Let R be a simple ring with eR and fR minimal right ideals, e and f idempotents. Show that $\mathrm{Hom}_R(eR,fR) = fRe$.
3. Let R be a simple ring and let eR be a minimal right ideal in R, $e^2 = e \neq 0$. Prove that $eR = eRe + eR(1 - e)$ is a vector space direct sum decomposition of R, where $eR(1 - e) = \{er - ere \mid r \in R\}$. Thus conclude that the mapping $T: eR \to eR$ defined by $(ere)T = ere$ and $(er - ere)T = 0$, is in $\mathrm{Hom}_\Delta(eR,eR)$, where $\Delta = eRe$.
4. In the proof of Wedderburn's theorem, reprove that $[M:\Delta] = n < \infty$ by using the following technique. Let $S = \{T \in \mathrm{Hom}_\Delta(M,M) \mid [\mathrm{Im}\, T:\Delta] < \infty\}$. Show that
   i) S is a two-sided ideal in $\mathrm{Hom}_\Delta(M,M) = R$, and
   ii) $S \neq 0$. Thus, conclude that since R is simple, $S = R$, whence $1 \in S$, and so M is finite dimensional.
5. Let R be a simple ring with 1 and with a minimal right ideal I. Prove that $R \simeq \Delta_n$, for some division ring Δ and integer n. Thus, conclude that a simple ring with 1 and with one minimal right ideal must satisfy the DCC on right ideals.

7.14 COMPLETELY REDUCIBLE MODULES

We saw in Theorem 7.12.15 that any module over a semisimple ring is the sum of irreducible submodules. By properly generalizing the definition of direct sum, we shall see that a module is a sum of irreducible submodules if and only if it is a direct sum of irreducible submodules. Moreover, we shall prove that if R is a ring with 1 such that every

R-module is the sum of irreducible modules, then R is semisimple. To achieve our results we shall use Zorn's lemma in an important way.

For the first few definitions and theorems of this section, R will be an arbitrary ring, not necessarily with 1.

Definition 7.14.1 Let M be a right R-module such that M is the sum of irreducible submodules. We say that M is *completely reducible*.

We regard the module 0 as a sum of zero irreducible submodules, so it is also completely reducible.

Definition 7.14.2 Let $\{M_\lambda\}$ be a collection of R-modules, indexed by a set Λ. Let f be a function with domain Λ such that $(\lambda)f \in M_\lambda$, all λ, and $(\lambda)f \neq 0$ for at most a finite number of the λ's. Then the set of all such functions is called the *direct sum* $\Sigma \oplus M_\lambda$ of the M_λ's.

For f_1 and f_2 in $\Sigma \oplus M_\lambda$, we see that $f_1 + f_2 \in \Sigma \oplus M_\lambda$, where $(\lambda)(f_1 + f_2) = (\lambda)f_1 + (\lambda)f_2$. Also for $r \in R$, we define $f_1 r$ by $(\lambda)(f_1 r) = [(\lambda)f_1]r$. It is easy to see that $\Sigma \oplus M_\lambda$ is a right R-module.

In the event that Λ is finite, say $\Lambda = \{\lambda_1,\cdots,\lambda_n\}$, we can identify each $f \in \Sigma \oplus M_\lambda$ with an element of $M_{\lambda_1} \oplus \cdots \oplus M_{\lambda_n}$, as defined in Definition 7.9.15 and Exercise 16, Section 7.9. Namely, we let f correspond to $((\lambda_1)f,\cdots,(\lambda_n)f)$. Thus, we can consider $\Sigma \oplus M_\lambda$ and $M_{\lambda_1} \oplus \cdots \oplus M_{\lambda_n}$ to be identical. In addition, if $\Lambda = P = \{1,2,\cdots,n,\cdots\}$, an element of $\Sigma \oplus M_\lambda$ may be thought of as a sequence $(m_1,\cdots,m_n,\cdots)$, where at most a finite number of the m_i's are not zero.

Now let M be an R-module and $\{M_\lambda\}$ a collection of R-submodules such that $M = \Sigma M_\lambda$ and such that if $x \in M$, $x \neq 0$, then x can be expressed in only one way as a finite sum: $x = m_{\lambda_1} + \cdots + m_{\lambda_k}$, $m_{\lambda_i} \neq 0$. With this condition, which of course generalizes the notion of linear independence, it is easy to show that $M \simeq \Sigma \oplus M_\lambda$. In this case, we say that M is the *internal direct sum* of the M_λ's and we denote this by $M = \Sigma \dotplus M_\lambda$. For convenience, we make a special convention. We will let 0 be denoted by $\sum\limits_{\lambda \in \phi} \dotplus M_\lambda$, and so $\Sigma \dotplus M_\lambda$ may at times be equal to the zero module.

Definition 7.14.3 Let M be an R-module. If $M = N \dotplus N'$, then we say that N' is a *complement* of N in M.

We now come to one of the main results of this section.

Theorem 7.14.4 Let M be a completely reducible R-module, and let N be a submodule of M. Then

i) N has a complement N' in M, and

ii) $N' = \Sigma \dot{+} M_\mu$, where $\{M_\mu\}$ is a subset of the set of irreducible submodules of M. (It may be that $\Sigma \dot{+} M_\mu = 0$).

Proof: We shall use Zorn's lemma in proving this theorem.

Let $\mathfrak{F}$ be the collection of all submodules K of M such that i) $N \cap K = 0$ and ii) K is the direct sum of irreducible submodules of M. Clearly, $\mathfrak{F} \neq \phi$, since $0 \in \mathfrak{F}$. We can partially order $\mathfrak{F}$ as follows: If $K_1 = \Sigma \dot{+} M_\tau$ and $K_2 = \Sigma \dot{+} M_\nu$ are in $\mathfrak{F}$, then $K_1 \leq K_2$ if $\{M_\tau\} \subseteq \{M_\nu\}$, that is, if the indices λ form a subset of the indices ν. Now let $\mathfrak{C}$ be a chain in $\mathfrak{F}$, say $\mathfrak{C} = \{K_\alpha\}$. Then $\bigcup_{K_\alpha \in \mathfrak{C}} K_\alpha$ is an element in $\mathfrak{F}$ and is an upper bound for $\mathfrak{C}$. By Zorn's lemma, $\mathfrak{F}$ has a maximal element, say $\Sigma \dot{+} M_\mu$.

Now let M_λ be an irreducible submodule of M. If $M_\lambda \cap [N \dot{+} (\Sigma \dot{+} M_\mu)] \neq 0$, then $M_\lambda \subseteq N \dot{+} (\Sigma \dot{+} M_\mu)$, since M_λ is irreducible (see Exercise 4, Section 7.10). If $M_\lambda \cap [N \dot{+} (\Sigma \dot{+} M_\mu)] = 0$, then $M_\lambda \dot{+} (\Sigma \dot{+} M_\mu) \in \mathfrak{F}$, contradicting the maximality of $\Sigma \dot{+} M_\mu$. Thus, every irreducible submodule $M_\lambda \subseteq N \dot{+} (\Sigma \dot{+} M_\mu)$ and so $M = N \dot{+} (\Sigma \dot{+} M_\mu)$.

Corollary 7.14.5 Let M be a completely reducible R-module. Then $M = \Sigma \dot{+} M_\mu$, where $\{M_\mu\}$ is a collection of irreducible submodules of M.

Proof: In Theorem 7.14.4, we let $N = 0$. Then $M = N' = \Sigma \dot{+} M_\mu$.

Corollary 7.14.6 Let M be a completely reducible R-module. Then every homomorphic image of M is completely reducible and every submodule of M is completely reducible.

Proof: Let $M = \Sigma M_\lambda$, where the M_λ are irreducible submodules, and let $f: M \xrightarrow{\text{onto}} N$ be an R-homomorphism. Then $N = \Sigma (M_\lambda) f$. Since each $(M_\lambda) f$ is either 0 or isomorphic to M_λ (Theorem 7.10.5), N is the sum of irreducible submodules.

Now let N be a submodule of M. Then, by Theorem 7.14.4, $M = N \dot{+} N'$, whence N is R-isomorphic to the quotient module M/N'. Since M/N' is a homomorphic image of M, M/N', and hence N, is completely reducible.

The converse to Theorem 7.14.4 is also true, that is, if each submodule N of M has a complement in M, then M is completely reducible. Before proving this, we first prove a lemma.

Lemma 7.14.7 Let M be an R-module such that every submodule N of M has a complement N' in M. Then every submodule P of M also has this property.

Proof: Let X be a submodule of P. Since X is also a submodule of M, there exists Y such that $M = X \dot{+} Y$. Since $P \subseteq M$, $P = P \cap M$

$= P \cap (X \dot{+} Y)$. We claim that

$$(*)\ P \cap (X \dot{+} Y) = (P \cap X) \dot{+} (P \cap Y).$$

Since $X \subseteq P$, we have $P \cap X = X$, so that this equality is equivalent to

$$(**)\ P = P \cap (X \dot{+} Y) = X \dot{+} (P \cap Y),$$

which would show that $P \cap Y$ is a complement of X in P.

To show (*), let $x \in P \cap (X \dot{+} Y)$. Then $x = x_1 + y_1$, $x_1 \in X$, $y_1 \in Y$, and $x \in P$. Since $x_1 \in P$ also, $y_1 = x - x_1 \in P$. Thus, $y_1 \in P \cap Y$ and so $x \in X \dot{+} (P \cap Y)$, whence

$$P \cap (X \dot{+} Y) \subseteq (P \cap X) \dot{+} (P \cap Y).$$

Next, let $x \in (P \cap X) \dot{+} (P \cap Y)$. Then $x = x_1 + y_1$, $x_1 \in P \cap X$ and $y_1 \in P \cap Y$. Then $x_1 + y_1 \in P$ and also $x_1 + y_1 \in X \dot{+} Y$. Thus, $x \in P \cap (X \dot{+} Y)$ and the proof is completed.

Theorem 7.14.8 Let M be an R-module, and suppose every submodule N of M has a complement N'. Then M is completely reducible.

Proof: We first show that M contains an irreducible submodule. Suppose M is itself not irreducible and let $x \in M$. Then let $\mathfrak{F}$ be the collection of all submodules M' of M such that $x \notin M'$. By Zorn's lemma, $\mathfrak{F}$ has a maximal element, say X. By hypotheses, $M = X \dot{+} Y$, for some Y. Now if Y is not irreducible, then, since Y satisfies the same hypotheses as M (by Lemma 7.14.7), $Y = W \dot{+} V$. Thus, $M = X \dot{+} W \dot{+} V$ and either $x \notin X \dot{+} W$ or $x \notin X \dot{+} V$, in each case contradicting the maximality of X. Thus, Y is irreducible.

Now take the collection $\{M_\lambda\}$ of all irreducible submodules of M. Then ΣM_λ is a submodule of M, whence $M = (\Sigma M_\lambda) \dot{+} N$, for some submodule N. If $N \neq (0)$, then by the above paragraph, N has an irreducible submodule, contradicting that $(\Sigma M_\lambda) \cap N = 0$. Thus, $N = 0$, and the proof is complete.

We are now ready to give another characterization of semisimple rings.

Theorem 7.14.9 Let $R \ni 1$. Then R is semisimple if and only if every R-module is completely reducible.

Proof: Let $R \ni 1$, and let R be semisimple. Then every R-module is completely reducible by Theorem 7.12.15.

Conversely, suppose that every R-module is completely reducible. Then, in particular, R_R (R as a module over itself) is completely reducible, and $R_R = \Sigma \dot{+} I_\lambda$, where each I_λ is a minimal right ideal in R. Since $1 \in R_R$, there is a unique way of writing $1 = i_1 + \cdots + i_n$, where $i_j \neq 0$

and $i_j \in I_j$ (and where the choice of subscripts is also unique). Then for $a \in R_R$, $a = 1 \cdot a = i_1 a + \cdots + i_n a$, whence $R \subseteq I_1 \dotplus \cdots \dotplus I_n$. Thus, $R = I_1 \dotplus \cdots \dotplus I_n$. Since each I_n is an irreducible R-module, R clearly has a composition series and hence satisfies the DCC on right ideals. Finally, if N = radical of R, then $N = 1 \cdot N \subseteq RN = (I_1 \dotplus \cdots \dotplus I_n)N = 0$, since each $I_j N = 0$ by Theorem 7.12.16. Thus, $N = 0$ and R is semisimple.

As a result of the theorems in this section, we can now prove a theorem due to Maschke, useful in the theory of group representations. In Example 5.1.10 the concept of a group ring was defined. If K is a field and G is a finite group, it turns out that $K(G)$ is semisimple, provided char $K \nmid |G|$. In order to prove this result it will be convenient to make several conventions. First, suppose M is a $K(G)$-module. By putting $m\alpha = m(\alpha e)$, for all $m \in M$, $\alpha \in K$, where e is the identity of G, we can consider M as a right vector space over K. Second, suppose M and N are two $K(G)$-modules. We shall write all functions $T: M \to N$ to the right of the elements of M, even if T is a $K(G)$-homomorphism. Thus, for the purposes of proving Maschke's theorem, T is a $K(G)$-homomorphism if T is a homomorphism of $(M,+)$ and if $(mr)T = (mT)r$, for all $m \in M$, $r \in K(G)$. This latter convention will make our notation more aesthetically pleasing in the next theorem.

We recall one simple fact concerning a group G. If y is fixed in G, then xy^{-1} takes on all values in G as x varies over G.

Theorem 7.14.10 Maschke Let G be a finite group, and let K be a field such that char $K \nmid |G|$. Then the group ring $K(G)$ is semisimple.

Proof: Since $1e$ (1 the identity of K and e the identity of G) is the identity for $K(G)$, it suffices, by Theorem 7.14.9, to prove that every $K(G)$-module M is completely reducible. By Theorem 7.14.8, M is completely reducible if every $K(G)$-submodule N of M has a complement N' in M, where N' is also a $K(G)$-submodule of M. Thus, let M be a $K(G)$-module and N a $K(G)$-submodule of M. Since M and N can also be considered right vector spaces over K, there exists, by Theorem 7.4.2, a right vector subspace W of M such that $M = N \dotplus W$, where this is a vector space direct sum (according to Definition 7.9.17). Since each $m \in M$ can be written uniquely as $m = n + w$, $n \in N$, $w \in W$, there exists an $E \in \operatorname{Hom}_K(M,N)$ such that $mE = n$. Moreover, it is easy to see that $\operatorname{Im} E = N$ and that E restricted to N (that is, $E \mid N$) is the identity on N.

The function E may not be a $K(G)$-homomorphism from M to N, so we will "average" over the group G to get a function F that will have these properties: i) F is a $K(G)$-homomorphism from M to N, ii) $F \mid N = 1_N$, the identity on N. We define F as follows: $F = \dfrac{1}{|G|}\sum_{x \in G} x^{-1}Ex$. A word or two is perhaps necessary so that we fully understand F. First, since char $K \nmid |G|$, $\dfrac{1}{|G|} \in K$. Second, for any $x \in G$, $m \in M$, we have $m(x^{-1}Ex) = [(mx^{-1})E]x$. This must be an element of N: for $mx^{-1} \in M$, since M is a $K(G)$-module; $(mx^{-1})E \in N$, by definition of E; and $[(mx^{-1})E]x \in N$, since N is a $K(G)$-module. Third, if $G = \{x_1, \cdots, x_r\}$, then

$$mF = m\frac{1}{|G|}\sum_{x \in G} x^{-1}Ex$$

$$= \frac{1}{|G|}(mx_1{}^{-1}Ex_1 + mx_2{}^{-1}Ex_2 + \cdots + mx_r{}^{-1}Ex_r).$$

To show that F is a $K(G)$-homomorphism, let $m \in M$ and let $y \in G$. Then

$$(my)F = \frac{1}{|G|}\sum_{x \in G} my(x^{-1}Ex) = \frac{1}{|G|}\sum_{x \in G} [(myx^{-1})E]x$$

$$= \frac{1}{|G|}\sum_{x \in G} [(m(xy^{-1})^{-1})E]x,$$

while

$$(mF)y = \frac{1}{|G|}\sum_{x \in G} [m(x^{-1}Ex)]y$$

$$= \frac{1}{|G|}\sum_{x \in G} [m((xy^{-1})^{-1}E(xy^{-1})]y$$

$$= \frac{1}{|G|}\sum_{x \in G} [(m(xy^{-1})^{-1})E]x.$$

Thus, $(my)F = (mF)y$, and this suffices to show F is a $K(G)$-homomorphism.

To show that $F \mid N$ is the identity on N, let $n \in N$. Then

$$nF = \frac{1}{|G|}\sum_{x \in G} n(x^{-1}Ex)$$

$$= \frac{1}{|G|}\sum_{x \in G} [(nx^{-1})E]x = \frac{1}{|G|}\sum_{x \in G} [nx^{-1}]x, \text{ since } E \mid N = 1_N$$

$$= \frac{1}{|G|}|G|n = n.$$

It is now easy to find a $K(G)$-module N' such that $M = N \dotplus N'$, as $K(G)$-modules. In fact, $N' = M(1 - F) = \{m - mF \mid m \in M\}$ is the desired module. We let the reader show this, and it may be helpful to realize that since $N = MF$, this means $M = MF \dot{+} M(1 - F)$. This completes the proof that $K(G)$ is semisimple.

In Theorem 7.14.10, the condition that char $K \nmid |G|$ is essential. Even in the most trivial example, when $K = Z_2$ and $G = C_2 = \{e,a\}$, with $a^2 = e$, we get a counterexample. For the element $e + a$ is nilpotent ($(e + a)^2 = 0$), and, since $Z_2(C_2)$ is commutative, the radical of $Z_2(C_2)$ is not zero, whence $Z_2(C_2)$ is not semisimple.

Exercises

1. Let R_1 and R_2 be rings such that $R_1 \subseteq R_2$ and such that R_1 and R_2 have the same identity.
   - **i)** Show that any R_2-module may also be considered an R_1-module.
   - **ii)** Show by example that an irreducible R_2-module need not be an irreducible R_1-module.
   - **iii)** Show that if M is an irreducible R_1-module, then M is an irreducible R_2-module.

2. Let M be a module with submodules N_1 and N_2. Suppose that N_1 and N_2 are completely reducible. Show that
   - **i)** $N_1 \cap N_2$ is completely reducible.
   - **ii)** $N_1 \oplus N_2$ is completely reducible, whence if $N_1 \cap N_2 = (0)$, then $N_1 \dot{+} N_2$ is completely reducible.

3. Let $(G, +)$ be an abelian group written additively. Prove that
   - **i)** G can be considered a Z-module, with Z the integers.
   - **ii)** There exists an abelian group G with a subgroup H such that H does not have a complement (as direct sum) in G. (Do not exhibit such a G—this could be easily done—but give an argument using facts about the ring Z).

4. Prove that if G is a finite group and K a field, then the group ring $K(G)$ satisfies the DCC on right ideals, regardless of char K.

5. Prove that if G is a finite group and if K is a field such that char $K \mid |G|$, then $K(G)$ has a nonzero radical and hence is not semisimple.

   Hint: Assume that char $K = p$ and that $|G| = pm$. Let $G = \{g_1, \cdots, g_{pm}\}$. Let $s = g_1 + \cdots + g_{pm}$. Show that $g_i s = s g_i = s$ for $g_i \in G$ and also show that $s^2 = ss = pms$, that is, $s + s + \cdots + s$, pm times. Show that $sK(G)$ is a nilpotent right ideal in $K(G)$.

7.15 HOPKINS' THEOREM AND "RIGHT VERSUS LEFT"

The rings Z and $Z_p(\infty)$ show that it is possible for either the ACC or the DCC to hold in a ring without the other also holding. However, if

$R \ni 1$, then the DCC in R implies the ACC. We shall prove this important result, which is due to C. Hopkins.

Lemma 7.15.1 Let M be an R-module and suppose M satisfies either the ACC or DCC on submodules. Then M is completely reducible if and only if M is the direct sum of finitely many irreducible submodules.

Proof: If $M = M_1 \dotplus \cdots \dotplus M_n$, where the M_i are irreducible, then clearly, M is completely reducible.

Now let M be completely reducible. Then $M = \Sigma \dotplus M_\lambda$, where the M_λ are irreducible. If Λ, the set of indices λ, is infinite, we may assume that $\{1,2,\cdots,n,\cdots\} \subseteq \Lambda$. We see that $M_1 \subseteq M_1 \dotplus M_2 \subset M_1 \dotplus M_2 \dotplus M_3 \subset \cdots$ violates the ACC, while $\sum_{i=1}^{\infty} \dotplus M_i \supset \sum_{i=2}^{\infty} \dotplus M_i \supset \sum_{i=3}^{\infty} \dotplus M_i \supset \cdots$ violates the DCC. Thus, M is the direct sum of finitely many irreducible modules.

Theorem 7.15.2 Hopkins Let R be a ring with 1 and DCC on right ideals. Then R satisfies the ACC on right ideals.

Proof: By Theorem 7.9.23, we need only prove that R has a composition series of right ideals.

We begin by observing that if N is the radical of R, then $R = N^0 \supset N \supset N^2 \supset \cdots \supset N^{m-1} \supset N^m = 0$, where m is the smallest integer such that $N^m = 0$. We form the quotient modules R/N, $N/N^2,\cdots,N^{m-1}/N^m$ and observe that each of these is a right R-module. Moreover, $(N^i/N^{i+1})N = 0$, so each N^i/N^{i+1} is a sum of irreducible R-modules, by Theorem 7.12.16. Thus, $N^i/N^{i+1} = \Sigma(x_\alpha + N^{i+1})R$, where each $(x_\alpha + N^{i+1})R$ is an irreducible submodule of N^i/N^{i+1}. Since R satisfies the DCC on right R-ideals, so does R/N^{i+1} and hence also N^i/N^{i+1} satisfies the DCC on R-submodules, and so $N^i/N^{i+1} = \sum_{j=1}^{n_i} \dotplus (x_j + N^{i+1})R$. Clearly,

$$N^i = \sum_{j=1}^{n_i} (x_jR + N^{i+1})$$

and $N^i \supset \sum_{j=2}^{n_i} (x_jR + N^{i+1}) \supset \sum_{j=3}^{n_i} (x_jR + N^{i+1}) \supset \cdots \supset N^{i+1}$

is a finite descending chain of right ideals in R that cannot be refined, that is, it is impossible to insert any other right ideal between two of the terms in this chain (because of the irreducibility of $(x_\alpha + N^{i+1})R$ in N^i/N^{i+1}). Putting all of these sequences, for $i = 0,\cdots,m-1$, together, we get a composition series for R, and so R satisfies the ACC.

As the reader is so well aware, all of our work so far has been concerned with right ideals and right modules. A natural question is: What theorems hold if all of our assumptions are made for left ideals and left modules instead of "right." The answer is very simple: Given a theorem we have proved, replacing "right" everywhere it appears by "left" results in another theorem. We will let the reader make the necessary verifications in the proofs. We simply go over one point that may be helpful.

Recall that if V is a left vector space over Δ, $[V:\Delta] = n < \infty$, then $\mathrm{Hom}_\Delta(V,V)$ is isomorphic to Δ_n. In showing this, we let $(e_1,\cdots,e_n)$ be a basis for V, we let $T \in \mathrm{Hom}_\Delta(V,V)$, we write $e_iT = \sum_{j=1}^{n} \alpha_{ij}e_j$, and we let T correspond to the matrix

$$\begin{bmatrix} \alpha_{11} & \cdots\cdots & \alpha_{1n} \\ \vdots & & \\ \alpha_{n1} & \cdots\cdots & \alpha_{nn} \end{bmatrix}$$

Now let $\{f_1,\cdots,f_n\}$ be a basis for the right vector space V over Δ. We now write linear transformations to the left of elements of V, that is, if $T \in \mathrm{Hom}_\Delta(V,V)$,

$$T(v\delta) = [T(v)]\delta, \quad \delta \in \Delta.$$

Now for f_i, we let

$$T(f_i) = \sum_{j=1}^{n} f_j\delta_{ji}$$

and consider the matrix

$$\tau = \begin{bmatrix} \delta_{11} & \cdots\cdots & \delta_{1n} \\ \vdots & & \\ \delta_{n1} & \cdots\cdots & \delta_{nn} \end{bmatrix}$$

Now let $S \in \mathrm{Hom}_\Delta(V,V)$, and write $S(f_i) = \sum_{j=1}^{n} f_j\gamma_{ji}$, and consider the matrix

$$\sigma = \begin{bmatrix} \gamma_{11} & \cdots\cdots & \gamma_{1n} \\ \vdots & & \\ \gamma_{n1} & \cdots\cdots & \gamma_{nn} \end{bmatrix}$$

We form the composite linear transformation $S \circ T$ and wish to show that the matrix for $S \circ T$ is simply $\sigma\tau$. Thus,

$$\begin{aligned} S \circ T(f_i) &= S\left(\sum_{j=1}^{n} f_j \delta_{ji}\right) \\ &= \sum_{j=1}^{n} S(f_j \delta_{ji}) = \sum_{j=1}^{n} S(f_j)\delta_{ji} \\ &= \sum_{j=1}^{n}\left(\sum_{k=1}^{n} f_k \gamma_{kj}\right)\delta_{ji} = \sum_{k=1}^{n}\sum_{j=1}^{n} f_k \gamma_{kj}\delta_{ji}. \end{aligned}$$

Thus, the k,ith entry of the matrix for $S \circ T$ is simply $\sum_{j=1}^{n} \gamma_{kj}\delta_{ji}$, which we observe is the product of the kth row of σ by the ith column of τ. Thus, the matrix for $S \circ T$ is $\sigma\tau$.

As we did in Section 7.5, we can now show that $\text{Hom}_\Delta(V, V)$ is isomorphic to Δ_n.

As a result of this discussion we get some interesting corollaries.

Corollary 7.15.3 Let R be a ring with radical zero and with DCC on left ideals. Then $R \cong \Delta_{n_1}{}^{(1)} \oplus \cdots \oplus \Delta_{n_m}{}^{(m)}$, where $\Delta^{(i)}$ is a division ring, $i = 1, \cdots, m$.

Proof: We simply check to see that all of the proofs leading to Theorem 7.13.6 still carry through when "right" is replaced by "left."

Corollary 7.15.4 Let R be a ring with DCC on either left or right ideals, and with radical zero. Then if $R \cong \Delta_{n_1}{}^{(1)} \oplus \cdots \oplus \Delta_{n_m}{}^{(m)}$, there exists a set of m nonisomorphic irreducible left R-modules and a set of m nonisomorphic irreducible right R-modules. Moreover, in neither case can we find such sets with $m + 1$ left or right R-modules.

Proof: Using the techniques of sections 7.12 and 7.13, we see that this decomposition of R is unique up to isomorphism whether this decomposition is obtained using left or right DCC. We leave the rest of the proof as an exercise.

Exercises

1. Prove Corollary 7.15.4.
2. Let M be an R-module and suppose $M = M_1 \dotplus M_2 \dotplus \cdots \dotplus M_n$, where each M_i is an irreducible R-module. Prove that M has a composition series.
3. Prove that every proper ideal in $Z_p(\infty)$ is finite. Hence, show by example that every proper submodule of a module M may satisfy the ACC, yet M need not satisfy the ACC.

4. Prove that if M is a module such that every proper submodule satisfies the DCC on submodules, then so does M.
5. Use the construction in Theorem 5.7.8 to embed $Z_p(\infty)$ in a ring with 1. Show that this ring does not satisfy ACC, and hence by Theorem 7.15.2, this ring does not satisfy the DCC. Thus, conclude that a ring without 1 may satisfy DCC, but when embedded in a ring with 1, the new ring need not satisfy DCC.
6. Let R be semisimple and let e be an idempotent in R. Prove that eR is a minimal right ideal if and only if Re is a minimal left ideal.
7. Let R be semisimple and let e be an idempotent in R. Prove that eR is a minimal right ideal if and only if eRe is a division ring. (By symmetry, we can show Re is a minimal left ideal if and only if eRe is a division ring. This would give another proof of 6.)
8. Let R be a simple ring satisfying the following conditions:
   i) eR is a minimal right ideal
   ii) there does not exist an infinite ascending chain $I_1 \subset I_2 \subset I_3 \subset \cdots$, where each I_j is an internal direct sum of right ideals of R.
   Prove that Re is a finite dimensional left vector space over the division ring eRe.

   Hint: Show that if $u_1, \cdots, u_n$ in Re are linearly independent over eRe, then $u_1R \dotplus \cdots \dotplus u_nR$ is an internal direct sum of right ideals. Apply condition ii).
9. Show that a simple ring R with DCC on right ideals satisfies the hypotheses of Exercise 8.
10. An R-module M is called *faithful* if $Mr = \{mr \mid m \in M\} = 0$ implies $r = 0$, where $r \in R$. Prove that if R is simple with DCC on right ideals, then there exists a faithful, irreducible R-module. Prove that if R is semisimple, but not simple, then no irreducible R-module is faithful.
11. A ring R is called *primitive* if there exists a faithful, irreducible R-module. Prove that the following example is a primitive ring but not simple.

    Example: Let M be an infinite dimensional vector space over a field F, and with basis elements $\{m_1, m_2, \cdots, m_n, \cdots\}$ that can be put in 1–1 correspondence with the positive integers. Let $R = \text{Hom}_F(M,M)$ and consider M to be an R-module. Show that M is a faithful, irreducible R-module. Use Exercise 4, Section 7.13, to show that R is not simple.

7.16 PROJECTIVE AND INJECTIVE MODULES

Since the 1940s, a new branch of algebra, known as homological algebra, has attracted the attention of a great many investigators. Although its origins lie in algebraic topology, it now has a wholly algebraic flavor. In this section we shall introduce two types of modules that arise in homological algebra, and we shall give two characterizations of semisimple rings in terms of these modules.

Throughout this section we shall assume that R is a ring with identity. We shall also once again write all functions to the right of elements, even if the functions are R-homomorphisms of R-modules.

To begin, let $\cdots A_{-n}, \cdots, A_{-1}, A_0, A_1, \cdots, A_m, \cdots$ be a sequence (finite or infinite) of R-modules and, for each integer n, let $f_n: A_n \to A_{n+1}$ be a R-homomorphism. This situation is depicted by either

$$\cdots \xrightarrow{f_{-2}} A_{-1} \xrightarrow{f_{-1}} A_0 \xrightarrow{f_0} A_1 \xrightarrow{f_1} \cdots \xrightarrow{f_{n-1}} A_n \xrightarrow{f_n} \cdots$$

or

$$\cdots \to A_{-1} \to A_0 \to A_1 \to \cdots \to A_n \to \cdots.$$

If $\operatorname{Im} f_n = \ker f_{n+1}$, we say the sequence is *exact* at A_{n+1}. If the sequence is exact at each A_n, then the sequence is called an *exact* sequence.

In particular, an exact sequence

$$0 \to A \xrightarrow{f} B \xrightarrow{g} C \to 0$$

is called a *short* exact sequence. It is clear that exactness at C implies $\operatorname{Im} g = C$, whence g is onto, while exactness at A implies $\ker f = 0$, whence f is 1–1.

Now let A, B, C, D be modules with homomorphisms $f: A \to B$, $g': A \to C, f': C \to D$, and $g: B \to D$. This is portrayed in the diagram

$$\begin{array}{ccc} A & \xrightarrow{f} & B \\ {\scriptstyle g'}\downarrow & & \downarrow{\scriptstyle g} \\ C & \xrightarrow{f'} & D \end{array}$$

We say this diagram *commutes*, or is *commutative*, if $f \circ g = g' \circ f'$. A diagram

$$\begin{array}{ccc} A & \xrightarrow{f} & B \\ & {\scriptstyle h}\searrow & \downarrow{\scriptstyle g} \\ & & C \end{array}$$

is called *commutative* if $f \circ g = h$.

The diagram

$$\begin{array}{ccccc} & & D & & \\ & & \downarrow{\scriptstyle h} & & \\ A & \xrightarrow[f]{} & B & \xrightarrow[g]{} & C \end{array}$$

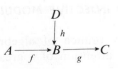

is said to be *completed* to the diagram

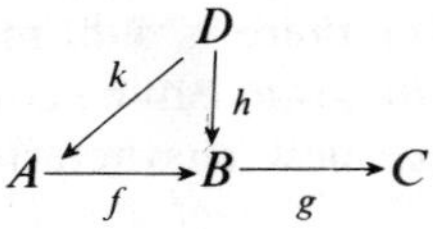

if

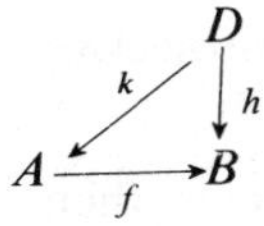

commutes. Similar definitions hold in analogous situations.

We are now ready to define two important types of modules.

Definition 7.16.1 Let P be an R-module. P is called a *projective R-module* if every diagram

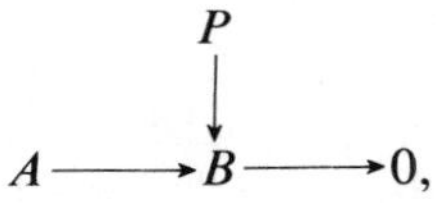

in which $A \to B \to 0$ is exact, can be completed to a commutative diagram

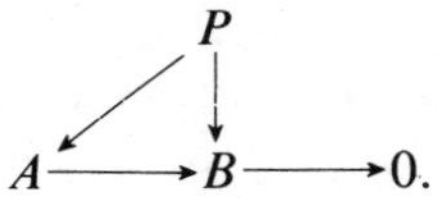

By reversing the arrows in the above diagrams, we get the "dual" concept, namely, that of injective module.

Definition 7.16.2 Let Q be an R-module. Q is said to be an *injective R*-module if every diagram

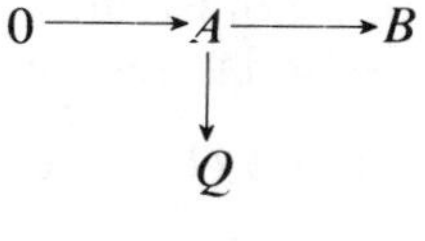

in which $0 \to A \to B$ is exact, can be completed to a commutative diagram

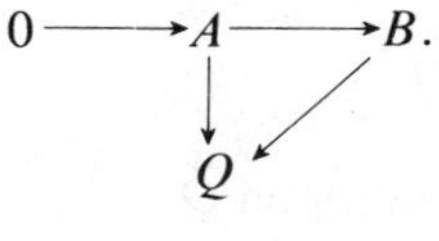

We should note in the above definitions that we do not claim there are nontrivial homomorphisms $f: P \to B$, say, whenever $A \to B \to 0$ is exact. We claim only that whenever there is a homomorphism $f: P \to B$, with $A \to B \to 0$ exact, then the diagram can be completed.

Of use to us in getting our new characterizations of semisimple rings is the following lemma.

Lemma 7.16.3 Let P be a projective R-module and Q an injective R-module.

i) Whenever $M \xrightarrow{g} P \to 0$ is exact, then $M = \ker g \dotplus N$, where N is a submodule of M isomorphic to P.

ii) If $0 \to Q \xrightarrow{f} M$ is exact, then $M = \operatorname{Im} f \dotplus N$, where $\operatorname{Im} f$ is a submodule of M isomorphic to Q. In particular, whenever Q is an injective submodule of M, Q is a direct summand of M.

Proof:

i) Since $M \to P \to 0$ is exact and P is projective, we can complete

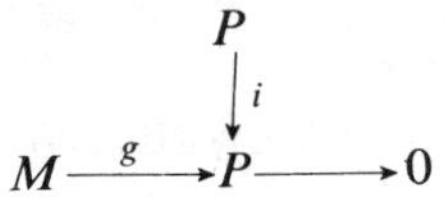

where i is the identity on P, to

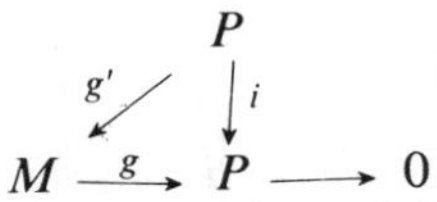

where $g' \circ g = i$. Now for $x \in M$, $xg \in P$, say $xg = y$, whence $xg = y = (y)i = (y)(g' \circ g) = (yg')g$. Thus, $(x - yg')g = 0$, and so $x - yg' \in \ker g$. Hence, $x \in \operatorname{Im} g' + \ker g$. To show that $M = \operatorname{Im} g' \dotplus \ker g$, we need to show that $\operatorname{Im} g' \cap \ker g = 0$. If $x \in \operatorname{Im} g' \cap \ker g$, then there exists $y \in P$ such that $yg' = x$, whence $y = (y)i = (yg')g = xg = 0$. Thus, $yg' = 0$, and so $\operatorname{Im} g' \cap \ker g = 0$.

To complete the proof of i), we must show $\operatorname{Im} g' \simeq P$. Since $g'g$ is the identity on P, g' is 1–1 by Exercise 11, Section 3.1. Thus, $\operatorname{Im} g' \simeq P$.

ii) Since $0 \to Q \xrightarrow{f} M$ is exact and Q is injective, there exists $f': M \to Q$ such that

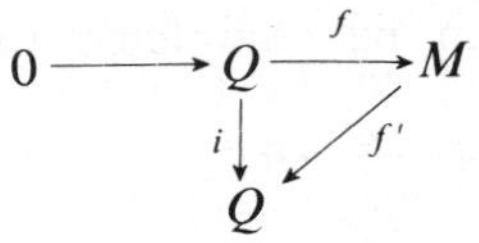

commutes, where i is the identity on Q.

Now for $x \in M$, $xf' \in Q$, so $xf' = y \in Q$. Thus, $xf' = y = (y)i = (y)(f \circ f') = (yf)f'$ whence $(x - yf)f' = 0$ and $x - yf \in \ker f'$. Thus, $x \in \operatorname{Im} f + \ker f'$ and $M = \operatorname{Im} f + \ker f'$. Suppose $x \in \operatorname{Im} f \cap \ker f'$. Since $x \in \operatorname{Im} f$, there exists $y \in Q$ such that $yf = x$. Then $y = (y)i = (y)(f \circ f') = (yf)f' = xf' = 0$, since $x \in \ker f'$. Thus, $\operatorname{Im} f \cap \ker f' = 0$ and $M = \operatorname{Im} f \dotplus \ker f'$.

By the exactness of $0 \to Q \to M$, f is 1–1 and $\operatorname{Im} f \cong Q$.

If Q is an injective submodule of M, then $0 \to Q \xrightarrow{f} M$, where $xf = x$, all $x \in Q$, is exact, and so $M = \operatorname{Im} f \dotplus \ker f' = Q \dotplus \ker f'$, since in this case $Q = \operatorname{Im} f$. This completes the proof.

It is interesting to note that the converses to i) and ii) are also true and can be used to characterize injective and projective modules. Thus, Q is injective if and only if whenever Q (or an isomorphic image of Q) is contained as a submodule of some module M, then Q (or its isomorphic image) is a direct summand of M. P is projective if and only if P is a direct summand of a *free* R-module (see exercises 14 and 16). We shall leave the proof of these facts to the exercises. Needless to say, these characterizations of injective and projective are at least equally important to those given in our definitions.

We may now easily prove two additional characterizations of semisimple rings.

Theorem 7.16.4 Let R be a ring with 1. Then the following conditions are equivalent.

i) R is semisimple

ii) Every R-module is projective

iii) Every R-module is injective.

Proof: 1. i) implies ii). Assume that R is semisimple, and let P be any R-module. We must show that P is projective. Thus, let $A \to B \to 0$ be exact and let

$$(*) \qquad \begin{array}{ccccc} & & P & & \\ & & \downarrow{\scriptstyle p} & & \\ A & \xrightarrow[f]{} & B & \longrightarrow & 0 \end{array}$$

be given. Since R is semisimple, P is completely reducible, say $P = \Sigma \dotplus P_\lambda$, where each P_λ is irreducible with generator x_λ. Since $x_\lambda R = P_\lambda$, we know how an R-homomorphism p' acts on P_λ once we know $x_\lambda p'$. In addition, since $P = \Sigma \dotplus P_\lambda$, the action of p' on P is determined by the action of p' on each P_λ. Thus, we shall define p' on each x_λ so that $p'{:}P \to A$ will complete (*). Since f is onto B (by exactness at B), there exists for each x_λ an $a_\lambda \in A$ such that $a_\lambda f = x_\lambda p$. We define p' by putting

$x_\lambda p' = a_\lambda$, and it is easy to check that

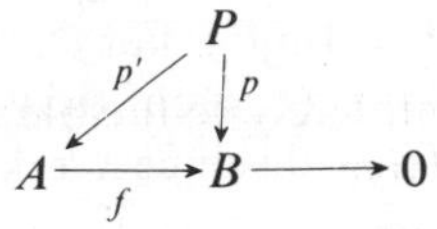

commutes. Thus, P is projective.

2. ii) implies i). Let M be an R-module. We shall show that M is completely reducible, whence, by Theorem 7.14.9, R will be semisimple. By Theorem 7.14.8, it is enough to show that if N is a submodule of M, then N has a complement in M.

Now the sequence $M \xrightarrow{\nu} M/N \to 0$ is exact, where ν is the natural homomorphism defined by $(m)\nu = m + N$, all $m \in M$. By Lemma 7.16.3, i), since $\ker \nu = N$, we have that $M = N \dotplus N'$, for some submodule N' of M. Thus, M is completely reducible and R is semisimple.

3. i) implies iii). Again, assume R is semisimple and let Q be an R-module. Suppose $0 \to A \xrightarrow{g} B$ is exact and

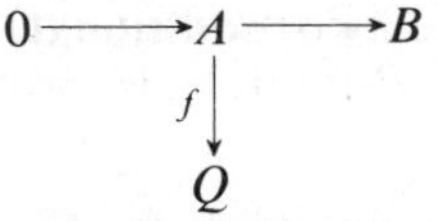

is given. Since R is semisimple, B is completely reducible, and, since $\operatorname{Im} g$ is a submodule of B, $B = \operatorname{Im} g \dotplus C$ for some submodule C. Suppose $b = ag + c$, $ag \in \operatorname{Im} g$, $c \in C$, for $b \in B$. Since g is 1–1, there is only one choice of a so that b can be represented in this manner. Thus, if we define $f' : B \to Q$ by $bf' = af$, then clearly

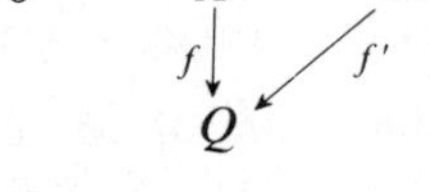

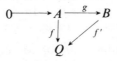

commutes and Q is injective.

4. iii) implies i). As in 2, it suffices to show that the R-module M is completely reducible. Thus, let N be a submodule of M. Since N is injective by hypothesis, N is a direct summand of M by Lemma 7.16.3, ii). Thus, M is completely reducible. This completes the proof of Theorem 7.16.4.

As a consequence of Theorem 7.16.4, it is possible to state the following.

Theorem 7.16.5 Let R be a ring with 1. Then the following conditions are equivalent.

i) R is semisimple.
ii) $R \simeq \Delta_{n_1}{}^{(1)} \oplus \cdots \oplus \Delta_{n_m}{}^{(m)}$, with each $\Delta_{n_i}{}^{(i)}$ an $n_i \times n_i$ matrix ring over a division ring $\Delta^{(i)}$.
iii) Every R-module M is completely reducible.
iv) Every R-module is projective.
v) Every R-module is injective.
vi) $R = e_1R \dotplus \cdots \dotplus e_nR$, where the e_iR are minimal right ideals, the $e_1,\cdots,e_n$ are mutually orthogonal primitive idempotents and $1 = e_1 + \cdots + e_n$.

Proof: Using our earlier theorems, we can show these are all equivalent once we demonstrate that vi) implies i). But we have actually done this already in proving Theorem 7.14.9.

Exercises

1. Define *projective* and *injective* left R-modules.
2. Prove that the right Z-module (Z is the set of integers) Z_Z is a projective Z-module.
3. Show by example that Z_Z is not an injective Z-module.
4. Let R be a ring with 1. i) Prove that every R-module is projective if and only if every left R-module is projective. ii) Replace "projective" by "injective."
5. Let $0 \to A \xrightarrow{f} B \xrightarrow{g} C \to 0$ be a short exact sequence. Prove that there exists a homomorphism $g': C \to B$ such that $g' \circ g$ is the identity on C if and only if there exists a homomorphism $f': B \to A$ such that $f \circ f'$ is the identity on A. Show that if either g' or f' exists, then $B \simeq A \oplus C$. (If either f' or g' exists, we say that the short exact sequence *splits*).

   Hint: See Proof of Lemma 7.16.3. Use the technique of i) to show that the existence of f' implies $B = \operatorname{Im} f \dotplus \ker f'$ and use ii) to show that the existence of g' implies $B = \operatorname{Im} g' \dotplus \ker g$.

6. Show that if N is a submodule of M, $0 \to N \xrightarrow{i} M \xrightarrow{v} M/N \to 0$ is exact, where $(x)i = x$, all $x \in N$, and $mv = m + N$, all $m \in M$.
7. Show that if P is projective, then every short exact sequence

$$0 \to A \to B \to P \to 0$$

   splits.
8. Show that if Q is injective, then every short exact sequence

$$0 \to Q \to B \to C \to 0$$

   splits.
9. Let P_1 and P_2 be R-modules. Show that P_1 and P_2 are projective if and only if $P_1 \oplus P_2$ is projective.

10. Let Q_1 and Q_2 be R-modules. Show that Q_1 and Q_2 are injective R-modules if and only if $Q_1 \oplus Q_2$ is injective.
11. Prove the following characterization of semisimple rings. Let $R \ni 1$. Then R is semisimple if and only if every short exact sequence of R-modules, $0 \to A \to B \to C \to 0$, splits.

    Hint: Use Exercise 6.
12. Give an example of a ring $R \ni 1$ and an R-module M such that M is neither a projective nor an injective R-module.

    Hint: Consider Z_3, Z_9, and Z_{27}, as Z-modules.
13. Prove the characterization of injective modules stated immediately before Theorem 7.16.4: Q is an injective module if and only if whenever Q (or an isomorphic image of Q) is a submodule of a module M, then Q (or the isomorphic image of Q) is a direct summand of M.

    Hint: If Q is injective, we have already proved that Q is a direct summand of any "containing" module. To show the converse, let

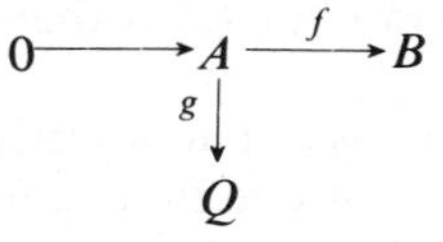

be given, with $0 \to A \xrightarrow{f} B$ exact. Let $D = (B \oplus Q)/K$ where $K = \{((a)f, -(a)g) \mid a \in A\}$. Let $\nu: Q \to D$ be defined by $(q)\nu = (0,q) + K$, and $\mu: B \to D$ be defined by $(b)\mu = (b,0) + K$. Show that ν is 1–1 and that

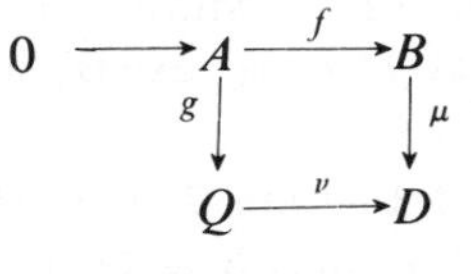

commutes. Then use the fact that $(Q)\nu$ is a direct summand of D to construct a map $h: B \to Q$ so that

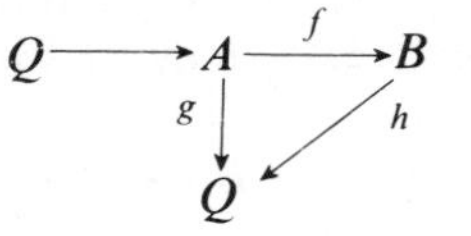

commutes.
14. *Definition:* Let R be a ring with 1. A module M is called *free* if M is isomorphic to $\sum_{\lambda \in \Delta} \oplus R_\lambda$, where each R_λ is isomorphic to R and the $\oplus$ indicates a direct sum of the R-modules R_λ (possibly with infinitely many direct summands). Prove that any module M is the homomorphic image of a free R-module.

Hint: Construct the free R-module $F = \sum_{m \in M} \oplus R_m$, with each $R_m \simeq R$ (we have one direct summand for each element in M). Define a map $h: F \rightarrow M$ by letting $(1_m)h = m$, where 1_m is the element in R_m corresponding to 1 in the isomorphism between R_m and R. Extend h to finite sums in the obvious way:

$$(1_{m_1} r_1 + \cdots + 1_{m_k} r_k)h = [(1_{m_1})h]r_1 + \cdots + [(1_{m_k})h]r_k.$$

15. The free R-module constructed in Exercise 14 need not be most "economical" in the number of generators. Show that if M is a *finitely generated* R-module (there is a finite set $m_1, \cdots, m_k$ of elements in M such that any m in M has the form $m = m_1 r_1 + \cdots + m_k r_k$), then F can be taken to be the direct sum of finitely many (in fact, k) copies of R.
16. Let $R \ni 1$. Prove that an R-module P is projective if and only if P is the direct summand of a free R-module.

Bibliography

This bibliography is not intended to be complete. Rather, its purpose is to provide the reader with a small number of sources that either give alternative approaches to material in this book or more fully develop topics mentioned in the text. The numbers following a reference indicate some of the topics, listed below, that are included in that reference. No attempt has been made to list all those topics contained in any particular reference.

1. General
2. Set Theory and/or Logic
3. Number Theory
4. Group Theory
5. Ring Theory
6. Linear Algebra
7. Group Representation Theory
8. Galois Theory and Field Theory
9. Homological Algebra

[1] Albert, A. A., *Fundamental Concepts of Higher Algebra.* Chicago: University of Chicago Press, 1956. 1,8

[2] Artin, Emil, *Galois Theory* (2nd ed.). Notre Dame, Ind.: University of Notre Dame, 1955. 8

[3] Artin, Emil, C. J. Nesbitt, and R. M. Thrall, *Rings with Minimum Condition.* Ann Arbor: University of Michigan Press, 1944. 5

[4] Barnes, Wilfred, *Introduction to Abstract Algebra.* Boston: Heath, 1963. 1,8

[5] Birkhoff, Garrett, and Saunders MacLane, *A Survey of Modern Algebra* (3rd ed.). New York: Macmillan, 1965. 1,6,8

[6] Burnside, William, *Theory of Groups of Finite Order* (2nd ed.). New York: Dover, 1955. 4

[7] Carmichael, R. D., Introduction to the Theory of Finite Groups. New York: Dover, 1956. 4

[8] Cartan, Henri Paul, and Samuel Eilenberg, *Homological Algebra.* Princeton: Princeton University Press, 1956. 9

[9] Coxeter, H. S. M., and W. O. J. Moser, *Generators and Relations for Discrete Groups.* Berlin: Springer-Verlag, 1957. 4

[10] Curtis, C. W., *Linear Algebra: An Introductory Approach.* Boston: Allyn and Bacon, 1963. 6

[11] Curtis, C. W., and Irving Reiner, *Representation Theory of Finite Groups and Associative Algebras.* New York: Interscience, 1962. 5,7
[12] Finkbeiner, D. T., *Introduction to Matrices and Linear Transformations.* San Francisco: Freeman, 1960. 6
[13] Fuchs, László, *Abelian Groups.* Oxford and New York: Pergamon, 1960. 4
[14] Hall, Marshall, *The Theory of Groups.* New York: Macmillan, 1959. 4
[15] Halmos, P. R., *Finite Dimensional Vector Spaces* (2nd ed.). Princeton: Van Nostrand, 1958. 6
[16] Halmos, P. R., *Naive Set Theory.* Princeton: Van Nostrand, 1960. 2
[17] Hardy, G. H. and E. M. Wright, *An Introduction to the Theory of Numbers* (4th ed.). Oxford: Clarendon, 1960. 3
[18] Herstein, I. N., *Topics in Algebra.* New York: Blaisdell, 1964. 1,6,8
[19] Herstein, I. N., *Theory of Rings.* Chicago: Department of Mathematics, University of Chicago (Lecture notes), 1961. 5
[20] Herstein, I. N., *Topics in Ring Theory.* Chicago: Department of Mathematics, University of Chicago (Lecture notes), 1965. 5
[21] Hoffman, Kenneth, and Ray Kunze, *Linear Algebra.* Englewood Cliffs, N.J.: Prentice-Hall, 1961. 6
[22] Hohn, F. E., *Elementary Matrix Algebra* (2nd ed.). New York: Macmillan, 1964. 6
[23] Jacobson, Nathan, *Lectures in Abstract Algebra.* Princeton: Van Nostrand.
vol. I, *Basic Concepts*, 1951. 1,4
vol. II, *Linear Algebra*, 1953. 5,6
vol. III, *Theory of Fields and Galois Theory*, 1964. 8
[24] Jacobson, Nathan, *Structure of Rings* (rev. ed.). Providence: American Mathematical Society, 1964. 5
[25] Jans, J. P., *Rings and Homology.* New York: Holt, 1964. 5,9
[26] Jones, B. W., *The Theory of Numbers.* New York: Holt, 1955. 3
[27] Kaplansky, Irving, *Infinite Abelian Groups.* Ann Arbor: University of Michigan Press, 1954. 4
[28] Kaplansky, Irving, *Notes on Ring Theory.* Chicago: Department of Mathematics, University of Chicago (lecture notes), 1965. 5
[29] Kelly, J. L., *General Topology.* New York: Van Nostrand, 1955. 2
[30] Kurosh, A. G., *The Theory of Groups* (2nd English ed.), New York: Chelsea, 1960. 4
[31] Kurosh, A. G., *Lectures on General Algebra.* New York: Chelsea, 1963. 1,2
[32] Ledermann, Walter, *Introduction to the Theory of Finite Groups* (5th ed.). New York: Interscience, 1964. 4
[33] LeVeque, W. J., *Topics in Number Theory.* Reading, Mass.: Addison-Wesley, 1956. 3
[34] Lewis, D. J., Introduction to Algebra. New York: Harper and Row, 1965. 1
[35] MacDuffee, C. C., *An Introduction to Abstract Algebra.* New York: Wiley, 1940. 1,3
[36] MacLane, Saunders, *Homology.* New York: Academic Press, 1963. 9
[37] McCoy, N. H., *Introduction to Modern Algebra.* Boston: Allyn and Bacon, 1962. 1
[38] McCoy, N. H., *Rings and Ideals.* Buffalo: Mathematical Association of America, 1948. 5
[39] McCoy, N. H., *The Theory of Rings.* New York: Macmillan, 1964. 5
[40] Mostow, G. D., J. H. Sampson, and Jean-Pierre Meyer, *Fundamental Structures of Algebra.* New York: McGraw-Hill, 1963. 1
[41] Northcott, D. G., *An Introduction to Homological Algebra.* Cambridge, Eng.: Cambridge University Press, 1960. 9

[42] Northcott, D. G., *Ideal Theory*. Cambridge, Eng.: Cambridge University Press, 1953. 5

[43] Pollard, Harry, *The Theory of Algebraic Numbers*. Buffalo: Mathematical Association of America, 1950. 3

[44] Robinson, Abraham, *Numbers and Ideals*. San Francisco: Holden-Day, 1965. 3

[45] Rotman, J. J., *The Theory of Groups: An Introduction*. Boston: Allyn and Bacon, 1965. 4

[46] Scott, W. R., *Group Theory*. Englewood Cliffs, N.J.: Prentice-Hall, 1964. 4

[47] Sierpinski, Wacław, *Cardinal and Ordinal Numbers*. Warsaw: Pánstworve Wydown, Naukowe, 1958. 2

[48] Stoll, R. R., *Set Theory and Logic*. San Francisco: W. H. Freeman, 1963. 2

[49] van der Waerden, B. L., *Modern Algebra* (rev. English ed.). New York: Ungar, 1953. 1,4,5,6,8

[50] Vinogradov, I. M., *Elements of Number Theory* (translated from 5th ed.). New York: Dover, 1954. 3

[51] Wilder, R. L., *Introduction to the Foundations of Mathematics*. New York: Wiley, 1952. 2

[52] Zariski, Oscar, and Pierre Samuel, *Commutative Algebra* (vol. 1). Princeton, N.J.: Van Nostrand, 1958. 5,8

[53] Zassenhaus, Hans, *The Theory of Groups* (2nd ed.). New York: Chelsea, 1958. 4

List of Special Symbols

S_1S_2: product of subsets of a ring, 283

ΣM_λ: sum of a set of submodules, 291

$\Sigma \oplus M_\lambda$: direct sum of an indexed set of modules, 297

$\Sigma \dot{+} M_\lambda$: internal direct sum of submodules, 297

Index